ANDREW CROSSE
and the mite that shocked the world

With best wishes,

Brian Wright.

ANDREW CROSSE
and the mite that shocked the world

THE LIFE AND WORK OF AN ELECTRICAL PIONEER

Brian Wright

Matador
9 Priory Business Park,
Wistow Road, Kibworth Beauchamp,
Leicestershire. LE8 0RX
Tel: 0116 279 2299
Email: books@troubador.co.uk
Web: www.troubador.co.uk/matador
Twitter: @matadorbooks

ISBN 978 1784624 385

British Library Cataloguing in Publication Data.
A catalogue record for this book is available from the British Library.

Printed and bound by CPI Group (UK) Ltd, Croydon, CR0 4YY
Typeset in 11pt Aldine401 BT Roman by Troubador Publishing Ltd, Leicester, UK

Matador is an imprint of Troubador Publishing Ltd

To Audrey Mead who, for so many years, has kept the story of Andrew Crosse the Electrician alive, and encouraged me to undertake this biography to correct so many misconceptions about this pioneering scientist.

Contents

Acknowledgements

I would like to thank the following people who have made contributions to this work:

Audrey Mead, for suggestions made when reading the manuscript.

Richard Porter, for his diligence in checking the manuscript, suggesting amendments and all his valuable comments.

John Porter, for supplying useful information.

Dr Anne Baker, BSc, DIC, PhD, The Natural History Museum, London.

Professor Richard Wall, BSc (Dunelm), MBA (Open), PhD (Liv), University of Bristol, for his views on the *acari*.

Valerie Wright, for drawing the diagrams.

Philippa Crosse for permission to include the illustrations of the oil painting and miniature of Andrew Crosse, and the painting of Cornelia Crosse.

Joan Stokes for initial work on the cover design.

Brian Henham for useful suggestions regarding the cover.

Introduction

Science in the 18th and early 19th century was generally in the hands of amateurs, in the true sense of the word - a lover of their subject, from the French *amator* (lover). Many of these were members of the clergy or 'gentlemen' with the time and money to engage their interest in whatever subject appealed to them. Until the first quarter of the 19th century science was not generally divided into specialisations, but was grouped together under the title of Natural Philosophy. Like any section of the population, these natural philosophers varied in intelligence, skill and dedication. Many of these gentlemen-scientists did make a contribution to various fields of science, but often comparatively little is known about their lives or their research. An exception to this is a gentleman-scientist, poet and landowner, Andrew Crosse, who was born and died at Broomfield, high in the Quantock Hills of Somerset, an area he loved and which inspired much of his poetry. He was not a typical member of the landed gentry as, despite having an estate, he was basically a republican as was his father before him. He spent a huge amount on electrical equipment so was never a rich man and, as he himself said, 'my family were learned and honourable men as long as I can look back; but they had the happy knack of turning a guinea into a shilling, and I have inherited that faculty pretty strongly.'

His research was in the field of electricity and the formation of crystals, an interest that he was to pursue for over fifty years until his death in 1855. He was doing pioneering work which resulted in him being the first to discover that thunderclouds were divided into different zones of alternating positive and negative charges, and his observations also led him to identify, in 1828, that the earth was negatively charged, a discovery that is generally credited to the Frenchman Jean Peltier in 1842. He was among the first people in Britain to do research on atmospheric electricity, leading to him being called the 'Thunder and Lightning Man', and most of his observations and conclusions remain valid to the present day. It was thanks to Andrew's work on atmospheric electricity that Michael Faraday realised that the only way to make an accurate electrometer to produce standard results when measuring electric potential, was to screen it from the minute extraneous electrical charges in the air. Andrew came up with what was later to be formulated as Joule's First Law of Thermodynamics a decade before Joule published it in 1840. His work on producing fresh water from sea water brought him to the attention of the Admiralty, he made improvements to the batteries used at that period and was a visionary in predicting the use of electricity for many purposes. Even as early as 1816 he startled guests at a dinner party by stating that 'by means of the electric agency we shall be enabled to communicate our thoughts instantaneously with the uttermost parts of the earth.'

Although living in an isolated part of the West Country he was by no means isolated from the scientific community, and so highly thought of was he, that many well-known scientists from both Britain and Europe felt that the journey to see him and his laboratory was well worth the effort. Among his many distinguished visitors were Sir Humphrey Davy, Michael Faraday and Sir Roderick Murchison from the world of science, the poets Robert Southey and Walter Savage Landor, and Ada Lovelace who devised computer programming for Charles Babbage, and was to have an affair with Andrew's oldest son. Many other notable figures of the 19th century made their way to his house/laboratory in Somerset, while others visited him at his London home.

He was a modest and very self-effacing man all his life, and also subject to bouts of depression and so was very disturbed when news of a curious finding from an experiment he was conducting in 1836 leaked out, the appearance of some small mites, it led initially to great excitement, but then to accusations that he had created life, something he never claimed. This story took on a life of its own with accounts appearing in the scientific and popular press not only in Britain, but in Europe and even America. Many people reviled him as they believed he had created life, which caused him great distress and, despite all his good pioneering scientific work, it is the mites that have ensured his fame (or infamy) has persisted to the present day. Exactly what these mysterious mites were remains an enduring mystery to the present day. Many people even believe he had inspired Mary Shelley to write her novel *Frankenstein*.

However, this huge fuss about the mites did not deter him from continuing his scientific work and even following all this bad publicity he still retained the admiration of the scientific community. Among the last experiments he was engaged in before his death was keeping blood liquid using an electric charge, suggesting he was interested in blood transfusions at that time. After his second marriage to Cornelia Berkeley in 1850, a girl forty-three years younger than him, his social circle widened to include many well-known people in the arts. It also thanks to Cornelia that we know about Andrew's earlier life, how his interest in electricity was sparked while still at school, and unexpected details such as how, while still a school boy, he was involved in an armed rebellion which came to the attention of the newspapers in Ireland, his unusual political views, and how he suffered many personal family tragedies but still continued his research to become the most dedicated and significant 'amateur' scientist of the 19th century.

Somerset still continues its connection with pioneering electrical developments. In 2010 Dave Pain, of the renewable energy company GotWind, announced the invention of a pair of Wellington boots incorporating a sole that converts the heat of the foot into an electrical current. This is carried through a cable to recharge the battery of a mobile phone in a holder on the outside of one of the boots. 'Power Wellies' were launched at the Glastonbury Festival in Somerset by the network provider Orange. This is a device of which Andrew Crosse would have undoubtedly approved. He would have loved to generate electricity while walking through his beloved Quantock Hills, keeping his feet dry, while using the power to operate a device that would have allowed him to communicate with others anywhere in the world.

CHAPTER ONE
The Early Years: 1740-1805

The beautiful Quantock Hills of Somerset, with its varied landscape of wooded valleys, known locally as combes, with magnificent trees, heather covered hill tops and areas of coarse grasslands seems an unlikely place to find a pioneering scientist, but it is here that Andrew Crosse, a researcher whose great life-long passion was electricity, was born, lived and died. The Quantock Hills are an area that even today is little known to many people. Designated as the first English Area of Outstanding Natural Beauty (AONB) in 1956, it has spectacular views of the surrounding country including, on a clear day, views of the Black Mountains in Wales across Bridgwater Bay and the mouth of the River Severn. The northern end of the Quantocks slopes down to the Somerset coast with its varied scenery and complex geology. There are few villages in the hills, most clustering on the lower slopes. During the 18th and 19th century it was a very isolated area but had a haunting beauty, as is still does today.

The Quantocks were recognised around the turn of the 18th century as a romantically picturesque area which had the advantage of being accessible from Bristol and even London. William Gilpin had written about the area in 1798, attracting such personages as William and Dorothy Wordsworth and Samuel Taylor Coleridge, while J.M.W.Turner was painting its scenery in the early 19th century. The Quantocks were wild, but not too wild. At that time the 'romantics' found Dartmoor and the Lake District intimidating, while the landscape of Scotland, Wales and Ireland was distinctly frightening. So it was to the Quantocks that the poets and artists of that time went to experience a romantic but safe wilderness. Having got used to the Quantocks, poets and artists later moved on to the wilder and even more picturesque Lake District.

Andrew Crosse's father, Richard (II), was born about 1740, the son of the Rev. Richard Crosse (I) and his wife Mary. He was rector of Cannington, a village lying a short distance from Bridgwater, Somerset. However, they seem to have lived for much of the time at Broomfield high in the Quantock Hills of Somerset. The early schooling of Richard (II) is unknown, but in 1756 he entered Corpus Christi College, Oxford, graduated in 1760 with a BA degree, but continued to study at Corpus Christi and was awarded an MA in 1763. The year 1766 was a momentous one for him since he inherited a 500 acre estate, Fyne Court, at Broomfield from his uncle, also called Andrew (1704-66), whose family had owned land there since 1634, and were probably tenants before that. However, it was not a straightforward inheritance. Uncle Andrew did not have a direct heir, so left his house and gardens at Wells in Somerset to his wife Francis but, wishing to leave the bulk of his estate to his nephew Richard (II), decided to set up a trust. He appointed three Trustees, Sir Charles Kemys-Tynte of Halswell House, Copplestone Warre Bampfylde of Hestercombe House and John Jeanes of Barford Park all about two miles (3.2 km) from Fyne Court. Part of his land holdings were to be sold off to settle a number of outstanding debts, including some valuable land near to the heart of the Fyne Court estate. The remainder of his properties, consisting of the Fyne Court estate and land at West Bagborough and Combe Florey were to be conveyed by the Trustees to Richard (II) and his two successive heirs for a total period of up to 99 years. This arrangement suggests he was aware of his nephew's character and had concerns that the landed estate he had worked so hard to create might be mismanaged and broken up. The lease arrangement he set up would prevent that happening for three generations. So Richard (II) became the first life tenant of Fyne Court.

'Uncle' Andrew aimed to establish at Fyne Court a house and pleasure grounds that he felt would reflect the status of the family, and indeed it did became an estate of note. He seems to have re-orientated, extended and re-faced the 17th century house. Fyne Court was surrounded by other estates of a similar size. Within a two mile (3.2 km) radius were Halswell House, Enmore Castle, Tetton House and Hestercombe House, and all were vying to create the latest fashionable elements in their houses and grounds. Halswell, one of the two manors of Goathurst, was described as the most impressive house of its period in Somerset, and had a number of romantic and well-designed follies including a stepped pyramid. Fyne Court was trying to equal these other gardens, since landscape gardening at that time was very competitive, although its garden follies and buildings were not up to the standards of the other estates (plate 2). They may have been designed by Andrew himself and built by local labour. However, the period from about 1725 to 1766 was to prove to be the heyday of Fyne Court's gardens, later generations having other interests.

Andrew created at Fyne Court his vision of an Arcadian pleasure ground following the prevailing fashion of the time (plate 1). He utilised two streams to create complex water features, including five linked ponds with cascades and an island in Five Pond Wood, and planted many trees. One of his most impressive creations was a serpentine lake, probably constructed between 1742 and 1766. Not only was this nine hundred feet (274 m) in length and up to sixty feet (18 m) wide, but was created on top of a hill, unlike most such water features that are usually to be found in valleys as were the lakes of his neighbours. This involved a huge amount of effort, with local labour working for many months to dig it out and build a huge retaining bank. It was fed by a leat which brought water from a spring. This large lake, the highest standing water in the Quantocks (200 m above OD – sea level), must have been an astonishing sight to visitors. Cornelia Crosse said Fyne Court was 'so named from the manorial fines having been collected there', although another theory is that the name comes from the Old English word *fyne*, meaning mould. While this seems unlikely on the face of it, the site is extremely rich in many types of fungi in the autumn, over one hundred having been identified.

Richard had travelled widely in Britain and Europe, initially after leaving university, and not just as part of the Grand Tour undertaken by so many upper class young men as a 'finish' to their classic education. This was often a chance not only to see the heritage sights of Italy, Venice and Greece, but to experience the other delights of the Continent such as new foods, exotic drinks and wines, and foreign whores. However, it is clear that Richard's interests were much wider than the average English traveller abroad, and he spent much time in France, a country not on the Grand Tour route, but which he obviously had a great love for and was to visit many times. He had a gift for languages and could speak several, and was described as an accomplished scholar. It is probable that it was Richard who built the library at Fyne Court to house his extensive collection of books, many of which were in French and Italian. Inheriting an estate in England did not curtail Richard's passion for travel. Having settled some outstanding debts of his late uncle and sorted out his own affairs he left for Italy in 1769.

He had not forgotten about Fyne Court, as a letter to him when he was staying in Rome from Henry Hobhouse (1742-92), dated 24 February 1770, shows he had asked him to order fir seeds to plant on the Quantock Hills, along with two hundred oaks and some pear and cherry trees, and to dispatch these from Bristol to Broomfield. The Fyne Court estate was being run by a manager, John Woods, who was following out Richard's plans for improvements to the lawns, wood and garden features. While in Rome Richard had been blessed by Pope Clement XIV during an audience, perhaps suggesting he had Catholic sympathies, a fact that Hobhouse refers to in his letter, presumably in a light-hearted rather than serious way: 'As his Holiness is so kind as to bestow his Blessing upon you I shall not be surprised to hear of his bestowing one of the vacant Hats of the sacred College upon you. I think you will make an excellent cardinal and greatly promote the Reconciliation of England and the Holy See ...'. The letter also shows that Richard was cutting short his intended stay at Naples.

About April Richard sent a box back to Hobhouse containing a number of items including a set of prints of Naples that his friend had asked him for. Richard was very fond of Italian literature and it would have contained a number of works in Italian. Hobhouse, in a letter to Richard dated 18 May 1770, confessed that his curiosity had got the better of him and he had examined the other contents of the box, but pointed out he was not the first to do so as 'ye Custom House officers had penetrated into its inmost Recesses, scrutinizing them with ye most piercing zeal, nor was this all, for when they had taken good care that the Revenue should not be defrauded; it was assigned over to ye officers of ye very Reverend Bp. [Bishop] of London, that they might examine lest it should contain Mass Books, Relics, *Agnus Dei*, or other Articles of Superstition; so ever watchful and anxious are our worthy Prelates to prevent the growth of Popery, which next to poverty they have ye most horrid Fears of; however if they had known both you and me, they might have spared these great precautions, for ye Box turning out to have neither Contraband or Superstition amongst its contents …'. Richard regularly sent back boxes of items he had purchased, and his friends often had some difficulty getting them released from the Custom House in London. Among other objects he sent back was a table of *pietra dura* work from Florence, engravings of Italian views and a lantern and other mementoes made by the monks of La Trappe.

By that Summer Richard was in Paris having been provided with introductions to the British ambassador and other influential persons, so was soon mixing with the best society in the French capital, where he was described as a handsome young man. He is said to have known and admired Anne-Robert-Jacques Turgot, Baron de Laune (1727-81), an economist, statesman and advocate of economic liberalism. He held high offices in France until he 'fell' in 1776. Richard had already decided he would travel on to Germany, and had written to his friend and neighbour Sir Charles Kemys-Tynte for introductions to the British ambassadors at Dresden and Berlin. However, it was not until 4 February 1771 that Tynte finally replied enclosing the letters of recommendation. He did not know the ambassadors, and it took him some time to get letters from someone who did. He also apologised for a delay in sending them as he had been very concerned about a dispute between two of his friends, Lord Poulett and Lord Milton, who had fought a duel with pistols. Poulett wounded Milton, but fortunately not fatally. The French had difficulty when introducing Richard, who was an untitled gentleman, so sometimes referred to him as le Baron.

The sealed letters of introduction to the ambassadors in Germany were still among the letters held by the family, so it is possible that Richard never got to Germany as he also went to Switzerland. There he met Louisa, a Swiss woman (her surname is unknown) about ten years younger than himself, and fell in love. In 1772 he and Louisa married, possibly in Geneva, and while there he received a letter from a friend in England, Mr Savage, who was an acquaintance of Voltaire (1694-1778) which, to Richard's disappointment, said he would not give him an introduction to the great writer, dramatist and philosopher as he was now too old to receive visitors.

Savage asked Richard 'If you return by Brussels, and can conveniently bring them, I wish you would buy me a good pair of lac'd Ruffles, value about three guineas, and give me credit till we meet.' The parish registers show that their first daughter, named Louisa, was born in 1773 and baptised in Broomfield Church, suggesting the family were living at Fyne Court at that time. However, she died within the year but was not buried in Broomfield church. One of the Fyne Court gardeners described the new mistress of the house, with her dark brown hair, as 'more beautiful than the flowers themselves.' Just four years after they married, Richard's wife died and was buried by torch light in Broomfield Church on 1 November 1775, and in January 1776 their second child, also called Louisa (as was their first child), was baptised in Broomfield church, so Richard's wife may have died from birth complications. After a brief interval of mourning, Richard continued his trips to the continent and particularly France, leaving his young daughter to the care of a nurse or relative.

Richard seems to have been a frequent visitor to the French Court of King Louis XVI, who came to the throne in 1774, at a time when the court was at its most extravagant. He also, travelled beyond France, Italy being a favourite destination, and he spoke the language fluently. The French Government and Court supported the American colonists in their desire to establish an independent Republican state. Benjamin Franklin made a secret visit to France towards the end of 1776, and American emissaries were at the French Court in 1777. In 1778 France went to war with Britain in support of the American colonials. Could all this talk and enthusiasm for republicanism have sparked Richard's interest while at the French Court? Richard had met and become friends with Benjamin Franklin who was lodging in Craven Street near Charing Cross, London from 1757. Franklin had been sent to London by the Pennsylvanian Assembly. Pennsylvania was a privately owned colony, and Franklin was to negotiate with its founder's two sons as they were not paying tax on their land holdings there despite deriving a considerable income, and the Assembly needed to raise money for defence. His negotiations were unsuccessful, but Franklin stayed on in London enjoying his contacts with figures from the world of science, arts and politics. He returned to America in 1762. Another famous acquaintance of Richard was John Hunter (1728-93), a renowned surgeon and anatomist of St. George's Hospital, regarded as the founder of scientific surgery he also established the Hunterian Museum of Anatomy.

Unlike many landowners of the time, Richard held very liberal views, and even confessed to being a republican in principle, this despite being sworn in as a Justice of the Peace on 23 December 1778. He was proposed by Sir Charles Kemys-Tynte, a neighbour and prominent member of local society. Richard also held the post of High Sheriff of Somerset in 1786. This was an unpaid law enforcement position, held for one year. The post holder was appointed by the Crown through a warrant from the Privy Council and was the Sovereign's judicial representative which, to some extent, complimented the post of Lord Lieutenant who was the Sovereign's personal representative. He added new property to the estate from time to time when in England, and had brought Broomfield Rectory and other bits of land from the former Heathcombe Manor by 1786. Eventually Richard decided to marry again and, being realistic, saw the advantages of marrying Susanna Mary Porter (born 1749), the daughter of Jasper Porter of Blaxhold Manor to the north of Fyne Court. His written offer of marriage to her addresses her simply as 'Madam', and the only real sentiment in the whole letter is where he tells her that even now he cannot think of his first wife without shedding tears! However, he credits Susanna with excellent business sense, explains his financial position candidly and goes on to point out that their eldest son, 'if they are blessed with one', would have his estates which are strictly entailed, and that any second son would have her property for his sole provision – which is what eventually happened.

They married at St. Mary-le-Strand Church, Westminster, on 30 April 1782. His marriage enlarged the Fyne Court estate as Susanna had inherited a large part of the Enmore Manor estate, Blaxhold Manor, lands in Enmore, and land at Spaxton and Broomfield the year before she married. These properties were, in effect, retained by Susanna, and was specifically returned to her in a bequest detailed in Richard's will. Susanna's inheritance caused ill-feeling in her family as she was the youngest of three children, having two older brothers who received only a small share of the property left in their father's will on his death in 1781. Her elder brother Jasper, a doctor, was furious about this and wrote to his brother Thomas, a sugar planter in

Demerara in the West Indies, in 1784, three years after their father's death, referring to him as an 'old rogue'. He urged Thomas to return to England so they could unite in a legal action in the Court of Chancery against Susanna to recover £4,000. To make matters worse from their point of view, Susanna had not only married Richard Crosse, but had recently given birth to their first son, Andrew, as Jasper notes in his letter: 'She has lately been delivered of a son – and by way of Farce to the Comedy compliments and congratulations have been sent to me on the Occasion by Mr. Crosse – how far such an Event was agreeable to me you may readily conceive when my Paternal Property is thereby alienated from our family and conferred on a sister's child – This Circumstance amongst various others will of course destroy Distant prospect of the Estate Devolving to either of us.' Jasper also wanted to sell the small parcel of property he had been left but was unable to do so as 'my honest sister refuses to part with the title deed …'.

Thomas did not, however, return and the matter was never pursued in court. He eventually made a fortune in the West Indies, and does not seem to have been too bothered about being done out of his inheritance. However, Jasper remained bitter about this for the rest of his life and had nothing to do with his sister or brother-in-law. This festering ill-feeling was clearly revealed when he made his will some years later which said:

> In consequence of being defrauded of my birthright and Paternal estate by the cruel and unnatural Will of my Father in 1779 which was effected by the Villainy and Artifice of my Sister to aggrandize her fortune and become his Executrix, I would stigmatise their memory to latest posterity and exhibit a picture of them in full length that I may deter the vicious from acts of injustice which disgrace humanity and assure the world that the memory of bad actions can only be effaced by public marks of detestation and abhorrence.

> Wherefore my Will is that £10 be deposited in the hands of the Overseers of the Parish of Enmore which they shall distribute equally amongst ten of the oldest men paupers of the said Parish on condition that on the fifth day of November each year they make two effigies representing a man and a woman which shall be fixed on two stakes and a copy of my Father's Will

shall be affixed thereto with a label in large characters of these words: 'To expiate the crimes of fraud and perfidy and make some atonement to the names of the Testator we commit this effigy to the flames at the request and in commemoration of our Benefactor.'

The ten men shall assemble at the Castle Inn at Enmore and walk in slow procession at the beat of the drum through the Village and carry the above effigies with my Father's Will affixed thereto as far as the Great Elm on the crossings near the Church when a Bonfire shall be provided for the purpose of burning the effigies – the oldest of the men shall then commit the said effigies to the flames in a solemn and audible voice repeating the above words. After performing the ceremony the men shall repair to the Castle Inn at dinner and receive the £10 divided amongst them agreeable to the Words of my Will on the 5th day of November every year provided that they perform the ceremony of burning the said effigies in the manner above recited.

In January 1795 Jasper died while on a trip to London, and his will was found in his saddlebags. It had not been signed or witnessed, and two local people had to swear it was his writing before probate was granted. It is not certain if this vindictive ceremony was ever carried out or, if so, for how long. If it was, how must Susanna have felt about her and her father being burnt in effigy and joining Guy Fawkes as a villain! Susanna was an intelligent and widely read lady. Her journal of the 1790s mentions some of the works she read and indicates her interests in reading. These also show she shared her husband's love of French literature, and her taste for writers of comedy and satire can be clearly seen. These included books by:

Madam de Genlis (1746-1830), who wrote more than eighty works covering historical novels, education and short comedies for young people.

Bernard-Joseph Saurin (1706-81), a French dramatist who also wrote many books including comedies, a satire on English snobbery (Les Moers du temps), and Sparticus (1760) which has remained popular ever since and made into a film.

Jean de la Bruyere (1645-96), French satiric moralist.

Blaise Pascal (1623-62), a physicist, mathematician and religious writer.

John Tillotson (1630-94), Archbishop of Canterbury. He wrote several books of sermons.

Alexander Pope (1668-1744), an English poet, famous for his satirical verse and translation of Homer.

Joseph Addison (1672-1719), English essayist, poet and politician.

Their first child, Andrew, who was to become the most famous family member and named after his great-uncle, was born on 17 June 1784, with a younger brother, Richard, born on 27 March 1786, although neither were baptised at Broomfield. Their father Richard would have seen the extravagances of the court of Louis XVI, but must also have been aware of the plight of many poor French people at that time. This seems to have influenced his views which indicate that he was in favour of the French Revolution and the overthrow of the French monarchy and aristocracy. His politics made him very unpopular in England. When he was four years old Andrew and his two and a half year old brother Richard, were taken by their parents to France, and a large part of the journey, which must have made quite an impression on both lads, despite their young age, is described in his mother's diary:

Wednesday Oct. 1st, 1788.
Left Broomfield with Mr. Brown, Mr. Crosse, my little Andrew, and two servants; drank tea, supped and slept at Piper's Inn. Andrew quite delighted with his journey. Thursday we left Piper's Inn, the two gentlemen in one chaise, Andrew, myself, and Sarah in the other; we called on Dr. Lovell at Wells, took fresh horses there, one which occasioned an alarm, but we leapt out of the chaise, and insisted on taking another.

We arrived comfortably at Bath, took a cold dinner at the Bear. Mem: We were charged four shillings for about three pounds of a breast of veal, and proportionally dear for other articles. We pursued our journey to Chippenham and slept there; the accommodations were good, but miserable attendants. Left Chippenham Friday morning, and came to Marlborough. We only stayed at Marlborough to take fresh horses, and went on to Newberry, where we took a cold dinner; and drank tea and supped at Reading. At Reading nothing appeared worth remarking, except the extravagance of the house and the affectation of the domestics.

From Reading, Saturday morning, we set off with good weather and good spirits; stopped at Hounslow for fresh horses, and arrived in London about three o'clock. What a beautiful entrance through Hyde Park; the innumerable grand carriages, passing and repassing, together with such an immense crowd of people formed a scene too pleasing to be forgot. We stayed in London [at the Bolt-in-Tun near Temple Bar], Sunday and Monday.

Tuesday morning we left and proceeded to Dartford, and from thence to Rochester, and where we took dinner, the ships in full sail on the river Medway was a delightful sight, and made my little Andrew ready to leap out of the chaise, so great was his joy. That evening we arrived at Citenbourn [Sittingbourne] in the evening. Supp'd and slept there. Wednesday we went on to Canterbury, took an early dinner and went on to Dover, where we were detained three days by contrary winds. We left the Royale Hotel at Dover, Saturday morning, being called at five o'clock; we took a hasty breakfast, and went on shipboard about seven o'clock, intending to sail to Calais; but the wind blew quite contrary, the sea was very rough, and there was scarce a soul on board but was sick. After being near six hours on the sea, sailing against the wind. The captain proposed to the passengers to go to Boulogne, to which some of them reluctantly consented, and within two hours we were in sight of it. A boat was now to convey us on shore, and it was then I really began to tremble.

My poor sick child was carried by French sailors into the boat, and I had no other way of making them know the value of him, but by the agony in which they saw me. The sail was up, and the boat much inclined on one side. But great was my joy when we saw forty or fifty women skipping and dancing in the water, with their petticoats above their knees; they presented themselves by the side of our boat to take us on their shoulders, and carry us on shore. Some of the women were of a gigantic make, and make nothing of carrying Mr. Brown and Mr. Crosse on their back; and Mr. Crosse humorously knighted his lady by bastinading her with his sword. My little Andrew was joyous beyond expression and having slept some hours aboard ship, played about the whole evening with uncommon alacrity.

Sunday we attended the cathedral service at nine o'clock in the morning, and for the first time I saw high mass performed. We left Boulogne Tuesday morning, Oct. 14th, dined at Montreuil and slept at Bernai. Rose at six o'clock after almost a sleepless night, as poor Andrew was extremely ill. We breakfasted on milk from earthen porringers; and pursued our journey. We arrived at Amiens about six o'clock in the evening, at the Hotel Royale, which is a most excellent house. I congratulated myself on leaving this place; but I was soon taught how little cause I had to rejoice. By agreement between Mr. Crosse and the coachman we quitted the public road to Orleans and travelled through by-roads, crooked and cross, and at last, towards evening, we came to an immense common, where the road was so uneven that we were every minute in danger of oversetting.

Night came on. The coachman was ignorant of the way, my poor Andrew lay asleep on Sarah's lap, and to increase my anxiety the coach door was open, which I was obliged to hold in my hand, not without dreadful apprehensions that the dear child would be dashed out of the carriage with every jerk that it made. My silent prayers to the Almighty were heard for our protection, and we arrived at Chartreuse without any bodily accident. We left this place the next day in a conveyance something resembling a covered cart. In this manner -.

Here the diary entry ends. The family remained at Orleans and at Rouen sufficiently long for Andrew to attend school. Andrew got up to the usual childish adventures. On one occasion he slipped away from their Swiss servant Barthelemy, and was found walking on a quay lost in admiration of the sailing ships by a French priest, who was fortunately a friend of his father. As is so often the case with young children and foreign languages he quickly learnt to speak French but almost completely forgot it in later years on his return to England. With the situation in France deteriorating and the danger of revolution becoming clearer, Richard sent his family back to England in the spring or early summer of 1789, at which time his wife Susanna was pregnant. However, he seems to have remained there himself, at least for a while. The civil unrest came to a head on 14 July 1789 when, after a battle with the mob, the garrison of the Bastille prison surrendered, marking the start of the French Revolution. Richard was in Paris when the Bastille was stormed and seems to have stood on the ruins of the prison the day it was taken, even wearing a tricolour cockade, which was later preserved in the family cabinet of family mementos. Soon after this Richard left France, taking two weeks to arrive back at Fyne Court as he had visited his friends the Hobhouses, Jenkyns and Whites on the way. His journey was not without its dangers, which lay not in France but at Bridgwater, only a few miles from Fyne Court.

Bridgwater was violently anti-Jacobin and a Tory stronghold. The anti-Jacobin movement that arose in Britain in the 1790s was due to the fear that the revolution in France would spread to Britain, and indeed there was a lot of unrest among the populace with increasing industrialisation and changes to agricultural practices that affected many people. A number had taken oaths of loyalty to the king and constitution, and occasionally burnt their political opponents in effigy. Somehow news of Richard's presence at the fall of the Bastille and his wearing of a tricolour cockade had reached the town, and Bridgwater was in a 'ferment of indignation.' Some of the more zealous citizens resolved to stop Richard on his way home and smash his carriage. However, a friend got a warning to him, and so he returned to Fyne Court by a route that avoided the town. In the autumn of 1789 Susanna gave birth to a daughter, Mary, who was baptised at Broomfield Church. However, the baby did not survive the year, but does not seem to have been buried at Broomfield, so presumably died when Susanna and the children were away from the estate.

Richard's ease of travelling through France at this very dangerous time suggests just how fluent he was in the language. The whole country was in an uproar, and by October 1789 the Royal family were imprisoned in the

Tuileries, a disused palace. Richard continued to visit France, but this would have become increasing dangerous as famine, high taxes and the attitude of the French aristocracy caused more and more disquiet and civil and political unrest. Richard clearly had liberal views and seems to have been sympathetic to the Revolution, or at least to the plight of the French people, which may have given him both the confidence and ability to travel safely despite his former connection with the French Court which, if he was wise, he would not have mentioned to those he met while in that country during the Revolutionary period. Richard was again in Paris in 1791. After a complex and confused time, King Louis XVI was executed on 21 January 1793 and Queen Marie Antoinette on the 16 October. That year France again went to war with Britain. Richard's trips to France were possible, even after war broke out since, despite the tension between the two countries, it was still possible for an English gentleman to travel in France as long as he was not a member of the military or government, although there was always a risk of being arrested as a spy.

Andrew had a memory of events and incidents from a very early age. For example he was able to remember quite clearly in later life a family dog called Rover which died when he was two years old! He was able to recall where the dog was fed and many other details about it. Andrew seems to have had a great respect for his father, but was also somewhat in awe and even fear of him. His tendency to consider philosophical matters seemed to have manifested itself at an exceptionally early age. Andrew used to tell how, when he was about four years old, he used to gaze up at the sky on a windy day and hope the clouds would disperse so he might 'peep into the glory of heaven beyond.'

As he grew older, his ideas on the location of heaven changed, so that by the age of fourteen he thought heaven was located in the sun, then he thought it lay in some remoter star, then in the space between the stars then, more conventionally, somewhere beyond human sight. As an adult, with his interest in the natural world around him, he formed a very modern view of the location of God's dominion: 'now it seems to me that heaven consists of a boundless sight and full comprehension of all the mighty mysteries which the Almighty has, in his infinite wisdom, cast around us, and that could we be permitted to comprehend all that is above, and below, and around, then indeed should we find ourselves in a heaven of heaven …'. Richard seems to have been a strict parent but always fair (as he saw it) and never harsh. He also had a reputation for integrity, something that was often remarked on to the young Andrew. Many people said that his father was 'an honest man', though one wonders if it was not privately accompanied by the thought 'despite his odd beliefs'. This seems to have irritated the young Andrew, and on one occasion, when his father was again being praised for being an honest man, Andrew was goaded into retorting 'Sir, would you have me the son of a rogue?' To which the speaker simply replied 'Young gentleman, when you are grown up, you will know what I mean!'

Richard seems to have made major modifications to the house, enlarging a moderate sized building by adding a double storey wing with a library on the upper floor with fitted bookshelves, and possibly building the music room (plate 7), both of which were to survive the disastrous fire of 1894. However, the music room may have been added by his son Andrew as, writing of his father in 1849, he says that his father had no ear for music, so with money always in short supply, would he have spent money on a room he was unlikely to use? Richard did build the courtyard with its service buildings such as coach house, stables, tack room, workshop and storage. This can still be seen today. He seems to have made some changes to the gardens in a first flush of enthusiasm for his newly inherited property, but garden design was not a passion with him as it was with so many other landowners at the time since his interests lay in foreign travel, books and attendance at the French Court, all expensive activities that were a big drain on his finances.

Richard's trips to the Continent inevitably had a considerable effect on the Fyne Court estate regarding both its day-to-day management and further development and improvements. Such changes would have happened in short bursts of activity when he was resident long enough to plan, fund and ensure that the work was carried out to his specifications. These would have included repairs and modifications to the house and other buildings, to the tenanted farms, and minor changes to the gardens and pleasure grounds. Some of the work was carried out when he was away as he was so often travelling for several months or more at a time. This would have been overseen by his wife and carried out by an estate manager, with Richard being kept informed of progress by letter. The greatest changes and improvements to the estate by Richard occurred in the periods 1766-70, 1773, 1775, intermittently in the late 1770s or early 1780s, 1786 and a few years in the 1790s.

The area where young Andrew spent his time when home in Somerset from school and university, and where he was to live for much of the rest of his life was described by the Rev. John Collinson in his *History and Antiquities of the County of Somerset* (1791). Broomfield he noted was 'a large parish, situated at the foot of the Quantock-hills, six miles north from Taunton, and seven west from Bridgwater, on high ground, beautifully varied with swelling hills, and deep romantick vales, and commanding a great variety of pleasing landscapes, and very extensive prospects, to which the Bridgwater river, the Bristol Channel, and the Welch mountains, particularly contribute. The lands, which are moderately fruitful are nearly divided between pasture and arable. The soil in general is shallow, and abounds with that kind of rag slate stone, divisible into thin laminae, which is found almost every where in the neighbourhood of Quantock. It is however, favourable to the growth of timber, and Spanish chestnut trees.' He described Fyne Court, although he did not use this name, as 'a handsome house near the church with beautiful grounds and elegantly disposed plantations.' Richard was one of the subscribers to Collinson's book.

It is not clear how much time the family spent at Fyne Court in the 1790s, but Andrew was sent to school in Dorchester, Dorset in 1790. Richard drew up his last will in 1795 while at the estate but his many trips abroad and passion for collecting books had taken its toll on the family's finances. When Thomas Porter returned from a stay in the West Indies in the mid-1790s he found that his sister, Susanna Crosse, was in dire financial straits and gave her £5,000, a huge sum, worth in today's money at least £350,000. They had obviously by now been reconciled after the rift caused by their father's bequest, although Thomas was not so bitter about it as his brother. The Crosses had got into this situation despite the fact that the majority of landowners found that their rental income from their estates increased by 40% to 50% between 1750 and 1790. It was to rise even more during the Napoleonic Wars of 1800-15.

A notable visitor to Fyne Court in 1799 was a young aspiring poet called Robert Southey, who was staying with Tom Poole at Nether Stowey. He was spending a walking holiday in the Quantocks for his health, having been advised to take fresh air and exercise. Southey just seems to have dropped in and was received hospitably by Richard and Susanna. However, their two children, Andrew and Richard, were away at school at the time. Robert Southey (1774-1843) was to achieve lasting fame. He went to Balliol College, Oxford where 'All I learnt was a little swimming … and a little boating.' He was a poet of the romantic school, and was later to be one of the 'Lake poets'. His first collection of poems had been published in 1794 a few years before his visit to Fyne Court. His work was to become so popular that he was made Poet Laureate in 1813, a post he held until his death. In addition to poetry he wrote a number of biographies and was a very prolific letter writer. In 1836 he published the first version of *The Tale of Three Little Bears*, today more commonly known as *Goldilocks and the Three Bears*. His wife, Edith, was the sister of Samuel Taylor Coleridge's wife.

Richard died at Fyne Court in 1800 and was buried in Broomfield Church on the 23 March. In his will he made careful provision for his family. His leasehold property in Broomfield was left to Susanna for life, and on her death passed to his second son Richard. Fyne Court seemed to be included in 'my real and personal estate of any kind and nature not before bequeathed … [which] I give and bequeath to my eldest son Andrew.' Andrew was fifteen at the time, so Fyne Court was run by Susanna on behalf of her son until her death in 1805. Susanna left the land she had inherited from her father, and which was returned to her under his will, to her second son, Richard, who died childless in 1846, when it passed to his older brother, Andrew.

CHAPTER TWO

From the Fort to the Brazen-nosed College: 1780-1805

The Crosses stayed long enough in Orleans, France during the 1780s for young Andrew to attend school there. He quickly picked up the language and could speak it perfectly, but on returning to England, gradually lost the ability to speak French as he had no occasion to use it and, as an adult, was not a good modern linguist. With the deteriorating situation in France Richard Crosse dispatched his family back to the safety of England in 1789. In 1790 Andrew, now six, was sent to a private tutor, the Rev. George White at Dorchester, Dorset. White seems to have held liberal views and was one of the instigators of a petition calling for the abolition of slavery, a fact that was mentioned on his tombstone at Glanvilles Wootton, Dorset. He is named as one of the executors in the will of Richard, Andrew's father.

At that time Dorchester was a small but busy market town on the river Frome, and had not spread much beyond its ancient town walls. There was no railway station when Andrew was there, so all travelling was by horse-drawn carriage or stage coach. The centre of the town would have looked very new and unified to Andrew, as much of it had been destroyed in a large fire in 1725. While staying with White, Andrew studied various subjects, including Greek in which he became proficient both in reading and writing. It was said that he learnt to write Greek before English! His writing was not always easy to read as the words often flew across the paper as he recorded his thoughts or the results of an experiment. Many years later Andrew's friend, John Kenyon, described his writing (plate 15) as being like the tracings of a spider on paper after a casual bath in an ink bottle! Andrew was a devout Christian, and this too manifested itself early. One evening the Rev. White and Andrew were gazing at a particularly impressive sunset, when the priest asked Andrew what he was thinking. To which he replied 'I was thinking that this must be like the Kingdom of Heaven opening to all believers.' Andrew spent a happy and productive time at Dorchester but, in due course, had to move on to his next school.

In February 1793, after spending an all too brief interlude with his family at Fyne Court, Andrew went to the Royal Fort School, a reference to it being built on the site of a Civil War fortification in Bristol, while the 'Royal' was in honour of Prince Rupert, who was made Governor of Bristol. The Master, (the title for Headmaster, assistant teachers being known as Ushers) was the Rev. Dr Samuel Seyer (1757-1831), a well-known classics scholar and expert on the complexities of Greek and Latin grammar. Andrew later described him as honest but narrow-minded and without any sense of justice. A natural remark for Andrew to make as it seems Seyer did not like his distinctive laugh, and since he was always up to japes, Andrew claimed he was caned on average three times a day for six years, although luckily was never flogged! School days at the end of the 18th century were very different from those of the 21st. However, a couple of years after Andrew left school, he was told by a member of Seyer's family that he was a great favourite of the Master, something he found very hard to believe! His mother's diary reports the parting, something every parent feels when their youngster goes to 'big school' but, in her case, it also gives an insight into how protective she felt towards her two boys. Something which was to shape Andrew's character in later life:

1st February 1796.

My dear Andrew went to school, more dear and better beloved than ever. Never shall I forget his expressive looks at parting. May the God of Mercy bless and protect him! Thursday, parted with my beloved Richard, whose engaging sweetness of disposition endears him to everyone who knows him. Happy prospect to look forward to these promising branches as a recompense for all my other troubles. Sweet children, both alike sharers of my maternal tenderness, my constant anxiety, and my daily prayers for their preservation and happiness! How delightful to be so beloved by children on whom the happiness of my life depends.

After Dorchester, with its almost one-to-one tuition, Andrew's next school was very different. He described the school buildings:

> The old court with its stone walls, the raised garden, the lilac bushes out of which I cut many a bow and arrow, the plain, neat, roomy house, the arch and study window, the row of elms and the two supereminent ones, which topped the whole, pointing out to many a schoolboy, returning from his vacation, that near that spot was to be his resting place for the next five months … .

Soon after arriving a bigger boy tried to force Andrew to lie about something and he later recalled how he hated the boy and 'never was happy till I was strong enough to thrash him.' One of his mother's favourite sayings was 'Never allow a mean or unworthy thought to enter your breast', something that Andrew was to take to heart and demonstrate time after time, not only at school and university, but during his long life. Andrew was described as a small, thin, but wiry boy, quick at his lessons, with a wild joyous temperament who delighted in fun and frolics. He recalled how, on one occasion, a school fellow came to him and begged him to help with a translation he was having difficulty with. The phrase, *Medi tutissimus ibis*, should be translated as 'the middle course is safest', but Andrew could not resist taking a liberty with it, and told his school fellow that it meant 'the stork is safest in the middle of the pond.' The Rev. Seyer was not amused and caned the unfortunate boy for his impertinence! This sense of fun and a certain disrespect of authority, which marked the young Andrew out as very much an individual, endeared him to his fellow scholars, and some of the friendships he made at school and university lasted all his life. Many of his young friends were to go on and become well-known figures of the 19th century. Among his special friends, who he was to be in contact with the rest of his life, was John Kenyon (1807-80) whom he described as the 'richest and most generous amongst us', John Eagles (1783-1855) and Richard Jenkyns (1782-1854). William John Broderip (1789-1859) was at school at the same time as Andrew, although it was after Andrew left that they became good friends.

It is interesting to contrast Andrew's life with that of his closest friends. Kenyon later matriculated at Christ Church, Oxford University in 1825, and graduated with a BA in 1828, the same year he was made a Fellow of All Souls College, Oxford. Granted a BCL (Bachelor of Civil Law) in 1831, he was called to the Bar in 1835, and granted a DCL (Doctor of Civil Law) in 1836. He was appointed Vinerian Professor of English Law, and held this chair until his death, as well as being Recorder of Oswestry in Shropshire. John Eagles later went to Wadham College, Oxford, gaining a BA in 1812 and an MA in 1818. He later took Holy Orders and was a writer and poet, having poetry published in *Blackwood's Magazine* among others and wrote a book of poetry. He gained a reputation as a naturalist and was an accomplished painter and etcher. Jenkyns was awarded a doctorate and took Holy Orders, becoming Master of Balliol College, Oxford 1819-54. He was a Canon of Wells Cathedral, Somerset, but was often absent fulfilling his duties in Oxford. He threw scholarships at Balliol open to competition rather than them being awarded by the Master and Fellows in turn as had happened until then. Dean Church said he was 'an unfailing judge of clever men, as a jockey might be to a horse.' He had a short mincing gait and an old fashioned (in the 1830s) pronunciation. He was a firm disciplinarian but won the affection of the undergraduates and Fellows.

Broderip graduated from Oriel College, Oxford with a BA in 1812. While there he had attended lectures on anatomy, chemistry and mineralogy. On leaving he entered the Inner Temple and was called to the Bar in 1817, and was appointed as a Metropolitan Police Magistrate from 1822-55. He was a very respected and influential naturalist, with a great gift for the observation of animal behaviour. Broderip put together an unrivalled collection of shells. He was elected a Fellow of the Linnean Society in 1824, Fellow of the Geological Society in 1825, and a Fellow of the Royal Society in 1828. He was a founding member of the Zoological Society and was, at one time, Vice President of that Society, as well as sometime Vice President of the Geological Society. A prolific researcher, he produced many papers on geology, fossils and molluscs.

Andrew quickly settled in at his new school, and his knowledge of Greek acquired at Dorchester proved useful soon after he arrived at the Royal Fort

School. He had to stand up in class and read, in Latin, from his Virgil. He had nearly completed the fifth book when he made a mistake in one word. Seyer demanded to look at the book from which Andrew was reading and found that the whole of the fifth section had been ripped out. Andrew had recited it all from memory! Yet another example of his phenomenal memory. Andrew explained that another boy had torn it out of his book six months earlier. Seyer's answer to this amazing demonstration of Andrew's ability to remember the text word for word (almost) for all that time was to give him a good caning! This was not to be the end of the incident, as every time Seyer was in a bad mood and annoyed with Andrew he would call him up to the front of the class, ask to look at his Virgil, and give him another caning for the damage to his book. Andrew's interest in science began to manifest itself while still at school, as did his scientific mind. One example of this, which made a big impression on his school fellows, and no doubt the staff as well, was described by Andrew himself:

> I was always very fond of making fireworks. One day, while learning my Virgil, I continued to carry on the business of pounding some rocket mixture; but, as ill luck would have it, Seyer discovered my twofold employment, and immediately took away the mixture from me in considerable wrath. I watched where he put it; it was on the window-sill of a room which was always kept locked; the window, though not glazed, had close iron bars through which nothing could pass: the case was hopeless; I could not recover my rocket mixture, but a happy thought struck me, I was resolved that no one else should enjoy the spoil which I regarded as so valuable. I had a burning glass in my pocket, and I thought of Archimedes and the Roman fleet; the sun was shining, and I soon drew a focus on the gunpowder, which immediately blew up. It was well that the house was not set on fire: as for me, I was reckless of all consequences.

While in general a happy and fun-loving boy, Andrew sometimes fell into an introspective mood. He would stand alone near the wall of the playground and ponder such weighty matters as, even if he were to live for a hundred years, time would still soon pass and the end would come all too quickly. Such thoughts tended to put him into a melancholy mood, but these periods were far outweighed by his happiness in sharing fun and mischief with his friends. The boys were encouraged to put on 'theatricals' and among those Andrew and his friends performed were 'George Barnwell' and 'The Drummer', in which Jenkyns major, destined much later to be a Head of Balliol College and Dean of Wells, played Mrs Abigail. On one occasion Andrew had a fight with a boy called Macdonald, and Seyer dragged Andrew, with his black eye and swollen nose, in front of the boys in the lower classes as an example.

For this humiliation, he used to imagine a variety of torments which he would have liked to inflict on the Master. Andrew was supplied with tartlets, game pies and cakes from his devoted mother, and was willing to share these not only with boys in his year, but even a few in the lower forms. The school was full of growing lads, but Andrew always recalled how he was always hungry because they were never given enough to eat. He was unlucky as he sat on the table of a school mistress at meal times and recalled that she 'half starved me with her economical ways; used to make me eat up the vile black potatoes, and what was called hashed mutton, which in fact was nothing more or less than a conglomerate of the fatty remnants of the past week.' They were served this unappetising dish every Thursday.

While Andrew was obviously outstanding in many respects, he was still a normal youngster. He recalled being expelled from his class by the French dancing master, who must have been in an unfortunate position, as not only did the boys regard dancing as embarrassing and unmanly, but held the dancing master in contempt, as they did all Frenchmen. This was at a time when Britain was at war with France and combating the ambitions of Napoleon Bonaparte. Andrew later said each boy thought he was a match for six foreigners, a view that probably reflects the same common belief among British sailors and soldiers at that time. No doubt the lads keenly followed the progress of the war when they could get news of British victories and the occasional defeat. Despite the strict school regime, or perhaps because of it, a number of boys, including Andrew, planned a rebellion. The reason?, they wanted longer school holidays, something Andrew was very much in favour of. They planned to barricade the schoolroom and had managed to obtain muskets from somewhere. They had agreed among themselves which boys would position themselves at the windows and, when they were shot down, which boys would take their place. With a touching lack of realism, every boy resolved to die at his post if necessary.

Luckily the plot was discovered before the final preparations were complete, the muskets seized, the ringleaders expelled, among whom was Andrew's friend John Kenyon, who was removed to Charterhouse School in London for two years before going on to university. Other participants were flogged, but somehow Andrew managed to escape this punishment. He recalled that one of the boys involved became a midshipman in Admiral Nelson's squadron, but was killed while boarding an enemy ship. News of the proposed revolt spread far beyond the bounds of Bristol. Some Irish newspapers covered it, magnifying the proposed schoolboy revolt into an act of political disaffection. They claimed that the British Government was so unpopular, that even a group of school boys were prepared to head a revolt of the citizens of Bristol. Andrew later commented 'So much for the truth of history.' The young Andrew used to sit at his desk but his mind was transporting him to dreams of classical times, and a future of 'unalloyed future happiness, fearing no enemy but Seyer, and believing firmly that those prodigies of perfection described in such glowing language by poets and historians were not unfrequently to be met with in real life.'

Andrew's early introduction to Greek was to spark a lifelong love of their classical literature. His favourite Greek writers were Theocritus and Thucydides, although he was not so fond of Homer, but he also liked the Roman writers Horace and Virgil. According to Andrew's second wife, Cornelia, his father was a friend of Benjamin Franklin (1766-90) and the scientist Joseph Priestley (1733-1804). Among Franklin's many interests were electricity and he is famous for, among many other things, the invention of the lightning conductor, which he patented in 1749, and his famous 'kite' experiment of 1752. In this he flew a kite, fitted with a metal spike, into the path of a thunderstorm. The string, which was damp, was a good conductor and tied to a metal key at its base. Then a strip of dry silk was attached to act as an insulator. Franklin found that at the height of the storm he could obtain sparks by bringing his knuckle near to the key, which proved that the kite had acquired an electrical charge from the storm, validating his theory that lightning consisted of electricity. Although some doubt has been expressed as to whether he actually carried out the experiment!

Franklin was in England between 1757 and 1762, and received honorary doctorates from St. Andrew's University in 1759 and from Oxford in 1762. While in England he attended meetings of the Royal Society and enjoyed the fashionable social and intellectual life of the time. During the period that Franklin was in England, Richard Crosse was at Corpus Christi College, Oxford (1756-63). It may have been there that he met this great scientist, literary figure, polymath and one of the founders of what was to become the United States of America. Franklin was in England again between 1764 and 1775 and 1783-84, which would have given Richard plenty of opportunities to meet and become friends with him. Another figure who may have had some influence on Andrew's later life was Dr Joseph Priestley, a Unitarian Minister, well-known for his research into Natural Philosophy, especially electricity, chemistry and pneumatics. He was an avowed republican, and became extremely unpopular for his outspoken support of the French Revolution. On 14 July 1791 his house in Birmingham was ransacked by a mob, destroying his library, notes and philosophical instruments during the rioting that broke out after Priestley and about eighty others held a celebratory dinner on the anniversary of the Storming of the Bastille.

It is probable that Richard knew these men, both of whom shared his republican principles and had an interest in electricity, so he may have discussed the mysteries of electricity to his son. However, Andrew himself attributed his interest in electrical science being thanks to the meagre school rations. When he was about twelve he came up with an idea for managing to get a meal while out of school. The drawing master gave lessons to a few of the boys at his house some way from the school. Andrew realised that there was a tavern not far from the master's house which displayed in its window tempting joints of boiled and roast beef to tempt in customers. He estimated that if he could become one of the group of boys who took drawing classes he could get out of school two or three times a week when he would have to pass the tavern or, more accurately, slip inside for a meal! Andrew contacted his father for permission to take the drawing classes and to ask for the money to pay for them. Richard was delighted at his son's sudden interest in the arts and readily consented to his taking the extra lessons, blissfully unaware of Andrew's ulterior motive. So Andrew's lessons began, via the local tavern. He long remembered the lunches of boiled beef, and how he won the sympathy of a lady at the tavern. She used to give him very generous portions realising he was only a schoolboy, a growing lad who was not being properly fed. Andrew explained how his interest in electricity was sparked:

> One day while discussing my beef, my eye fell upon a bill containing the syllabus of a course of lectures on Natural Science; the first of the series was on optics. I conceived a great wish to hear the lectures; I asked and obtained permission of Mr. Seyer, to subscribe to the course. The second course was on electricity; my future tastes were decided.

Although Andrew was happy at school, he was more than delighted when the holidays came round and he could return home to his beloved mother, with whom he had a very close relationship and obviously loved dearly. So excited was he on returning home that he often turned head over heels in delight! While at home his mother introduced him to the world of English literature, descriptive books on travel to strange and exotic lands, and works on the marvels of nature. Andrew enjoyed the wit of Jonathan Swift, a writer and satirist, best known for *Gulliver's Travels*, and Henry Fielding, dramatist, satirist and novelist, whose most famous work is *Tom Jones*. He also began to look at bound volumes of the *Philosophical Transactions*. Fyne Court possessed a fine library put together by both his father and mother, and Andrew began to eagerly devour its books during the school holidays when the family were in Somerset. However, his father took care that Andrew did not neglect his more formal education, and he was made to read from the Greek classics for three hours every day.

Andrew's brother, Richard, had been sent to Dr Valpy's School at Reading in Berkshire. Richard Valpy, a Jerseyman, was described as a liberal, even 'whiggish' gentleman, and had a reputation as a domineering headmaster. He wrote adaptations of Shakespeare and was keen on staging Greek plays for the locals. It is not recorded what the locals thought of them. The two brothers were very close and the holidays at Fyne Court provided a welcome change from school, enabling them to play and explore the pleasure grounds created by their great uncle and maintained by their father. The two boys, like most children, had a great imagination and lived in a world of their own. Though the world of the young Crosses was rather more organised than those of many other children. Between them they created a whole new language, and peopled their world with Hoblegees, creatures that looked like large fir cones. The two boys used to run down the long passages of Fyne Court pursued, in their imagination, by these creatures, although this was more in fun than fear as they did not see the Hoblegees as objects of terror.

Their imaginary world, complete with its own peculiar laws, language and institutions, was designed as a 'Model Republic.' Could the boys' time in France at an early age, and their father's time spent travelling in the newly founded French Republic with its aims of *liberté, égalite et fraternité* have formed the pattern for their imaginary world? Their father made no secret of his support of republican principles, and both Andrew and Richard were strongly influenced by him. The two boys approached their model republic with an earnestness that made their imaginary world almost more truthful than real life. This elaborate childhood world existed for several years, until age and other interests caused it, like so many childhood imaginary worlds, to pass away. The boys' apparently idyllic childhood came to an abrupt end in 1800 when their father died, and although Richard was a strict parent, he was obviously greatly loved by both boys and his daughter. His daughter was not forgotten in his will, drawn up in 1795:

> I give and bequeath to my daughter Louisa … all the estates now rented of me by Mr. Joseph Skates … all rent and arrears of rent which may be due to me … from the said Joseph Skates … I give and bequeath to my daughter Louisa a miniature picture of my mother which is inclosed in a small case in one of the drawers of the library table. I give and bequeath to my daughter Louisa my silver bread basket and likewise my silver tea kettle together with the lamp and stand thereto belonging hoping that she will always keep them in remembrance of her affectionate father. I do likewise give and bequeath to my said daughter Louisa one silver coffee pot and one dozen of the best table spoons and one dozen of the best tea spoons. Item I give and bequeath to my said daughter Louisa one hundred volumes to

be chosen for her out of the books in my library by the Reverend Mr. John Jenkyns of Evercreech in the County of Somerset and the Reverend Mr. George White Rector of Huntspill in the same county who I am confident will select such as are best adapted to the cultivation of her mind.

Among the many land and income bequests to his wife, along with various household items, and land bequests to his two sons, he says:

It is my will that none of my books be sold after my decease – let them be carefully kept for my son Andrew those excepted which I have bequeathed to my daughter Louisa and my wife Susanna and likewise excepting those in the room next to the library commonly called the Humble Room which I give and bequeath to my son Richard all my drawings prints and pictures whether placed in the library or elsewhere I give and bequeath to my eldest son Andrew.

The will ends:

I commend my soul to the mercy of my Great Creator humbly hoping through the merits and intercession of my blessed redeemer to obtain pardon for a misspent life may the almighty enable my dear daughter to tread in the steps of that best of women her departed mother may he grant her peace in this world and happiness in the next may my dear sons be diligent and active in their respective professions ... honour God benefit society from the purest motives and finally secure their own eternal welfare may they pity their father but imitate [their] uncle.

Richard was buried in Broomfield Church on 23 March that year. He appointed the Rev. John Jenkyns, the Rev. Edmund Lovel Liberal and the Rev. George White to be his executors and guardians of Andrew and the estates he inherited until he was twenty-one. Susanna took over the running of the Fyne Court estate while Andrew returned to school after the funeral and resumed his studies. Despite his liking for practical jokes, which sometimes got him into a lot of trouble, Andrew was eventually made Head Boy, probably because of his popularity with the other pupils and the fact that he was clearly an outstanding scholar. The art lessons continued, his attendance, as before, being via a decent meal on the way! Soon after his attendance at the talk on electricity, Andrew began to put his newly acquired knowledge into practice. One of his school fellows, John Jenkyns, the son of his father's friend, the Rev. John Jenkyns of Evercreech, recalled how he and Andrew both delighted and surprised their friends, while Andrew often seems to have used electricity to frighten the younger boys with shocks. One example of this was noted in a letter by Jenkyns, written just after Andrew died. Andrew made a simple but effective electrical machine from the glass tube of a broken barometer which was vigorously rubbed with a piece of leather obtained from a pump, creating a static charge. This charge was then stored in a Leyden Jar which Jenkyns had made from a bottle that had been sent to one of the school boys containing 'physic from the apothecary'. This was used to give an electric shock to a younger boy as part of an elaborate prank Andrew set up. This young boy was William Broderip, who was later to become a close friend of Andrew, and described what happened:

> When the electrical experiments began, Crosse was in the sixth form; and I was in the first and lowest, a child under seven years of age, and known to the 'big fellows' of the sixth only as 'a Black', a thing to be bullied and belaboured. I well remember being brought up by Woodford – then I think in the fifth – to what I took for an old witch who was standing by an upright sort of doorless box; one of the 'presses', as they were called, which stood in the hall. At the back of the box was a transparency representing a place which is said to be paved with good intentions; and before it, suspended and apparently dancing, pitchfork in hand, a frightful medieval devil.

> While I gazed in horror, a shock shot through my terrified frame, which I must have borne tolerably well, for I was afterward let into the secret, and assisted in bringing up other 'Blacks' to the scratch. The old witch was Andrew in a great coat with a pocket handkerchief tied under his chin and covering his head … .

The 'devil' was apparently suspended by a single human hair which was invisible to the onlooker. Such activities earned him the not unflattering nickname of 'Conjurer', almost anticipating a nickname by which he was to be known by local people a couple of decades later, the 'Wizard of the Quantocks'. After the success of these initial experiments, Andrew's enthusiasm for electricity increased and he determined to buy a piece of electrical machinery. For six months he saved up every farthing of pocket money and, with great determination, passed by the tavern, with its tempting array of cooked meats, despite a return to being hungry and half-starved. Eventually he had enough money to buy an electrical 'cylinder', from Mr Nicholls's Philosophical Instrument Maker's Shop on The Parade in Bristol. However, shortly afterwards an accident befell his machine, which Andrew mentions in a letter written to his mother on 8 October 1801:

> I received your letter the day before yesterday, and have taken this opportunity to answer it. As to my cylinder, &c., as they were not of so much value, I am consoled about their loss; but I have good news to tell you; there is peace. I suppose you have heard it before, but the articles are not yet signed; when they are there will be illuminations, bonfires, fireworks, and all the rejoicings that can be invented. The inhabitants of Bristol are mad with joy. As to the book you sent me – it is not very entertaining, but I hope you will send me some other soon. I am in good health, and hope you and Saturn are. Last Tuesday the boys did English verses on the peace … .

The peace he refers to was a treaty negotiated to end the war between Britain and the Danes, Swedes and Russians. It is probable that it was the rotating glass cylinder of Andrew's electrostatic generator that got broken. Shortly after this letter he again wrote home to his mother asking for five guineas to buy a new electrical machine. This was a seventeen year old asking for, what was then, a great deal of money. Susanna granted his request and sent him the money. So it was not long before Andrew was making his way back to Nicholls's shop with his five gold guineas. In the shop he began to discuss electricity with Nicholls, and he must have been impressed when Andrew said he was curious about some experiments carried out by a namesake of the instrument maker that he had seen mentioned in *Nicholson's Dictionary*. Nicholls said that he was the person mentioned in the book, and Andrew was amazed that this was not only the man mentioned in print but someone who was a real electrician. The boy listened with great respect to all Nicholls had to say, and later recalled how this 'seemed to me an epoch in my life.' Andrew continued his interest in electrical matters in addition to his school studies, but this enjoyable part of his life could not continue forever. In 1802 he left school after six generally happy years there, which he often looked back on fondly in later years, despite the starvation rations and regular canings.

Andrew matriculated at Oxford on 7 May 1802. Matriculation at Oxford University, where it is known as Responsions, is the formal admission of a student to the university. This involved taking an entrance examination, consisting of relatively simple questions in three subjects, Latin, ancient Greek and mathematics. Andrew entered Brasenose College as a Gentleman Commoner reading the Classics, Latin, Greek, Logic and Divinity, but fortunately this syllabus did not affect his natural talent for scientific thinking or his passion for it. The 18th century has been described as the period characterised by the drunken Oxford undergraduate and Brasenose was perceived as a place where the prosperous sons of gentlemen got a small measure of education and did a great deal of fox hunting, horse racing and drinking. At the time that Andrew was there the College was one of the wealthiest in Oxford and had become the college of the country gentry.

Unlike his school days Andrew did not enjoy his time at Brasenose. This is clear from the few references he made to it in later years compared to the many recollections of his time at school. He heartily disliked wine, but as this was the main drink of student parties at that time had no choice but to drink it. He himself said he did not have the moral courage to refuse to go to the parties thrown by his fellows. Indeed, in one of his letters to his mother he said that 'Oxford was a perfect hell upon earth', and expresses what sounds like despair: 'What chance is there for an unfortunate lad just come from school launched into every species of extravagance, no one to watch or care for him – no guide?' Over indulgence in drink was not just confined to the students. Andrew described how he often saw his tutor carried off 'perfectly intoxicated.'

Andrew was now mixing with members of the aristocracy, with their very clear inbred views on life and the class system and, to his later regret, he adopted many of their prejudices. Andrew's natural liberality was submerged under the 'upper class' influence of his fellow students. On one occasion, when reading Aristotle's writing on Friendship, his tutor said 'Don't you think this rather too romantic?' To which Andrew replied 'I think a man ought to make every sacrifice for his friend.' He was upset when he saw the smile of derision on all his fellows' faces, and took no further part in the discussion. This fear of ridicule haunted much of his time at Oxford. Later he was to say that 'it took some years to rub off the prejudices of class which I had acquired at Oxford.' After three not very happy years, Andrew graduated with a BA, and it must have been with a great sense of relief that he returned to Fyne Court.

Andrew adored his mother Susanna, and had developed a particularly close relationship with her after his father died in 1800 when he was just sixteen. Andrew described her as a 'pure, simple, and innocent being, with a lofty and generous mind.' Andrew's second wife, Cornelia, with keen insight, talking about the death of Andrew's father felt that 'had a few more years of life been granted to this judicious and affectionate parent, it would have been well for his son, now left to the charge of a mother whose only fault, but very grave fault, was an over indulgence of her favourite child. The natural impetuosity of his temper required a firmer hand than that of a women to guide him in his early career.' Andrew was to present a complex character as an adult, with conflicting emotions and views, shaped by the upbringing and experiences of his early life.

While Susanna was running the estate on Andrew's behalf it is unlikely that any major changes to either the house or grounds were made. However, his happiness at being home for good and not having to return to his hated university, was to be short-lived. His mother had not been well for some time and was ailing. Andrew was twenty-one on the 17 June 1805, which should have been a happy time, but Susanna was once again really ill. The villagers, to celebrate Andrew's coming of age, rang a peal on the church bells, but Andrew ran up to the church, only a few hundred yards from the house, to stop them, asking how they dared to ring the bells when his mother was so ill. When he returned to the house his mother said 'What, shall I not hear the bells ring for the coming of age of my eldest son?' To which Andrew replied 'No, mother; I will allow of no rejoicings while you are ill and suffering.' On 3 June 1805 his mother died, leaving Andrew and his brother distraught. She was buried at Broomfield Church on 10 July. In her will, dated 21 March 1805, drawn up only three months before her death, she made various land bequests to her sons Andrew and Richard, and also included bequests and statements that give insights both to her character and her relationship with Andrew:

> ... I give and bequeath unto my said son Andrew the sum of one hundred pounds and also Boydell's edition of Milton in three volumes folio and one Octavo volume of Fitzosborne's Letters, also I give unto my said son Andrew my chaise and harness coach horses and cart and an equal half part or share of my cows sheep and all my other livestock ... I also give to my said son Andrew the pair of silver candlesticks purchased by myself and a dozen of silver tea spoons and a silver soup ladle marked in my own hand and I request my said son Andrew to give his sister Louisa a gold chaised watch and steel chain I used to wear and also a gold seal and chain which were their Grandmothers. I assure my dear son Andrew and intreat him to believe that he is equal to my other son in my affectionate regard and that my sole reason for giving more of my property to my youngest son Richard than to himself is that my son Andrew is amply provided for by a patrimonial estate.

From now on, only a few months after graduating from university, Andrew was the master of the Fyne Court estate (plate 3). It seems that he had hoped to go on the Grand Tour after university as his father had done, to visit the classical world, particularly Greece, his favourite ancient land, but it was not to be. In a letter to his school friend John Kenyon in 1817 he wrote 'I well remember when, at one-and-twenty, I said I should be miserable if I thought I should die without having seen Greece and Italy; and yet now I must sit down contented with only an historical acquaintance with those countries, having a thousand other subjects to attend to.' He had an extreme diffidence, perhaps caused by shyness, which was probably instilled in him by his mother. He was very reluctant to speak publicly, but once persuaded was able to address audiences and convey his enthusiasm to them. This applied not only to scientific audiences but even rowdy crowds at political meetings.

He had a great sense of 'fair play for all', which is why he was a republican landowner, but also played a part in society in both Somerset and London. He suffered periodic bouts of depression, but had a great sense of fun and enjoyed jokes. He often felt he was isolated in the fastness of the Somerset hills, but loved them passionately. He hated country towns but loved London where he had a house and many friends, and often went there. He would also visit London when he was suffering from one of his periodic bouts of depression as this often relieved the problem. In his fifties he formed many more friendships and acquaintances after his second marriage. Andrew often expressed his feelings in poetry, and the first four verses of 'Humility and Defiance' seem to express this conflict within him:

What thoughts conflicting in my bosom rise!
This strikes me down, that lifts me to the skies!
Now I recline an infant at the breast,
Now stride a warrior with forbidding crest.

Here grovel low a helpless, earthly clod,
There pant defiance to the oppressor's rod;
At first with not a finger to oppose,
Then every pulse with hostile fury glows.

Or, soft as rill which pour their sacred stream
In nightly murmurs on the poet's dream;
Or firm as rocks whose echo laughs to scorn
The puny summons of the huntsman's horn.

The windows of my soul at once reveal
A twig of osier and a bar of steel:
Thus good and ill, and light and shade, combine,
And, though distinct, in folds together twine.

CHAPTER THREE
A Return to Fyne Court:
1805–1820

Andrew and Richard were deeply upset by their mother's death, particularly so because of the closeness that had developed after their father had died in 1800. Andrew, as the eldest son, had inherited the Fyne Court estate, but in practice it had been run by his mother, presumably with the help of a land agent. In his will Andrew's father left his leasehold properties in Broomfield 'held under the late Sir Charles Kemys Tynte Baronet or his widow' to Susanna for life, and after her death to his second son Richard. His freeholdings, the moiety of Shattocks Down, were also left to Susanna 'for and during the term of her natural life.' After her death they were to pass to his youngest son Richard. In addition, he left 'my real and personal estate of any kind and nature not before bequeathed … to … my eldest son Andrew. With the death of his mother so shortly after he finished university, Andrew had had no opportunity to acquire knowledge of the day to day needs of running an estate. His classical education was no help in this task, and his second wife, Cornelia, noted that Andrew had 'no business habits and was wanting altogether a common prudence; he implicitly trusted, without discrimination, in all those around him.' He obviously struggled to come to grips with the complexity of his new life, and had problems with some dishonest people and was a victim of both his own and others' mismanagement. Years later, Andrew wrote:

> If I were to write a book, its object should be to show the mistakes people make at the commencement of their career. A boy comes from school, or a young man from Oxford or Cambridge, with a taste for the classics, and perhaps some knowledge of mathematics; but what does he understand of

the management of his property, the duties of a magistrate, or the ordinary business of life? Agents, ever ready to assist the inexperienced, transact the young landowner's business for him, and his estates soon become involved. After years of discomfort, this truth dawns upon him, that if a man wishes anything to be well done, he must do it himself, and so it goes on; each man buys his own experience, but sometimes it is bought too dear.

Andrew was living at Fyne Court with his brother Richard and his half-sister Louisa, and they seemed to have enjoyed themselves. One person commented that their household was more noted for hospitality than economy! However, Andrew was not confined to Somerset as he also spent time in London with his friends there. One of his friends at this time was Theodore Hook, and they enjoyed each others company, both in Somerset and London. The young men got on well as they shared a great sense of humour and a liking for practical jokes. Hook himself said that at school he principally distinguished himself for mischief and deceptiveness. He spent one year at Harrow School, and Matriculated at Oxford, but never resided there and spent only two terms at St. Mary Hall before leaving to resume his more exciting and high-spirited life. Andrew's pranks tended to be harmless and not designed to humiliate his victim, but Hook had no such qualms. Hook achieved rather more respectable distinction when, aged only sixteen in 1804, he wrote a number of comic operas with his father, James. As he grew older his practical jokes became more and more elaborate. One involved writing 4,000 letters! Andrew and he were close friends when they were both in their twenties, and Andrew recalled Hook's quickness in coming up with comic verse. On one occasion he was dining at Hook's lodgings when another guest, Mr Winter, a Tax Inspector, arrived. Hook immediately called out:

Here comes Mr. Winter, inspector of taxes,
I'd advise ye to give him what e'er he axes,
I'd advise ye to give him without any flummery,
For though his name's Winter, his actions are summery.

Their friendship ended in 1813 when Hook used his contacts to get appointed to the post of Account-General of Mauritius on a salary of £2,000 a year, despite having no experience of accountancy. Four years later £12,000 was embezzled by a deputy official, but Hook was held responsible and jailed for two years and his property seized. He later became editor of *John Bull* (a Sunday paper), and wrote several novels. He died in debt in 1841 and his property was seized by the Crown. Despite this he has been described as one of the most brilliant, genial and original figures of the Georgian period.

Not surprisingly, with all the responsibilities of a landowner thrust on Andrew, he considered other careers. He is believed to have tried two or three terms as a trainee lawyer, but it was not for him and he soon abandoned all thoughts of this, although a number of his friends followed this course. However, if he had succeeded in the law it could have come in useful! The Fyne Court estate was held by Andrew as tenancy as set up by his great uncle in 1766, and in 1808 Andrew began an action of 'common recovery'. This was a legal process by which land was transferred instead of using a conveyance. At this time a number of actions involved a 'legal fiction', in this case involving a notional tenant, who was theoretically ejected to effect the transfer. This action concerned the estate and the inheritance of Andrew Crosse (1704-66), and young Andrew wanted to take back the fee simple [freehold] of the estates from John Tyndale Warre Bampfylde, who was the heir of one of the original trustees, Copplestone Warre Bampfylde.

Having recovered from the death of his mother in 1805 Andrew took over the running of the estate. About this time Andrew met George Singer (1786-1817) in London, another enthusiast of electrical science. After his father's death, Singer helped his mother with the family business, a feather and artificial flower manufactory at their home in Prince's Street, Cavendish Square. However, he spent his spare time in the laboratory / lecture hall he built at the rear of his mother's house. He made almost all his equipment himself, and improved the design of existing apparatus, and at one time built a Voltaic Pile consisting of 20,000 silver and zinc plates. From at least 1808 he was giving lectures and demonstrations at his mother's house and from 1810 also lectured at the Russell Institution, by which date he was describing himself as a 'Lecturer on Chemistry and Natural Philosophy.' He used the money from his lecturing and demonstrations to fund his research. They became close friends, and Singer often stayed at Fyne Court where they engaged in studying various aspects of static electricity.

Singer provided Andrew with a cylindrical electrical machine and battery table which held fifty Leyden Jars. The electrical machine was used to create a static electrical charge. A handle was used to turn the glass cylinder rapidly against a cloth pad and the electrical charge drawn off by means of sharply pointed brass conductors placed close to the glass. The charge could be 'stored' in the Leyden Jars. Andrew was mainly involved in testing the power of his newly acquired electrical machine under different conditions, and exploring the charging powers of positive and negative conductors. Andrew and George Singer planned and carried out a long series of experiments to explore static electricity. Although known for over 2,500 years, it was dismissed by Sir Isaac Newton as merely a source of amusement rather than a serious study, something Andrew and George Singer obviously did not agree with.

Singer often visited Fyne Court, and he and Andrew used to take long walks in the hills, discussing the results of their work and planning further experiments, exploring the landscape and its geology, but both were also able to appreciate its beauty. This was the period when Andrew began his serious research into various areas of Natural Philosophy, learning the practicalities of chemistry, studying geology and, of course his great passion, electricity. Andrew, when his attention turned to a subject or matter for investigation, always wished to examine it from his own, often unique, point of view. He always made it clear that this was not because he felt his opinion was superior and he greeted each new discovery equally with genuine gratification, whether they were made by others or himself. Indeed, to a large extent the only aim of his life was to uncover the truth and reveal the marvels and mysteries of nature. He was a true scientist as he never accepted a fact as true without proving it was so by experiment, unless the rationale of the subject was such that it was incontrovertible. He was working at a time when discoveries were being made by many 'gentlemen scientists', but which often led to more questions than answers. Another trait of the true scientist that Andrew exhibited was that if an experimental result suggested something contrary to received knowledge, he would spend months or years in trying to identify the true cause. He and other scientists of that period often made discoveries that were not, apparently, related to each other. The links to make up the full story or explanation were sometimes decades off, and this often also applied to the practical applications of their discoveries.

In 1806 Fyne Court had an unexpected visit from Robert Southey, whose reputation as a poet had begun to flower following the publication of the first of his epic poems, *Madoc*, the previous year. This time it was Andrew who was the master of the estate, and the two seem to have taken an instant liking to each other, although after this initial meeting were only to see each other occasionally. About 1807, while still grappling with the complexity of running his estate, Andrew began his first experiment on electro-crystallisation, an interest which was to last for years. His interest was sparked by the existence of a cave system called Holwell Cavern, in the parish of Broomfield. Found by quarry workers about 1800, it is unique in being the only known cave in the Quantock Hills. He was drawn to it for a number of reasons. With his romantic streak it inspired poetry, but his scientific side was fascinated by its rock formations. Its walls were covered with crystals of aragonite, a mineral consisting of calcium carbonate, in various formations and sizes. His interest was aroused by the method by which crystals were formed. He thought that the crystals were created by the dripping of water laden with 'carbonate of lime' (calcite), but that there was some other agency involved. With further thought he felt that the crystals that lined the roof were caused by some 'upward attraction'. Could that be an electric charge? Andrew decided to try an experiment:

> The water of this cave contains ten grains of carbonate of lime and a minute portion of sulphate of lime in each pint. I took some of this water and filled a wine-glass with it, and by means of two platina wires connected to it with the poles of a voltaic battery, composed of 200 pairs of five inch plates, in Wedgwood troughs, filled with water alone. During the first nine days no alteration took place at either pole, except the usual disengagement of the gases at either end. On the tenth day I perceived by the aid of a lens, a deposit of crystalline carbonate of lime at the negative pole: at the end of

about three weeks the whole of the carbonate of lime contained in the glass was arranged in a crystalline form around the negative wire. These crystals were mostly irregular, but some of them were rhomboids. I then removed the wires and found by test no lime remained in the water.

He repeated the experiment again, but this time in the dark. He arranged in the cellar a similar set-up, using a Voltaic battery consisting of forty pairs of plates. Crystals formed at the negative pole after six days. Other experiments involved dripping water from Holwell Cave on to a porous insulated brick for weeks at a time, and he wrote a paper on it which was published in Volume One of the *Proceedings* of the newly founded Somerset Archaeological Society. After this initial series of experiments on the formation of crystals, family and estate matters occupied much of his time, and his work on electro-crystallography was put aside for some years. On 17 May 1809 Andrew married Mary Ann Hamilton in Broomfield Church. He was the first owner of Fyne Court to marry in that church since it began keeping records in 1630! She was the daughter of Captain John Hamilton of the 61st Regiment of Foot, whose family owned estates in Co. Fermanagh, Ireland, while her mother, Bridget, was the only daughter of George Davy of Tiverton in Devon. Mary Ann was born in London about 1776, and is known to have been resident in Bath, that most fashionable of Georgian cities, in 1809, the year she married Andrew. When she married him Mary Ann was about thirty-three years old which, at that time, was regarded as quite late to marry. Andrew was twenty-five, although it was not unusual for a younger man to marry an older woman.

Marriage was in the air that year. In 1809 Andrew's half-sister Louisa married Joseph Porter, something that caused a certain amount of scandal since Joseph was described as one of Andrew's servants. However, he may have been related to the family in some way as Andrew's mother's maiden name was Porter. He was mentioned in her will drawn up in 1805: 'I give to my servant Joseph Porter if he should be living with me at the time of my death but not otherwise twenty-five guineas.' Joseph was granted a Gamekeeper's Licence in 1805, 1806 and 1807, which may indicate he was their gamekeeper, but more likely was the estate's land agent with responsibility for many aspects of running the estate, which covered a considerable area, and incorporated land not adjoining the main estate such as a holding at Blaxhold.

On 26 June 1809 Louisa, aged thirty-six, married the thirty-nine year old Joseph at St. Michael's Church, Minehead. This seems to be another example of a member of the Crosse family not being too concerned with the social conventions of the day. After his marriage Joseph seems to have given up his work on the Crosse estate and the following spring Louisa and Joseph went to stay with her half-brother Richard at Over Stowey, sometimes called Upper Stowey, where he had settled when he moved out of Fyne Court when Andrew married. The vicar of Over Stowey, William Holland, described the couple when they attended his church on 1 April 1810:

> Prayers here in the morning and Mr. and Mrs. Porter, Mr. Crosse's sister and brother-in-law made their appearance at Church but no Mr. Crosse nor his new Bride. They behaved well at Church and tho' the lady has so very good a fortune and was a Gentlewoman, yet he who was a servant appeared full as well as she did. The singers in the Gallery showed off today for Mr. Porter, they say is a famous man at the Baseviol.

Soon after their marriage the couple moved to Minehead and lived the life of a lady and gentleman. Joseph had long been interested in music and now had time to fully devote himself to it. Six tunes that he composed were published in *A Collection of Tunes for Choirs and Congregations* by Thomas Hawkes in 1833. This was very popular with the Methodist church in the West Country. As Louisa grew older she suffered some form of mental problem and needed a lot of care, which was provided by relatives of Joseph until her death in 1849. During this sad period, Andrew was a frequent visitor to his half-sister. Joseph died in 1852, and was buried alongside his wife in the churchyard of St. Michael's church, Minehead. In his will Joseph left several bequests of nineteen guineas to various friends and relatives including Andrew and his two sons, John and Robert.

Andrew settled back into life with his new wife and was obviously very much attached to Mary Ann. They seem to have alternated their time between Fyne Court and London. Andrew was always very close to his younger brother Richard, who followed the Crosse family tradition in being a somewhat unusual person with strong views on many matters. Andrew felt that few people were equal to his brother's intellect, and that he was very fortunate in having a 'metaphysical brother'. This was very useful in counteracting Andrew's materialistic tendencies which he felt were a natural outcome for one whose main interest was in the physical sciences and who had an estate to run. Andrew once commented 'He argues more closely than anyone I ever conversed with: like Dr Johnson, a fallacy won't stand before him.'

Richard was a brilliant mathematician and had a particular passion, in reality amounting to an obsession, for the decimal system. One of the radical changes brought about by the French Revolution was the introduction of the decimal system based on the measurements of a team of French surveyors who, despite immense difficulties, managed to measure the earth's circumference. The decimal system replaced the old French form of measurements in which almost every town and village used their own units. Tallyrand introduced the new unit of measure called the metre, after the Greek word for measure. They also introduced the Revolutionary Calendar that had twelve months, each consisting of three weeks of ten days, leaving five fête days at the end of September, and a further day every fourth year called Revolution Day. This new calendar was dropped after about ten years as it was very unpopular, particularly as everyone only had a rest day every tenth day instead of every seven. Richard was not alone in thinking that this system should be introduced into Britain, but was one of the most dedicated to putting his beliefs into practice. Cornelia wrote:

> Mr. Richard Crosse was an ardent supporter of the decimal system. He literally carried out his principles in all things. His clocks were divided into ten hours: his weights and measures were all on the metrical system. And so strictly mathematical was he in all his ideas, that when he built a house it was in the form of a double cube, each room being also mathematically proportioned. Mr. Crosse used to call his brother the three M's; for his favourite studies were music, mathematics and metaphysics. And his mental influence upon Andrew was immense… .

Long after the French had abandoned decimal time, Richard was still using it. His clock would have showed that each day was ten hours long, with one hundred minutes to the hour and one hundred seconds to the minute. His decimal dwelling at Pightley, Spaxton, known as Hill House, no longer exists, having been demolished by 1890. Richard was successful in persuading the woman who kept the Globe Inn at Over Stowey to sell her beverages by the 'new measures', which almost certainly makes this the first pub in England to sell beer in decimal measures! After this success Richard stated that: 'As for the old system I mean to abandon it entirely.' He also said that he would not vote for any MP who did not promise to put forward the adoption of decimal yards and inches in Parliament. Further details of Richard's unique character is to be found in the diary of William Holland, the vicar of Over Stowey. Holland describes the day he called on him, on 26 September 1810:

> I walked over to call on Mr. Crosse this morning. I found him busy about his Astronomical Matters in a neat undress and I had a good deal of talk with him. He has a Decimal Thermometer, and a curious thing to tell which way the wind blew. He had indeed so many new things in his head that I asked him whether he had any particular horror about the Old Rules and Customs. He answered if there were no change there would be no improvement. True, but the improvement should be made evident before the changes took place. He breakfasts at 6 in the morning and is for going to bed at 6. Why then I said you must live by yourself but man is formed for society and must conform in some degree to the society he dwells among, especially in things of little moment or he must be content to live by himself. Then I proposed that he should go and live on top of Dowesbury and have a little hut and Observatory for himself. He laughed heartily at this. I then took my leave of him as his Decimal dinner was ready to which he often invited me and I as often declining, intimating that I had a dinner at three which if he could partake of after his Decimal dinner I should be glad to see him. He seems a pleasing good tempered man but somewhat enthusiastic on Mathematical matters. I know not what servants he has but I saw only one young girl and she without a cap, which I did not much approve of.

On 27 March 1810 Richard married Jane Greensill in St. Michael's Church,

Minehead, Somerset. In a letter to Andrew he described her as a 'young woman that I have the highest opinion of; as to learning mathematics; she will learn anything to please me.' On the 5 April 1810 the *Taunton Courier* carried the following announcement 'Marriages – Tuesday se'nnight at Minehead, Richard Crosse Esq. of Stowey to Miss Jane Greensill, niece to Mr. E. Jones, Feathers Tavern, Minehead.' Jane's uncle, Edward Jones, was the owner of the Plume of Feathers on the Parade at Minehead, the most impressive inn in the town. Holland's disapproval is clear from his diary entry on 27 March 1810:

> Our ringers were ordered to ring the bells for Mr. Crosse who has taken the Park Cottage (as they call it) and brought his wife home, a niece of Jones the landlord of the inn at Minehead, a sad connection for a young man of family and fortune. His sister married a servant man in the family, Mr. Porter, and they were both with him and certainly countenanced the whole business and the aunt from Minehead saw the dinner well dressed and a pretty society of them sat down to it alas! He is a young man of some abilities but his head is cracked. The sister has a very good estate, which she bestows on this manservant, a pretty hopscotch indeed.

Richard, like Andrew, had clearly been unused to the domesticity of a household with a woman's touch for quite a while. Their mother had died in 1805 when he was aged nineteen and had been at Balliol College, Oxford from May 1804, presumably spending the vacations at Fyne Court. He lived there with his brother and sister before taking a house at Over Stowey about four and a half miles (7 km) from Fyne Court. He expresses this in a letter to Andrew the week he got married: 'At present I am quite unsettled and in confusion, not ever being used to domestic affairs.' Unlike Andrew, who was a devout Christian all his life, Richard does not seem to have been particularly religious, which must have led to some fascinating metaphysical discussions between the two brothers. This lack of belief, not surprisingly, upset the vicar, who noted in his diary on 20 May 1810:

> Mr. and Mrs. Porter were at church and I bowed to them and I think spoke to them. But neither Mr. Crosse nor his wife have been to church since they were married, a strange couple indeed. He, I fear has no religion for

he has not been at church since he took the house he is in. I shall not call upon [them] unless he comes to church.

Despite his disapproval of Richard's sister marrying a 'servant', at least they went to church and his disapproving attitude to them seems to have softened somewhat. However, a month had passed and Richard and Jane had still not attended a service, as Holland noted on 24 June 1810:

> Mr. Porter was a kind of Steward to Mr. Crosse when the sister cast her eye upon him and is I believe a Relation of the family. They have been for some time at Mr. Crosses the brother who married the Bar Maid at Minehead. But they have not been to church so I cannot call, a sad degradation of a respectable family.

On 10 March 1810 Andrew and Mary Ann had their first child, John, who was born at their London house in Marylebone. Shortly after the birth the new family returned to Fyne Court and John was baptised in Broomfield Church on 21 May 1810. Andrew's family rapidly increased. Their second child, a girl, Maryanne, was born in 1811 and baptised in Broomfield Church on 5 April that year. The following year another son, Robert, was born at Fyne Court on 30 April 1812, and baptised in Broomfield Church on 7 June. Another boy, Richard, was born on 16 September 1813 and baptised in Broomfield Church on 27 September. The haste to get him baptised may suggest he was poorly, but he was to live until he was twenty-five.

Andrew's interest in science showed no diminution. He had turned to the study of atmospheric electricity, something he had often discussed with George Singer when they were together. To study this Andrew erected one and a quarter miles (2 km) of copper wire one sixteenth of an inch (1.6 mm) thick (plate 8), from trees and poles around the estate (plate 9). This was suspended at a height of 100-110 feet (30-33.5 m) above the ground. The wires were insulated at various points where fixed to a support, but these had to be lowered occasionally to clean them of spider's webs which turned the insulators into conductors. The wire had to be very securely fixed as it had to resist the weight of considerable numbers of swallows that perched on it in the Autumn prior to migrating, and the impact of wood pigeons and owls that frequently flew into it with considerable force.

Andrew later reduced the length to 3,000 feet (914 m), and then to 1,800 feet (548 m) which he found to be just as effective. It was subsequently shortened again, so that by the 1840s it was around 600-900 feet (182-274 m) long, with which he was still able to gather electricity from the atmosphere. This, which he referred to as his 'exploring wire', led into the gallery above his main laboratory in the music room (plate 7), known to close friends and family as the philosophy room. There it could be connected to a battery of fifty Leyden Jars which it would rapidly charge. Andrew provided a very detailed account of how the wire was constructed and used in *Electricity: its phenomena, laws and results* by Edwin Sidney (1843).

While a number of French scientists, L.G.Lemonnier, G. Beccaria and H.B. Saussure had carried out research on atmospheric electricity during the 18th century, almost no such investigations took place in Britain at that period. Andrew was one of the earliest scientists in Britain to carry out research into the free electricity present in the atmosphere and clouds. This acts by induction upon the earth and electromagnetic devices. His observations and experiments were carried out over many years to build up a valuable body of data. There is always free electricity in the atmosphere, which is sometimes positive and sometimes negative, but usually positive. The electricity in the atmosphere is due to the accumulation of huge static charges which seem to be generated by friction of the air upon itself. Other factors which produce atmospheric electricity include evaporation from the earth's surface, chemical changes on the surface of the earth, expansion and condensation of the moisture in the atmosphere, and temperature variations.

The intensity of the atmospheric electricity varies through the day and through the seasons, and weather conditions have a huge influence on the amount of free electricity in the air. The potential increases with altitude at the rate of 30 volts per foot (30.5 cm). Fyne Court lies 656 feet (200 m) above sea level. Andrew's 'exploring wire' was supported about 100 feet (30 m) above ground level, so that Andrew could easily, in ideal conditions, be 'capturing' at least 22,680 volts via his wire. Because of its geographic location the area often has thunderstorms developing nearby or passing over it, and at such times there was a huge amount of free electricity present. Many years later it was thanks to Andrew's work on atmospheric electricity that Michael Faraday realised that the only way to make an accurate electrometer to reproduce standard results in measuring electric potential was to screen it from the minute extraneous electrical charges in the air. The first true electrometer had been invented in 1766, but until the 1830s, when Faraday understood the effect atmospheric electricity had on them, they were not very accurate.

Andrew also used another way of exploring atmospheric electricity as he described in 1843:

> I once raised about a mile of string, with a copper thread twisted throughout its whole length, by the aid of three large kites. I found, in clear fair weather, so much electricity in the string that it gave rather severe sparks, or little shocks, to the person who touched it. The trouble, however, attending on this mode of experimenting, and the imminent danger in thunder weather, obliged me to discontinue the use of it.

He was following a method supposedly first carried out by Benjamin Franklin in June 1752 when he flew a kite from a church tower in Philadelphia to confirm that lightning was a form of electricity. The kite string was wet to act as a conductor, but he kept the end dry where he was holding it, and the end was attached to an iron key which was connected to a Leyden Jar. The kite was not struck by visible lightning, if it had Franklin would almost certainly have been killed. Franklin said he received a mild shock when he later moved his hand near the key. The only witness to this experiment was said to be his son, and doubts have been expressed as to whether he actually carried it out. Nobody else was able to duplicate his experiment in the way he described, so there is some doubt whether he actually did it. The following year Professor Georg Richman, a Swedish physicist working in St. Petersburg, Russia, tried it and was killed when a foot (30 cm) long spark from a conductor struck his head. The first known victim of high voltage experiments in the history of physics!

Andrew was well aware of the danger of such a method even in good weather, and the potential fatal consequences of trying it in a thunderstorm. It was the results of a series of observations Andrew carried out with his 'exploring wire' that first brought him to the attention of the scientific community when the results were published in George Singer's *Elements of Electricity and Electro-Chemistry*, published in 1814. Andrew's observations, made in the period c.1808-14 are still valid today, so his first published results are worth quoting:

1st. In the usual state of the atmosphere, its electricity is invariably positive.

2nd. Fogs, rain, snow, hail, and sleet produce alterations of the electric state of the wire. It is usually negative when they first appear, but sometimes changes to positive, increasing gradually in strength, and then gradually decreasing, and changing its quality every three or four minutes. These phenomena are so consistent, that whenever the negative electricity is observed in the apparatus, it is considered as certain there is either rain, snow, hail or mist in its immediate neighbourhood, or that a thunder-cloud is near.

3rd. The approach of a charged cloud produces sometimes positive and at others negative signs at first. During this display of electric power, so awful to an ordinary observer, the electrician sits quietly in front of the apparatus, conducts the lightning in any required direction, and employs it to fuse wires, decompose fluids, or fire inflammable substances; and when the effects are too powerful, he connects the insulated wire to the ground, and transmits the accumulated electricity with silence and safety.

4th. A driving fog or smart rain frequently electrifies the apparatus nearly to the same extent as a thunder-cloud, with similar changes.

5th. In cloudy weather, weak positive electricity usually prevails: if rain falls, it generally changes to negative, but the positive state is resumed when the rain ceases.

6th. In clear frosty weather the positive electricity is stronger than in a fine summer's day; and the intensity of the electrical sign at different seasons is expressed in descending order in the following list, commencing with those effects are most considerable.

> 1st. During the occurrence of regular thunder-clouds.
> 2nd. A driving fog accompanied by small rain.
> 3rd. A fall of snow, or a brisk hail-storm.
> 4th. A smart shower, especially on a hot day.
> 5th. Hot weather succeeding a series of wet days.
> 6th. Wet weather following a series of dry days.
> 7th. Clear frosty weather, by day or night.
> 8th. Clear warm summer weather.
> 9th. A sky obscured by clouds.
> 10th. A mackerel back or mottled sky.
> 11th. Sultry weather, the sky covered with light hazy clouds.
> 12th. A cold rainy night.

To this may be added the least electrical of all – a peculiar state of the atmosphere which sometimes occurs during the prevalence of north-easterly winds: it is characterised as particularly unhealthy, and is remarkable in producing a sensation of dryness or extreme cold, which is not accompanied by a corresponding depression of the thermometer.

The usual positive electricity is weakest during the night. It increases with the sunrise, decreases towards the middle of the day, and increasing as the sun declines, it then again diminishes and remains weak through the night.

This fact is one of the most instructive resulting from these observations, and is confirmed by most of the regular experiments on atmospheric electricity that have been made. It clearly proves that the electricity of the atmosphere is influenced by the same causes that promote the equal distribution of moisture.

Having come to the notice of some parts of the scientific community in Britain thanks to Singer's publication, a work of considerable importance, Andrew's pioneering work gained even wider notice when *Elements of Electricity and Electro-Chemistry* was translated into French (1817), Italian (1819) and German (1819). The 'exploring wire' terminated inside Andrew's laboratory and was used to charge a 'battery' of Leyden Jars. This consisted of fifty Leyden Jars amounting to 73 square feet of coated surface. To charge this using a 20 inch (51 cm) cylindrical machine required 230 vigorous turns of the wheel. Hard work! However, using his copper 'exploring wire' Andrew could charge and discharge this twenty times in a minute. To do this he had a large brass ball suspended from the ceiling immediately over the Jars and connected, by means of a long wire, with the conductor in the gallery. This ball was raised from and let down to the battery by means of a long silk cord passing over a pulley in the ceiling. When the atmospheric electricity generated was charging and discharging the Leyden Jars it caused loud bangs like cannons going off. Andrew himself described how, during one day in November when the weather was driving rain and dense fog, his wire, at this time 1,600 feet (487 m) long, became electrically charged. The brass ball in the atmospheric conductor was an inch apart from the receiving brass ball:

> About four o'clock in the afternoon, whilst I was still reading, I suddenly heard a very strong explosion between the two balls, and shortly after many more took place, until they became one uninterrupted stream of explosions, which died away and recommenced with the opposite electricity in equal violence.

> The stream of fire was too vivid to look at for any length of time, and the effect was most splendid, and continued without intermission, save that occasioned by the interchange of electricities, for upwards of five hours, and then ceased totally.

Andrew fully understood the power of the atmospheric electricity that he was attracting, and if the load became too great he was able to throw a switch and earth it. He was well aware that if something went wrong it could be fatal. He described in 1843 how, on one occasion, he received a shock from atmospheric electricity gathered by his 'exploring wire' when it was still 3,000 feet (914 m) long. He was experimenting by holding a small penknife against the terminus of the wire in his laboratory when there was a loud bang, the tip of the penknife he was holding was fused, and a 'small perforation' made in two of his fingers. His fingers were badly swollen and his whole hand paralysed, although fortunately this wore off after a few hours and he was able to use his hand again. As far as we know he never suffered any really serious injury, unlike some other early electrical scientists, a few of whom were killed.

The explosions and bright flashes of light while Andrew was conducting his experiments was the reason he became known locally as the 'Thunder and Lightning Man'. There is no doubt that many local people were scared of him. One of the advantages of this fear was that he had more game on his land than his neighbours as poachers were afraid to come onto the estate! So he had plenty of pheasants and, it seems, large numbers of rabbits. Andrew was noted as a 'capital shot'. His fish ponds were abundantly stocked with perch and some of his guests used to spend an hour or two fishing. Cornelia noted that because of all the bangs and flashes issuing from Andrew's laboratory, they were never burgled!

Not only did Andrew come to the notice of a wider public in Singer's work published in 1814, but Singer persuaded Andrew to give a lecture at Garnerin's Lecture Hall and Gallery on 28 December that year. This was where André-Jacques Garnerin presented talks and demonstrations on galvanism, the medical and other uses of electricity and various subjects of a scientific nature. The placards announcing the evening's entertainment described Andrew as the 'Electrician from Somerset' who would give a talk on 'Electricity and the Elements'. This was the first occasion that Andrew spoke in public. The evening also included a display of 'Phantasmagoria', that is a magic lantern display of various instructive and novelty slides where levers caused movement of part of the image. Such displays were very popular and amazed audiences with their novelty and the mystery of how the pictures moved. Two notable figures visited Garnerin's that evening. Mary Wollstonecraft Godwin, the mistress and later (1816) the second wife of the poet Percy Bysshe Shelley (1792-1822), who accompanied her. This visit is noted in Mary's diary:

Wednesday, December 28th. Shelley and Clara out all morning. Read *French Revolution* in the evening. Shelley and I go to Garry's Inn to get

Hogg; he is not there; go to Arundel Street; can't find him. Go to Garnerin's. Lecture on electricity; the gases, and the phantasmagoria; return at half-past 9. Shelley goes to sleep. Read *View of French Revolution* till 12; go to bed.

It is this visit by Mary to Garnerin's that has caused some writers to claim that Andrew was the inspiration for the novel *Frankenstein or the modern Prometheus*, as it was Mary Shelley that wrote the book about a scientist who created life. It is not clear from her diary entry how long they actually spent at the lecture hall. Did they sit and listen to what was on offer, or did they just pop in searching for their friend Thomas Hogg (1792-1862)? The idea for *Frankenstein* came to Mary in 1816 when she spent the summer on the shores of Lake Geneva, where Lord Byron was also staying. She began her story after Byron suggested having a ghost story competition. Mary completed her work when she returned to England and it was published in 1818. It has become one of the most famous horror stories, but which few people have read today.

In 1931 the film *Frankenstein* was made by Universal Studios, directed by James Whale with Boris Karloff playing the Creature. There are more differences between the film and Mary's book than similarities because the film was based on a play, itself loosely based on Mary's book, by Peggy Webling that was staged in the 1920s. In the novel the details of how Dr Victor Frankenstein actually builds his Creature and animates it are very vague. Only in the film does Frankenstein acquire the body bits by grave robbing, while one of the most memorable and spectacular scenes in the film is the harnessing of a lightning bolt to give the Creature life. Sequels followed. *The Bride of Frankenstein* (1935), *The Son of Frankenstein* (1942) and *The Ghost of Frankenstein* (1942). The film has been spoofed a number of times over the years, perhaps one of the funniest is *The Young Frankenstein* (1975) directed by Mel Brooks which features Gene Wilder as Dr Frankenstein. In all of these films lightning provides the 'spark of animation', and so most people believe that this is what Mary said in her novel. It is this mistaken belief that has now firmly passed into popular folklore and has helped ensure Andrew Crosse is still remembered. Hollywood is not known for its historical accuracy!

Mary was probably familiar with the principles of electricity before she attended Garnerin's, and certainly would have been before she wrote her novel, as her lover, Shelley, had been fascinated with chemistry and electricity since he was at school. Contemporary reports describe how his room at Oxford University was packed with a variety of scientific and electrical equipment, and he was always delighted to give demonstrations of his electric machine and galvanic battery. However, in Mary's novel the creature is brought to life by chemical means, and there is not a single mention of lightning or electricity. Some extracts from the book show both the importance to Frankenstein (the name of the scientist not the Creature), of chemistry, and clearly shows that his creation's animation was due to his chemical apparatus:

The Main Focus of Frankenstein's Study in Shelley's Book.

His Field of Study.
From this day natural philosophy, and particularly chemistry, in the most comprehensive sense of the term, became nearly my sole occupation.

Giving Life to his Creation.
It was a dreary night of November that I beheld the accomplishment of my toils. With an anxiety that almost amounted to agony, I collected the instruments of life around me, that I might infuse a spark of being into the lifeless thing that lay at my feet. It was already one in the morning; the rain pattered dismally against the pane, and my candle was nearly burnt out, when, by the glimmer of the half-extinguished light, I saw the dull yellow eye of the creature open, it breathed hard, and a convulsive motion agitated its limbs.

Cleaning up the Equipment that Conferred Life on the Creature.
… yet, before I departed, there was a task to perform, on which I shuddered to reflect: I must pack up my chemical instruments … .

… and in the meantime I sat upon the beach, employed in cleaning and arranging my chemical apparatus.

Andrew's other claim to 'popular folklore fame', is the belief that he himself accidentally created life in 1836, and sometimes the two claims seem to have become entwined in people's minds. While there is no doubt that Mary was at Garnerin's Lecture Hall when Andrew was giving his talk, there is no real reason to suppose that it inspired her to write the novel two years later. Indeed, in the very detailed book *In Search of Frankenstein* by Radu Florescu (1999) which examines the myths and facts of the story, Andrew does not appear at all! Singer mentioned Andrew and his work again in 1815 in the *Philosophical Magazine* (46, 163) and he also encouraged Andrew to publish an account of his work in that journal the same year. Entitled 'Experiments in Voltaic Electricity', this was Andrew's first paper.

Andrew occasionally enlarged the estate, which had been much reduced since 'uncle Andrew' had left it to his father. In 1814 Andrew was negotiating the purchase of land on Broomfield Hill and Common 'to permit a line to be drawn through the whole property between us. This will diminish neither property, but will increase the value of both.' Despite his marriage, rapidly increasing family, and working hard to get the maximum income from the estate, he still had time to carry out civic responsibilities. He was sworn in as a Justice of the Peace on 13 January 1815, witnessed by Charles Kemys Tynte (who had proposed him), Thomas Mullins and Henry Parsons. Andrew held this post until his death. Justices were not required to have any formal legal training, and their role was to dispense summary justice, deal with local administrative applications in Common Law and appoint Constables. Andrew was also an Overseer of the Poor from about the same date. The position of Overseer, of which most parishes had two, was created under the *Poor Law Act* of 1579. By the 18th century they, along with the churchwardens, were responsible for setting and collecting the Poor Law Rates from parishioners and distributing the funds for the relief of the poor.

Under an amendment to the Act in 1722 each parish was authorised to establish a workhouse, and the relief could be declined if the applicant refused to go into it, a fate many considered almost worse than death. However, Broomfield, like many other small country parishes could not afford to build a workhouse, and did not have enough poor to justify it anyway. They did have a Parish Poor House, a small building which was situated to the west of the churchyard, but this seems to have been demolished by 1839, and the introduction of new Poor Law regulations meant that the parish's poor were removed to the Union Workhouse in either Bridgwater or Taunton. Andrew did not like this new system, and said 'Those wretched prisons should more aptly be termed Dis-union Houses', since they separated men and women even if they were a married couple.

Charity was given directly to the needy in various ways. Benefactors left fields to the parish, so that their rental income could be used for charitable purposes, and others left sums of money to be invested. Andrew and his fellow Overseer would have been responsible for this income and seeing it was used as directed, and for supervising the Parish Poor House until the change of legislation. He would have seen that the roast beef and plum pudding, with bread and vegetables, was in sufficient quantity, and a pint of beer, were provided at a dinner for six poor men and six poor women of Broomfield each Christmas and each Easter Day. Twelve loaves were provided for the poor each Sunday. Other Broomfield charities provided six shillings and articles useful in childbirth just before the event, while another provided small sums to be distributed on St. Thomas's Day, 21 December. John Jeanes, one of the trustees of 'uncle Andrew's' will, left money to be invested, the income of which was used to buy 'implements of husbandry' to be given on 2 April each year to 'the poor people of Broomfield as were honest and industrious …', but it was conditional that the tools must not be sold or pawned. Andrew would have attended regular meetings with the vicar, churchwardens and members of the Parish Vestry to consider such matters as the rate they should set, how much had been collected, who had not paid, who needed help and how much had been expended on giving assistance to the poor of the parish. Despite these social duties, Andrew did not neglect science.

The year 1815 saw the birth of Andrew's second daughter, Susanna, who was baptised in Broomfield Church on 4 June that year. He also seems to have had some major work done on Fyne Court House that year, which he mentions in a letter to John Kenyon dated 23 July: '… I have been more busy that ever winding up my last business with workmen of all descriptions. I have now totally finished with the carpenter, mason, smith, plumber and glazier on my house and premises, having left nothing not even a hinge, or a handle of a drawer, but what is completely in order.' In this letter Andrew also expresses his wish to see Napoleon Bonaparte if he lands at Plymouth. Napoleon had surrendered to Captain Frederick Maitland of HMS *Bellerophon* on 15 July 1815. He was transported in the *Bellerophon* to Torbay in Devon, anchoring off Brixham on 24 July. Captain Maitland received orders from Admiral Lord Keith that no one, except the ship's crew and officers was to come on board. However, the attempt to keep the news that Napoleon was on his ship secret failed when a seaman told a baker who had rowed out with supplies, and had not been allowed aboard, the reason why supply ships were being kept away. When the baker rowed back to shore with the news it soon became widely known that the former Emperor was on board. Maitland kept boats from coming alongside, but made no further attempt to conceal Napoleon's presence. Two days later *Bellerophon* received orders to proceed to Plymouth where Lord Keith was anchored aboard his flagship, the *Ville de Paris*.

Andrew had a keen interest in French affairs, and followed events before and after the Napoleonic Wars. This was not surprising as he had lived there for a time as a small child. His family was there during an exciting and historically important period for the country, and he must also have heard about his father's adventures during his continental travels both before and during the Revolution. Andrew clearly stated why he wanted to 'get a peep' at Napoleon:

> It must be gratifying to rest one's eyes upon a man who will live to the end of time, whose name will be in the mouths of all nations, when our bodies are mouldered to dust. Excepting him and Wellington, I have no great ambition to see the continental kings, who will fill up the intervals of history, like notches in a prisoner's stick.

Andrew rode to Plymouth and was lucky enough to glimpse Napoleon on the evening he arrived. He was one of the great many people who boarded small vessels to be carried out to surround the *Bellerophon*, hopefully to catch a sight of the defeated Emperor. The owners of these small boats must have made a small fortune carrying passengers out to the naval vessel. The next day Andrew was aboard one of these boats when Lord Keith ordered *Bellerophon* to put to sea and await the arrival of HMS *Northumberland*, which had been designated to carry Napoleon into exile on the island of St. Helena. The vessel that Andrew was in was a sailing boat and was able to follow the *Bellerophon* for some distance, giving Andrew the chance to see Napoleon on deck once more. On returning to Fyne Court Andrew made a note about this historic event that he had been lucky enough to have witnessed:

> I left home on Wednesday morning about eight o'clock, reached Exeter on my mare about four o'clock, left Exeter ten o'clock the same night, reached Plymouth Dock at half after five Thursday morning, saw Bonaparte about six o'clock same night. He started in the Bellerophon, without signal, at about one o'clock, Friday, August 4th, 1815, was met by a sloop-of-war, who exchanged signals with the Bellerophon; followed by the Eurotus frigate with French officers of rank aboard, also by the [blank] and Glasgow frigate and Mackerel schooner. The Bellerophon bore eastward, and I followed her some hours; was on the water from twelve to two; sailed ten miles from dock, and about twenty-five or thirty in all. Saw Bonaparte between decks, afterwards, in the cabin window, the curtain of which was drawn by a French lady; got within thirty yards of him, and was told by Captain Maitland to keep off.

Andrew must also have been aware that HMS *Bellerophon* was one of the most famous warships of the Napoleonic period. A 74-gun third rate Ship-of-the-Line, launched in 1786, she fought at the battle of the Glorious First of June under the command of Captain William Johnstone Hope. In 1798 she fought at the Battle of the Nile under Captain Henry D'Esterre Darby, and in 1805 she took part in the Battle of Trafalgar. There she was fifth in Admiral Collingwood's Southern Division and was heavily engaged in the battle, fighting the French *L'Aigle* to a standstill, despite the death of her Captain, John Cooke, command being taken over by her First Lieutenant. Andrew's close friend John Kenyon often visited him and had become very fond of the West Country, so that on his first marriage in 1802 Kenyon rented a house, known as Woodlands, between Nether Stowey, where Tom

Poole lived, and Holford four miles (6.4 km) away where Alfoxton, the house of his other school friend, Langley St. Albyn, was located. Kenyon rented this house until 1815 when, with the end of the Napoleonic War, travel on the Continent became easy again, so he, and many others, once more travelled abroad to visit Italy, Germany, Austria and Greece.

In 1816 Andrew showed an example of how he was able to foresee the practical use of electricity in everyday life. He was at a dinner party given by his school friend Langley St. Albyn at Alfoxden House when he startled the other guests by stating that 'by means of the electric agency we shall be enabled to communicate our thoughts instantaneously with the uttermost parts of the earth.' While the possibility of sending messages down a wire had been demonstrated as early as the 18th century, most, if not all, of these early attempts (1729 in England, 1753 in Scotland, 1774 in Switzerland, 1804 in Spain and 1812 in Germany) would have been unknown to him. Andrew was to live long enough to see the laying of an electric telegraph across the Channel, connecting England with Europe in 1851. In 1816 Andrew began another complex legal action to overturn provisions of his great uncle's will regarding the holding of land at Broomfield as a tenant rather than a freeholder. Andrew agreed to a £10,000 bond of indemnity to John Tyndale Warre in respect of missing, forgotten or non-existent earlier conveyances of the estate to Thomas Mullins, who was authorised to hold all the Fyne Court lands with the proviso that Andrew and his heirs should be 'accommodated for ever.' This was separate to that taken in 1808, but also seems to have involved an artificial transfer of property from one individual to another.

The year 1817 brought bad news for Andrew as his great friend, George Singer, fell ill due to 'breaking a blood vessel in the lungs.' Up to that time Singer had been in good health, was strongly built and, apparently, had a calm demeanour. His doctor forbade him to read, a difficult order for someone with such an active mind, and to get plenty of rest, but this did not help. Singer died of pulmonary consumption, unmarried, on 28 June 1817 at his mother's house in London, aged only thirty. The following year his collection of scientific apparatus was sold at Stewart's Auction Rooms. Andrew wrote to his friend John Kenyon a few days after Singer died, lamenting his passing and considering the nature of death, but went on to say, prophetically as it was to turn out: 'I who say this am not tormented by Blue Devils. I can be comparatively happy in all situations and places, and could live a thousand years as I now am without feeling *ennui*; but I know that were I to experience the loss of a child, or any other misfortune of that nature, I should suffer more pain than I ever felt pleasure.' It was in this year that Andrew again turned his attention to crystals and the part that electricity might play in their formation. He succeeded over the next thirty years in producing a number of metallic and other crystals found in nature, and even substances that were not found in the natural world. Unfortunately, with the loss of his good friend Singer, Andrew had no-one with whom to share his exciting results. Composing poetry continued to play a large part of his life and often reflected his inner feelings, such as this example:

The Three Trenches.

Three circling trenches round my heart I throw,
To keep at bay each intermeddling foe.
Within the first the world may enter free,
Whate'er their sect, opinion, or degree;
Safe o'er the next, I greet a fair array,
Serenely smiling as a summer's day;
To pass the third, alas! how few contrive!
And of those dearest few, how few survive!

His poems also reflected his great love of nature and his beloved Quantock Hills. He was an observant naturalist and often made notes of the behaviour of birds and animals seen on his walks. Andrew was also a careful observer of natural history. He recorded a curious incident one day at Fyne Court. He was looking out of his laboratory window into the courtyard and saw a robin dragging the apparently dead body of another robin round and round on the ground. It did this several times until it suddenly stopped and threw itself onto its back with hard-distended wings and upturned legs. This other bird then came back to life and seizing the other bird, pulled him round and round several times. Then both birds flew off to the nearby trees. He was also a great lover of trees, of which his estate had a great many large and impressive examples, something often mentioned by visitors to Fyne Court. During the Summer, the hills are covered with foxglove flowers, and one of his poems concerned this plant:

To The Foxglove.

Dearest of all the flowers that grace
    The healthy hill or tangled brake,
That to the sun turn glowing face,
    Or bow them o'er the shady lake!

That climb some friendly stem to show
    Their beauties to the wanderer's eye,
Or, dimly seen, their fragrance throw,
    Sweet duty! ere they droop and die!

Dearer than all the rainbow hues
    Or tropic tints on shrub or tree,
Or sketched by pencil or by muse,
    Art thou, surpassing flower, to me.

Surpassing! ay, thou dost surpass!
    For in thy spotted bells I view,
Mirrored as in some fairy glass,
    Past days my kindling thoughts renew!

Thou seem'st to smile with such intent,
    That as on thee abstract I gaze,
I fain would lose what fate has sent,
    And dream the dreams of bygone days.

It seems that illness frequently afflicted his family, and Andrew's second wife, Cornelia, said that he often used to walk all the way into Taunton, a distance of some five miles (8 km), even on a cold dark winter's night to seek medical advice for his sick children. Convinced that only he could do the errand, he would not send a servant. His first wife, Mary Ann, suffered prolonged ill-health, often being confined to her bed, particularly in her later years. This probably contributed to the chaos of the household described by Lady Lovelace during her stays at Fyne Court in the 1840s. It is therefore rather ironic that Collinson, in his *History and Antiquities of the County of Somerset* (1791) in writing about Broomfield says that: 'This parish has always been remarkably healthy, even in times of general sickness elsewhere.' Andrew himself had problems with his 'nerves', and according to Cornelia, 'from the age of fifteen to the time of his death, he suffered more or less from nervous attacks.' These seem to have been triggered by the death of his father, and he certainly does not seem to have shown such symptoms at school before this event. He also later suffered from depression, which often lasted for long periods and again, according to Cornelia, 'he was one of those almost morbidly anxious persons who feel and suffer all things intensely.'

In January 1818 a fourth son was born to Andrew and Mary Ann and named Andrew, but was only to have a short life. The following year was to turn out to be a dreadful year for the family. It started well with rejoicing as their third daughter, Isabella, was born on 3 April 1819, but the following month their fourth son, Andrew, aged only seventeen months, died and was buried at Broomfield on 4 June. The beginning of July saw the death of four year old Susanna who was buried at Broomfield on 8 July. With all these tragic events, it was not until the 8 November that Isabella was baptised in Broomfield Church. It is hard to imagine the feeling of the parents as they stood in the church where they had so recently buried two of their beloved children. Not surprisingly, Andrew suffered one of his periodic bouts of depression at this time. Child mortality was common during the Victorian period and death was part of everyday life for all classes of society. Patent medicines were available and doctors had a limited range of medicines available. People used old folk medicines and herbs, particularly in country districts, but new discoveries in science were also beginning to make an impact. While electricity was not understood by most people and some even regarded it as a form of magic, many did believe it had its use in medical treatments, something that had been suggested long before Andrew was even born.

John Wesley had become interested in electricity in the 1740s and began to practice electrotherapy. In 1760 he published a small book called *The Desideratum, or electricity made plain and useful*, in which he described various electrical apparatus he had used and even details of some of the patients he had treated. He advocated its use to treat a wide range of diseases such as tuberculosis, toothache and epilepsy. The therapeutic benefits of electricity were also recommended by Joseph Priestley in his *History of Electricity* (1767). During the 18th century it was used to treat royalty and the aristocracy, and this patronage gave it a respectability so that many people felt it was a good cure for all sorts of problems. Even 'electrified water' was believed to be an effective medicine. The poor of the district often used to turn up at Fyne Court to ask Andrew to use his electrical machine to cure paralysis and rheumatic problems. He would usually oblige, giving his 'patients' a mild shock, which seemed to be beneficial to many people.

Cornelia recalled how a farmer, aged over sixty, was paralysed on his left side and also had a 'distressing complaint' of the salivary glands. When he first went to Andrew for treatment he had difficulty even getting out of his gig, but he was 'electrified' twice a week for six weeks, and towards the end of the treatment he was so much better that he could not only walk to Fyne Court, but his throat problem was also completely cured. Sir Richard Phillips, in his description of Andrew's laboratory in 1836, mentions seeing a medical discharger in his main laboratory. Today electricity is still used medically to stimulate the brain, treat neurological disorders, to rehabilitate wasted muscles, to relieve muscle spasms and, in some cases, to promote the healing of wounds.

When he spent time at his London house in Charles Street, Marylebone, Andrew often met up with his old school friend John Kenyon. For thirty years Kenyon was a prominent figure in London society and knew most of the literary and scientific figures of the day. The delightful and enlightening breakfasts and dinners that he gave are often mentioned in the biographies of the notable figures that he invited. Robert Southey said he was 'one of the best and pleasantest men whom I have ever known; one whom everybody likes at first sight, and likes better the longer he is known.' He made a point of always asking any prominent foreigner to a small dinner party before launching them into Society. While many were welcomed at his table, he made a point of excluding literary critics and those he regarded as belonging to a mutual admiration clique. He had the knack of bringing the right people together. When in London, Andrew sometimes met up with both John Kenyon and his other old school friend, John Eagles. We don't know their nicknames, if any, but they often referred to Andrew as 'Devil Crosse', somewhat different to his nickname at school – Wizard Crosse. These friends, along with Kenyon's brother Edward, were frequent visitors to Fyne Court over many decades, and John Kenyon also stayed with their friend Tom Poole at Nether Stowey.

CHAPTER FOUR
Penury to Perpetual Motion: 1820–1835

It seems that Andrew may have been planning to spend more time in London in 1821 as an advertisement appeared offering Fyne Court House to let: 'The house is roomy and well calculated for the accommodation of a large family. There is every kind of attached and detached offices, a coach house and stabling for ten horses …'. It does not seem to have found a tenant, not too surprisingly as any prospective tenants would probably have been put off by all the scientific equipment and chemical apparatus that the house was filled with. So Andrew and Mary Ann remained in Somerset, and a note in the *Taunton Courier* that year notes that he took the chair at a meeting in the Assembly Rooms, Bridgwater, to consider the formation of a Church Missionary Society for the town and its neighbourhood.

Andrew's eldest son John was making good progress at school in 1822. He is believed to have attended Christ's Hospital, often called the Bluecoat School, Newgate Street, London, where he proved, like his father, to be good at classical languages. The other two boys, Robert and Richard, also seemed to be doing well with their education. Andrew was reading the Classics with the two youngest boys, and was preparing an analysis of the Greek verbs, a language he was always good at. Despite all seeming to go well with the children at this date, Andrew was concerned at how fast time is passing. He was thirty-eight years old, but this concern could not have been caused by any fear of an early death in the footsteps of his father since he had died in his 60s. Such depressive thoughts may have simply been inspired by the fact of his boys growing up. John was eleven, Robert nine and Richard eight. These thoughts were expressed in a letter, dated 10 March 1822, to John Kenyon, which also includes the surprising statement that he had been considering becoming a priest:

> How the years fly, and how we are all changed! a few more years, and nothing will remain of us but some chance fusty manuscripts, half worm-eaten, showing perhaps some remains of my iron-ribbed letters. The report of my being about to enter into holy orders is correct. I fear I am utterly unworthy of taking upon me so sacred a function. God bless you ... .

His wife, Mary Ann was still suffering from bouts of illness and his business affairs were not doing too well. Although never extravagant with money, he was often careless with his expenditure, and certainly spent much money on electrical apparatus, even though he made much of it himself. As an example of his economy, he required huge numbers of batteries, each of which had to have its own vessel. So every time they finished a bottle of wine, he used to knock the top off and use the base as a container to make a battery (plate 11). The Crosse family had, at one time been quite wealthy and had owned land in various parishes in West Somerset, but Andrew's father Richard had spent a lot of money on his continental travels and building up his collection of books. Andrew had not expected to inherit much in the way of riches as his father had often told him that 'he could only leave him bread and cheese.' Several times Andrew was heard to remark 'my family were learned and honourable men as long as I can look back; but they had the happy knack of turning a guinea into a shilling, and I have inherited that faculty pretty strongly.' His resources were stretched by the expenses of his family, in maintaining Fyne Court House and the grounds, rebuilding farm buildings, and all the other outlay involved in running an estate. He sought relaxation in poetry, and would write on almost any subject. He continued his investigation into atmospheric electricity and electro-crystallisation, writing his notes in the handwriting that some people found hard to read, even himself on some occasions! He had the theory, which has gained much acceptance today, that it was possible to tell a person's character by looking at their handwriting. He satirised his own writing in a poem:

Belshazzar's soul was sore amazed
When on the mystic lines he gaz'd
Traced on his palace wall;
When Daniel rose, high gifted-seer,
The fatal prophecy made clear:
But Daniel, were he now alive,
In vain might scratch his head and strive
Thy meaning to explain;
Thy mazy pen would bid defiance
To saints and devils sworn alliance,
All efforts would be vain.

Despite his obvious 'scientific brain', his literary side was able to provide flights of fancy. On one occasion having been to Plymouth to see off a friend who was sailing to India to join his regiment Andrew stopped the night at Exeter as he was not only suffering from fatigue but was feeling very low. After a brief meal he went to his room, but had scarcely laid down on the bed when a sudden train of thought came to him, so intense that he described it as an inspiration. When he described this he said he was convinced that he was not asleep and it was not a dream. In his mind he roamed over the universe, and saw the unbounded glories of creation, and it appeared, he said, as if his soul had left his body and was free to reach the outer limits of space, or to 'annihilate space with the intensity of its perception.' It seemed as if centuries were condensed in those moments of ecstatic life he was experiencing, and all nature's laws became clear – he felt immortal. Presumably this 'vision' was brought on by both extreme tiredness and depression. If it was a dream, then according to those who believe that the subject of dreams are significant, Andrew's could be interpreted as meaning that he would soon be freeing himself from a confining situation. He would be experiencing a new found sense of independence and freedom. Perhaps this was a subconscious wish! Others might suggest it was an 'out of body experience'.

Andrew was a true man of the Quantocks and loved walking in the hills. Quantock means 'hill country', from the Celtic *cuan* (hill) and *toich* (country). He would go into the hills at all times of the day or night, and in all weathers, even when it was at its most extreme. On one occasion he nearly lost his life when a tremendous storm overtook him while walking at night. He expressed this love in a paper he wrote for a meeting of the Somerset Archaeological and Natural History Society:

> In my walks over the Quantock Hills my attention has been called to their products, their minerals, the woods which adorn their sides, the varied and magnificent views from their highest tops, the distant channel bounded by the Welsh mountains, and a thousand accessories which it is impossible to behold with common sensations; but far stronger are they when I reflect that I drew my first breath within their precincts, and that those from whom I derived my existence sleep beneath their soil. As life draws on, the memory of the past is added to the enjoyment of the present, and things in themselves common and trifling become sacred in our eyes. Over these wild and beautiful hills, at all hours of day and night, in all seasons, have I wandered, and never in vain. It has been said that Julius Caesar ascended the highest point of the Quantocks, and that, on beholding the splendid view around, he exclaimed, *'Quantum ab hoc'* ['How much is seen from this'].

Andrew was a keen geologist and during his walks noted the rocks and minerals that he encountered. While mostly of sandstone, the Quantocks have metallic deposits that from time to time have been exploited commercially, something that he was later to try himself. Buckingham Mine was opened in 1786 at Dodington near Over Stowey where Andrew's brother lived, and several thousand pounds worth of copper ore was extracted. Andrew said that 'A mining gentleman, of high reputation in Cornwall, paid me a visit of some duration, and in our walks over the Quantock Hills he gave it as his opinion, that at some future time this vicinity would become the principal mining district of the west of England.' This 'mining gentleman' was Robert Fox the younger (1789-1877), a geologist, natural philosopher and inventor. He seems to have been inspired by Andrew's work on electro-crystallisation to begin his own series of experiments from 1829, on the artificial production of metal-bearing veins by means of the long term application of an electric current. He presented his results at the Bristol meeting of the British Association for the Advancement of Science in 1836. Fox was an active member of the British Association, a key person in the establishment of the Royal Cornwall Polytechnic Society, and was elected a Fellow of the Royal Society in 1848.

About 1825 a mason employed on the Fyne Court estate found a piece of curious stone in a lane on the estate and brought it to Andrew. Andrew, thinking it might indicate a copper lode, returned with him to the find spot carrying a pickaxe. The spot was on a steep hill with a rise of 400 feet (122 m) within half a mile (0.8 km), with confused looking strata on each side of the lane. The first blow of the pickaxe broke off a piece of slate containing copper carbonate ($CuCo_3$). The next day Andrew got two of his labourers to open the ground on each side of the lane, when they revealed pieces of copper pyrites as large as eggs. Excited by the potential of the discovery, Andrew engaged a couple of local miners, who sank a small shaft twenty feet (6 m) deep finding copper pyrites interspersed with hydrous peroxide of iron. A Cornish agent, presumably Fox or someone recommended by him, offered to follow this up and an adit, a horizontal tunnel, was driven into the hill and a forty foot (12 m) shaft was sunk. From this a considerable amount of copper-rich ore was dug out, including a single stone of pyrites weighing eight and a half pounds (3.85 kg) which contained twenty per cent copper. The work continued for a while until, for reasons that are not clear, it was abandoned, presumably because it was not continuing to be profitable. Andrew was very fond of trees, and his estate had many fine and large specimens. There were frequent sales of young trees grown on the Fyne Court estate, as well as timber and bark which was used by local tanners. In a paper written for the Somerset Archaeological and Natural History Society he shows both his love of trees, gives a description of some of those on the Fyne Court estate, and shows his knowledge of arboriculture:

> In a tremendous storm which took place some time since, and which only
> lasted twenty minutes, I lost two beech-trees which stood side by side. One
> of them exceeded a hundred feet in height, and contained nine tons of
> timber. Thirty-five tons of beech timber were also blown down in its
> immediate vicinity. The spectacle during this short-lived hurricane was

awful. The silver, Scotch, and larch firs grow to a very unusual bulk. Some years since, a group of silver firs, twelve in number, each averaging the height of one hundred feet, overshadowed my house.

At the present time I have Spanish chestnut-trees which measure twenty-three feet in circumference ... The ash flourishes so well in this district, that it is quite the weed of the country. No one who is interested in planting can observe, without pleasure, the tall, smooth, silver stems of this tree, rising up in parallel pillars, so as to form, in due time, a flourishing plantation. The great enemy of this tree in its youth is the rabbit, as the squirrel is the great destroyer of the larch and Scotch fir.

It is much to be lamented that more attention is not devoted to planting. It is true that the time has not been when the planter was remunerated more than he can now expect to be; still, much may be done, and thousands of unproductive acres throughout Great Britain may be rendered highly advantages to the owner and the public by enclosing and planting them ... One of the principal mistakes of landed proprietors with respect to the culture of trees, is suffering their young plantations to remain for years without being properly thinned out.

Their gardeners and labourers hoe out the superfluous carrots and turnips, but little or no attention is paid to the thinning of plantations either young or old; indeed, they are in general irreparably injured before any mischief is dreamed of. Great care and incessant attention is requisite in this department, which will repay the planter to an extent little anticipated. One fine tree is worth a hundred small ones, both in value and beauty, and to produce this one many smaller must be sacrificed, to give the larger room to expand on all sides.

It must be borne in mind that wood is mostly composed of carbon, and that the carbon of the tree is extracted principally from the atmosphere, by means of the absorbent power in its branches; and that if those branches have not sufficient room to expand, it is absolutely impossible for the tree to attain any size. Again, it frequently happens that the cultivator, in order to preserve the number of his trees, lops off their branches unmercifully, and in so doing destroys the feeders of each tree, which these branches are. A vulgar notion prevails, that the branches to a great extent take off from the size of the body of the stem, so that one frequently observes tall thin skeletons of trees, denuded of most of their branches, disgracing the beauty of the landscape by their unsightly appearance.

Andrew himself was well educated and, unlike many of his class, was a keen advocate of education for the 'humbler classes', another example of his democratic, republican leaning. He said: 'There is no real difference between men but education.' The early 1820s saw Andrew becoming involved with political matters, particularly in support of his fellow men. This was a particularly hard time for many people, who had been suffering from the effects of the industrial and agricultural revolution from around 1800. In 1801 starving Somerset labourers marched twenty-four miles (38 km) to try and get the price of food lowered. The increasing hardship for the agricultural workers of Somerset can be clearly seen with the rising amounts given each year by the Overseers of the Poor to help destitute families and individuals. Agricultural workers were paid one shilling a day or one shilling and fourpence for a long summer's day work with an allowance of cider or beer. Women earned sixpence or eightpence in summer plus cider or beer. In contrast beef, veal and lamb cost fourpence per pound, a fowl two shillings, a goose three shillings and a bushel of wheat five shillings and fourpence. A four-pound loaf cost one shilling, candles four shillings and sixpence per dozen, sugar one shilling and a penny and tea three shillings and sixpence per pound.

Andrew wrote a paper entitled 'Ought an excess of agricultural produce to be the cause of a proportionate degree of poverty to the cultivators, and consequently the owners of the soil?' The main point of his argument was that the production of excessive produce or an increase in population was not a bad thing as many were claiming at that time. He felt that the policy of encouraging people to emigrate to other parts of the Empire was a mistake as it depleted Britain of able-bodied labourers and potential recruits for the army and militia when required. While the Napoleonic War had been over for a few years, there was still great distrust of the Europeans, particularly the French.

In January 1822 Andrew went to a meeting in Taunton attended by members of the gentry, magistrates and various landowners, chaired by Mr A. Sandford. This had been called to discuss the problems being experienced in agriculture, that were badly affecting both the labourers and landowners. It was a heated meeting. One attendee pointed out that 'An oppressive taxation is the evil under which the whole country is suffering, and it is in vain to expect that war taxes and peace prices can exist together.' As an example of this a vicar pointed out that in his parish the increase in rates was absorbing most of the profits from industry. In 1793 the Rates amounted to £82, but by 1821 they had risen to £2,000. Another vicar blamed the 'inadequate duty on foreign corn', although someone else said all restrictions on foreign corn should be removed, not a popular idea with most people at the meeting. A petition was proposed, although someone else thought that this would be a waste of time 'and would share the fate of thousands of other petitions, which were like so many murdered babes smothered in parchment.'

It was generally felt that the only hope for the country was a complete reform of the House of Commons. Although the war had been over for seven years it was generally agreed that the benefits of the peace had not materialised and 500,000 people were then facing financial ruin. A farmer pointed out that his stock had dropped in value from £4,000 to £3,000 in two years. The Chairman graphically described the plight of the agricultural labourers in Somerset: 'Would to God that those who deny the existence of the miseries of the agriculturalist, or doubt their unhappy extent would enter the habitations of the yeomen of this once opulent county, and witness the privations to which they are now reduced; their hopeless days and sleepless nights; their sorrowing families; and their exhausted means of bestowing on the objects of their affection the comforts to which their honest industry had entitled them.' One gentleman pointed out that in 1792 the price of food and other items was about the same as then and the amount of tax collected by the government was £16 million, but that the taxes collected in 1820 had amounted to £70 million. Andrew, with his strong democratic and philanthropic views, stood up and addressed the meeting on this subject about which he felt so strongly:

Though not in the habit of public speaking, I should deem myself a traitor to my country if, at an awful crisis like the present, I was to refrain from expressing my sentiments. I see infallible ruin before me. I am perfectly free from all political opinions and speak the sentiments of an unprejudiced man. I am in the habit of intimacy with many distinguished persons, both Whigs and Tories, but am free to think and act for myself; and my opinion is most decisive, that absolute and irretrievable ruin must overwhelm us unless we are saved by an efficient and constitutional Parliamentary reform. [After expressing his admiration of the British Constitution he continued:]

I have no malevolence towards ministers, but I am perfectly convinced that all the miseries with which the country is inundated are solely to be ascribed to the Pitt system. Which has been wrong and pernicious from beginning to end. So long, therefore, as the present ministers remain in power, real improvement in public affairs cannot be expected. Within a few years the taxes had been quadrupled, and three-fourths of them must be taken off before their pressure would cease to be intolerable. One half of the National Dept must be reduced, for, having been created by a fictitious currency, it is impossible to cope with it now we have returned to cash payments: had I been more accustomed to public speaking I should have given my feelings a better utterance, but I have honestly and conscientiously avowed my opinions.

Andrew, with much deep feeling, went on to exhort landlords to be merciful to their tenants during this period of extreme difficulty for so many people. He also said that tenants should be 'industrious to their landlords.' Then continued:

If members of Parliament and ministers will show no example of economy, it behoves every individual to set them an example of retrenching any superfluous expense in private life.

In the end it was decided to draw up a petition:

'To the Right Honourable the Lords Spiritual and Temporal, in Parliament assembled. We, the gentry, clergy, freeholders, and occupiers of land in the district of the once opulent Vale of Taunton, most humbly represent to your honourable House, that the cruel distress throughout the district in which we reside has arrived at an unparalleled height, and is daily increasing to an alarming extent. That the progressive decline in the value of all productions of the earth, accompanied by an overwhelming burden of taxation, such as never was endured by any country, has swallowed up the capital of the farmer, and brought the greater proportion of independent yeomen to the brink of ruin, which, without the most speedy relief, must terminate in the annihilation of that most excellent and invaluable body of men. That your petitioners therefore pray, that the strictest economy and retrenchment may be enforced in every department of the State.'

This was a period of great social deprivation and a lot of political agitation. Although Andrew had become involved in politics, he tended to support those he felt would best serve his fellow men rather than supporting a particular party, although his inclinations were to support the Whig party. The Whigs were a reforming and constitutional party that sought the supremacy of Parliament over the Crown and was, later in the 19th century, to be succeeded by the Liberal Party. Several times he proposed or seconded the candidate for Bridgwater, his close friend and neighbour Charles Kemys Tynte of Halswell Park who was a Whig MP in 1820, 1832 and 1835. As an example of Andrew's apolitical attitude, on one occasion he was present at a Whig dinner and found himself seated next to the President. He suggested to him, in a whisper, that they should take this public opportunity to toast the health of a political adversary who had acted honourably in a particular matter. However, the reply he got was 'Better not, better not; it won't do.' This upset Andrew who felt he was not understood and remained silent for the rest of the meal since 'how could I sympathise with such ungenerous prejudices, even though the opinions of these men were the same as my own?' Andrew's behaviour is almost identical to the incident when he was at university and upset by the attitude of his fellow students.

Andrew was not adverse to addressing the crowd at the hustings. In Bridgwater this was in Cornhill on the spot where the old market cross had stood until removed in the 1790s. This was a time when political rallies often deteriorated into rioting and it was not uncommon for the militia to be called out to quell the unrest. On one occasion, while speaking at a political meeting a member of the opposition called out 'Oliver Cromwell!, Oliver Cromwell!', to which Andrew immediately replied 'Gentlemen, I thank you for the compliment, and if I were Oliver Cromwell, I would sweep all such as you from the face of the earth.' This could have precipitated trouble, but although the crowd pushed and shoved each other, fortunately it came to nothing more serious. After this meeting a gentleman came up to him, shook his hand and said 'Why, Crosse, you don't care for the whole world.' To which Andrew replied 'Not if I think they're wrong, and I am right.' Despite this rather pompous seeming remark Andrew's fairness and concern for 'ordinary people' was well-known. While attending a political rally, the speaker's platform was so crowded that Andrew, standing at the edge, barely had room to get both his legs on it and was in danger of falling off. However, his legs were supported by one of the opposition, a 'red-hot Tory', as Andrew later described him, to prevent him falling, despite the criticism being espoused from the platform against his 'props' party.

However, not all of the meetings at which Andrew spoke were quite so good natured. On another occasion when Andrew was talking to the crowd, a group of farmers hissed and booed, and their heckling prevented him from being heard. A commercial traveller from the North of England noticed the extreme hostility of this group and asked a bystander who the speaker was and why the farmers were so angry with him. 'Why, don't you know him? That's Crosse of Broomfield, the thunder and lightning man; you can't go near his cursed house at night without danger of your life; them as have been there have seen devils, all surrounded by lightning, dancing on the wires that he has put up round his grounds.' The view that Andrew was practising the 'Black Arts' up at Fyne Court was not uncommon amongst many of the less educated locals who were still apprehensive about witchcraft. Election campaigns were often noisy and rowdy, but a gentleman who attended a meeting at which Andrew spoke, later recalled that in the middle of all the commotion Andrew had said something that had remained clear in his memory for many years: 'I value one ounce of knowledge more than a ton of gold; but I value one grain weight of human kindness more than a ton of knowledge.'

Andrew was generally popular with people due to his real, and at that time very unusual, absence of all prejudices of class, his consideration for others, and his unswerving integrity. One day a fellow magistrate said to him: 'You have immense influence in the county', to which Andrew, characteristically replied: 'I despise all influence. I don't think I possess any; and if I did, I would not exert it; I only desire the good of my fellow-creatures.' He was regarded as an ultra-liberal by many people, a somewhat more acceptable term than a republican, which is where his inclinations obviously lay. In 1825 death once more visited the Crosse household as his daughter Maryanne, aged fourteen, died, and was buried in Broomfield Church on 17 July. Andrew was not popular with everyone as a frightening incident at Fyne Court, reported in the local paper in June 1827, shows:

> Some villains a few nights since attempted to destroy the premises of A. Crosse esq. of Finecourt House, Broomfield by placing some lighted combustibles under the thatch of his stables, whereby the rafters were partly consumed, but fortunately the intended mischief proceeded no further. A reward of 50 guineas is offered on conviction of the perpetrator. If anything could heighten the atrocity of this diabolical attempt it would be found in Mr. Crosse's habitual benevolence to the sick and poor of his parish. The occupants of several of the cottages on the [out]skirts of the Common at Broomfield are known to be of the most profligate habits and it is conjectured that some of these upon whom Mr. Crosse has been called to exercise his functions as a Magistrate have thus vindictively evinced the turpitude of their feelings.

The Autumn of 1827 was a memorable one for Andrew as he had a visit from one of the most eminent scientists of the 19th century. Sir Humphrey Davy (1778-1829) was staying with Thomas Poole at Nether Stowey, but was suffering from the illness that was to prove fatal within two years. This was almost certainly the result of years of sniffing and even tasting chemicals. Davy was a chemist who had been knighted in 1812, spent two years travelling in France in 1813-14, despite Britain being at war with the country, and who had been awarded a medal for his scientific discoveries by Napoleon. He was President of the Royal Society 1820-26 and a pioneer of electrochemistry, who had used electricity to isolate the elements sodium, potassium, magnesium, calcium, strontium, chlorine and barium. He determined the properties of iodine, demonstrated that diamond was a form of carbon and discovered nitrous oxide (laughing gas). His name was widely known as in 1816 he produced an oil lamp, at the urgings of Cornish miners, that would not cause explosions. This was commonly known as the Davy Safety Lamp. Poole had known Davy since he was a young man, and Davy dedicated his last work *The Consolations in Travel, or the Last Days of a Philosopher* (1830) to him. Poole wrote to Andrew on 11 November 1827 about this impending visit:

My Dear Friend,

I have heard again from Sir H. Davy. He says, 'I am going to London to-morrow, and after staying two or three days to try a new plan of medical treatment, which my physicians recommend, I shall come westward, and I profit by your kindness and I adopt whichever of the three plans shall promise to be most satisfactory. If I take Mr. Crosse's house Lady Davy will come with me. With respect to society, I want only a friend, or one or two persons at most to prevent extreme solitude, and I am too weak to hold much conversation, and wholly unfit to receive any but persons with whom I am in the habits of intimacy. I shall not probably be at Stowey before Wednesday or Thursday next. I am upon the strictest diet, and a wing of chicken and a plain rice or bread pudding is the extreme of my gormandize. God bless you, etc.' Thus for Sir H. I wish he could give a better account of himself. On his arrival you shall hear from me appointing a time when we will call on you at Broomfield.

A second letter from Poole, dated 'Saturday night' was sent to Andrew regarding the visit:

My Dear Friend,

You have been, I doubt not, expecting to hear from me and Sir H. Davy. He is, I am in hopes, better than when he arrived, but still in a feeble state. We propose doing ourselves the pleasure of calling on you on Monday morning. He is anxious to see you and Broomfield ... .

Yours, my dear Crosse, sincerely,   T. Poole
Sir H. desires me to say everything from him.

It was with some difficulty that Davy had driven over to Fyne Court with Poole and Andrew warmly welcomed them both and proudly showed Sir Humphrey over the house. Davy had been fatigued by the journey and was walking languidly, but at last they entered Andrew's main laboratory. Andrew never forgot how Sir Humphrey's eyes lit up and a glow came over his countenance as he looked at the furnaces and other equipment, and for a while he seemed quite like his old self again. No doubt Andrew's unbounded enthusiasm for science also helped to stimulate his famous visitor. This visit, and the chance to meet this great scientist, was something that Andrew greatly valued. Davy, who was only forty-eight when he visited Fyne Court, was to die in Italy just two years later.

Andrew's eldest son, John, matriculated at Exeter College, Oxford on 4 March 1829, while his second son Robert matriculated at Balliol College, Oxford on 2 December 1830. By the 1830s his interest in political matters seemed to have waned somewhat, or he had simply become disillusioned. At that time he noted that: 'My brother and I are determined Reformers, but have little time to waste on politics', although in a letter of the late 1830s he bemoans the fact that, among other things, he was kept busy with politics! Despite his busy life, and having the courage to address crowds of potentially hostile people at political meetings, he was described as suffering from 'nervous attacks', presumably anxiety attacks, from the age of fifteen, which was when his father died. He feared an early death, and wrote 'The ill health I suffered in my younger days made me imagine that I should never see thirty.' This must have been reinforced by the early death of two of his children in 1819, and the loss of Maryanne in 1825. As so often, Andrew expressed his thoughts in poetry:

On A Sudden Illness.

So, Death, by my frail door thou fleetest,
    And, as thou passest by,
With warning hand thou lightly beatest,
    To hint that I must die!

And though thou say'st not at the portal
    When thou shalt step inside,
T. is kind to tell me I am mortal,
    And check me in my pride!

How many a tree my fathers planted,
    I've lived to see decay!
How many a flower whose scent enchanted,
    Is past for aye away!

How many a string whose tones enthralled me
    Is rudely rent in twain!
How many a voice which sweetly called me
    I ne'er shall hear again!

And while creation dies around me,
    Shall I escape the tomb,
To herd with those whose sufferings wound me,
    Yet flee the general doom?

Have I not closed eyes which were lighted
    With joy as I drew near?
Have I not seen those prospects blighted
    On which the sun shone clear?

Have not I felt, since Nature made me,
    Far more than death can bring?
For should a thousand deaths invade me,
    The past would blunt their sting!

Say, does not all that floats about me
    Scoff at life's vain pretence?
The worm I trample seems to flout me,
    And bids me to go hence!

The cloud above, the wave below me,
    All beckon me away!
Each sight I gaze on does but show me
    That here I must not stay!

Better to writhe in death's last anguish,
    With hope of some relief,
Than in this weary world to languish
    The sport of joy and grief!

[T. in the second verse is probably his friend and near neighbour Charles Tynte.]

Andrew seems to have a near brush with death, or so he believed, brought on by his tendency to boyish behaviour even as an adult. The exact date of this incident is unclear. When returning home one day Andrew was walking beside one of the ponds in the grounds of Fyne Court when he saw a cat sitting by the edge. He suddenly sprang forward to catch the animal with the intention of throwing it into the water. However, it was too quick for him to catch hold of it firmly, and he only held it for an instant, but it was long enough for the cat to wriggle round and bite him severely on the hand. He automatically threw it from him, but in doing so noticed that its hair was 'stivered', that is bristled up, indicating that the cat was ill. Later that day it died, according to Andrew, of hydrophobia (rabies)!

However, all seemed well with Andrew and the incident was forgotten as the weeks went on. However, one morning, about three months after this occurrence, he suddenly felt a great pain in his hand, at the same time experiencing a raging thirst. He called for a glass of water, but just as he was about to raise it to his lips a sudden spasm shot across his throat and, to his horror, he thought he was about to become a victim of rabies contracted from the cat. For the next hour his mind was filled with thoughts of death, something that was never far from his thoughts at the best of times. He later said that 'the torments of hell itself could not have surpassed what I suffered.' The pain, which had started in his hand, passed to his elbow and up to the shoulder, by which time he was quite convinced he would die.

After a while, although the pain was still terrible, he began to reflect on his condition and said to himself 'either I shall die, or I shall not; if I do, it will only be a similar fate which many have suffered, and many more must suffer, and I must bear it like a man: if, on the other hand, there is any hope of my life, my only chance is in summoning my utmost resolution, defying the attack, and exerting every effort of my mind.' Having resolved to 'fight' the condition he decided that not only was mental exertion necessary but so was physical activity. Accordingly, he took a gun and went out into the grounds to do some shooting, despite the considerable pain in his arm. He found nothing to shoot, but spent the whole afternoon in strenuous walking, making a huge mental effort to fight the disease. By the time he returned to the house he was feeling much better and was not only able to eat some dinner, but was able to drink some water without ill effects.

On waking the following morning he found that the aching pain had gone down to his elbow and later he only had pain in his wrist. On the third day he was free of pain altogether. It is perhaps surprising that he was able to recover from such a serious disease so relatively easily. Was it rabies? Andrew later described the circumstances to Dr John Kinglake of Mount Street, Taunton, who considered that Andrew had indeed suffered an attack of hydrophobia which could possibly have proved fatal had he not 'struggled against it by a strong effort of mind.' However, it is unlikely that Andrew had caught rabies, an infection of the central nervous system. If treated immediately it is possible to prevent it, but untreated and once the victim begins to show the symptoms, death is nearly always inevitable. If Andrew had caught rabies he would initially have suffered from a fever, headache, nausea and vomiting. This is often accompanied by excessive salivation, drooling and watering of the eyes. In the second phase he would have experienced spasms of the throat and gullet, excessive thirst, hydrophobia, hallucinations and manic behaviour, followed by paralysis, coma and death; not the symptoms he was exhibiting, so Kingslake was wrong in his opinion.

Andrew, as a keen observer, never passed up any opportunity to study the world around him. Among his many discoveries was that concerning fog:

There are two distinct species of fog, which take place in the atmosphere. The one is comparatively rare, is highly electrical, and produces quite different effects from the other, or common fog, which contains so little electricity as only to be manifested by the aid of a delicate condenser. When the electric fog occurs in a freezing wintry night, each shrub or tree, or even on a blade of grass, in a freezing state, shoots out in a crystalline arrangement, forming a succession of radiations from the twig which becomes their centre; till at last the whole shrub or tree becomes covered with innumerable aggregations of acicular crystals of ice. I have seen a dead thistle supporting a crown of these needle crystals of at least ten inches in diameter. Now this is by no means the case, in an unelectrical fog, during which, in a night similar to the above (excepting that the electric agency is wanting), as the moisture is deposited upon the branches of the trees, upon each of which it is frozen by the severity of the cold instead of appearing in a crystalline form, as in the former instance, it simply cases the stem with a smooth cylinder of ice, like barley-sugar.

In 1828 Andrew spent a lot of time researching atmospheric electricity using his 'exploring wire', strung from poles and trees around the estate. This produced some exciting and unexpected results regarding the make-up of thunder clouds. When one came near his 'exploring wire' he noted that the gold leaf electrometer he had at its terminal end was indicating a positive charge, then there was a gap, then it showed a negative charge. This pattern was repeated several times depending on the size of the cloud, the charge getting more powerful as the centre of the cloud passed over and lessening as the cloud moves away. He also noticed that the leaves of the electrometer opened and shut rapidly some time before the storm appeared, indicating great atmospheric electrical disturbance, but after it passed the free atmospheric electricity was less than normal. Andrew had discovered that thunder clouds were divided into different zones of alternating positive and negative charges, apparently the first person to discover this. Up to this time 19th century scientists had thought that storm clouds were simple dipolar structures. He also realised from his observations that the earth was negatively charged, a discovery that is generally credited to the Frenchman Jean Peltier in 1842.

An undated letter, but which belongs to the period 1830-34, throws light on Andrew's activities during this time. His walks in the hills continued and he noted that he had walked to the house of Thomas Mullins, described as a 'gentleman' and solicitor, at Goathurst in a record time of thirty-eight minutes, four minutes less than he had ever done it before. Mullins estimated that the distance covered was four miles (6.4 km). Andrew mentions that he had not owned a horse or mare for the previous two years, and financially things seemed to have been tight as he goes on: 'I find this plan agrees with my health and pocket, the latter of which is somewhat necessary to attend to, as my two elder sons are at their respective colleges.' John, who had gone to Exeter College, Oxford, graduated with a BA in 1833 and became a student at Lincoln's Inn the same year. Robert, who had gone to Balliol College, Oxford, graduated with a BA in 1834.

In June 1831 Andrew gave a talk on Galvanic Electricity to the Taunton Mechanics Institute and demonstrated a powerful Voltaic battery he had constructed. If he did not have a horse or mare then he presumably walked into Taunton or Bridgwater, where it was possible to get a stage coach to Exeter, Bristol, Bath or London. In the 1830s a stage coach, *The Herald*, left Taunton at 11.30 am and arrived in Bath at 5.50 pm. Donkey carts were much used in the Quantocks then, and he may well have used this form of transport to travel to the nearby towns. A railway station opened in Taunton in 1842 connecting it with Bridgwater and, two years later with Exeter. It was to be further extended over the next thirty years.

Andrew often spent time at this period with his good friend Tom Poole (1766-1837), who was the owner of a tannery at Nether Stowey five miles (8 km) from Fyne Court. This had brought wealth to his family since the 18th century. Poole was well-known for his democratic views, and was a philanthropist and sponsor of the arts. About 1807 he founded a Womens Friendly Society (which still holds an annual church service and procession), established a school at Nether Stowey in 1813, and in 1817 founded the Quantock Savings Bank, of which Andrew was a Trustee. He was a great friend of the Wordsworths, the poet Robert Southey (1774-1843), and Samuel Taylor Coleridge (1772-1834) who stayed at Nether Stowey on a number of occasions between 1794 and 1807.

Described as having a bombastic manner and a short temper, Tom nevertheless had an attractive personality but took snuff to excess, which later ruined his voice.

When Coleridge, Southey and Poole got together they came up with a plan to set up a new society, called a Pantisocracy, meaning equal rule for all, on the banks of the Susquehanna River in New England, America. This was a serious suggestion, but the group never carried it out for various reasons. With Andrew's republican leanings and his wish to see equality of education and fairness for all, it is more than likely that he would have discussed this aspirational but unrealistic plan with Tom. Would he have considered joining this band of 'brothers' in their enterprise? Unlikely, as he loved the Quantock Hills too much, and was certainly more down to earth than these famous poets. In November Andrew attended a meeting of patrons to form the Taunton and West Labourers Friendly Society. Andrew's experimental work had become more ambitious and carried out on a larger scale. He actually seems to have had hopes of perfecting a perpetual motion machine:

> I have lately constructed a voltaic battery of ONE THOUSAND AND TWENTY-FIVE pairs of metallic plates; also an electrical battery, composed of talc plates coated with tin-foil. This last battery being interposed between the poles of the voltaic battery, charged with common pump-water becomes instantly charged, and an intensity sufficient to deflagrate metallic leaves, explode fulminating powders, cause iron wire to perpetually scintillate, &c. &c. I have hopes to be enabled thus to form an apparatus capable of giving perpetual LIGHT, HEAT, and MOTION.

Andrew's Talc Battery seems to have been a new type which he invented in 1831-32. Talc is a naturally occurring mineral, hydrated magnesium silicate. What is also interesting is that Andrew seems to have realised that the various types of energy – light, heat and mechanical, all have the same origin, and could be changed from one form to another. This was in the early 1830s, but the same idea was published in 1840 by James Joule as the First Law of Thermodynamics. He was constantly looking for ways to improve his scientific equipment, and about 1831 he noted that he had 'just discovered a method of doubling the power of cylinder electrical machines, both cheap and simple.' He considerably increased the power of a Voltaic battery when he brought the copper plate of one pair almost in contact with the other pair, and found that each separate pair of plates was much more efficient. He put together 1,200 pairs of zinc and copper cylinders to this design, with water as the electrolyte. This was a major improvement in this type of battery and he published his method in a Report of the British Association for the Advancement of Science:

> The average size of the cylinder being about equal to a four-inch plate, four pairs communicate a charge to an electrical battery sufficient to cause iron wire barely to scintillate, and will just decompose water; 100 pairs cause the gold leaves of an electrometer to diverge $\frac{1}{3}$ of an inch; 200 pairs open the same $\frac{2}{3}$ of an inch; 300 pairs cause the same to strike their sides, and fire gunpowder placed loosely on a brass plate, the opposite poles being connected with an electrical battery; 500 pairs give a smart shock, fire gunpowder readily, give a visible stream of fire to the dry fingers, and cauterise the skin as though with a red-hot wire; 1200 pairs being connected with an electrical battery fuze the point of a penknife, deflagrate brilliantly metallic leaves, tin-foil, and even stout silver sheeting &c., &c.

Andrew used a battery of this construction for eighteen months without any noticeable diminution of charge, making it ideal for his long-term research into crystal formation. He had recently created crystals of metallic silver and muriate of mercury in the form of four sided pyramids by passing a low electric current through solutions for long periods. He gave two lectures to the Taunton Mechanics Institute on one of his favourite subjects, atmospheric electricity. His time seemed to have been fully occupied and so he turned down the invitation by his friend Charles Tynte to accompany him on a tour through Ireland, and then on to Switzerland and Italy. Andrew said he was a 'fixture – erratic in mind but chained in body.' A letter written to a friend in May 1832 reveals what occupied Andrew at this time, and shows once again how important was his scientific research:

> I received your letter the day before yesterday. The kindness of it I shall never forget. I am in the midst of all sorts of business, – selling hay, barking oak, cutting down poles, gardening, &c. &c. Far above all, I am working

like a slave in my laboratory, and have two fires constantly burning night and day. I have formed crystals on several new plans, and I am preparing a very extensive apparatus. I wish my means were half as ample and extensive as the apparatus I would fain construct! I do not go to London to see the geegaws and frippery and childish nonsense of the coronation. How much mankind has to learn before they begin to be ashamed of such trash!

I have just put together a water battery of sixty-three large zinc and copper cylinders, each cylinder equal to a nine-inch square plate. It gives a small but intense constant stream of light, between two charcoal points the heat of which will fire gunpowder. I am about to increase it to 100 pairs. Five thousand of such cylinders as these would make a glorious exhibition, but they would cost £500. Each pair of cylinders is contained in a glass jar, which holds about three pints. The shock through the thin part of the skin, even quite dry, is almost intolerable. It is my belief that 1,000 of such cylinders, or even less, would produce potassium from alkali. I am half stewed with the heat of my furnaces, which I am obliged to watch closely.

The problems of running the estate and financial problems were never far away, and towards the end of the 1830s Andrew must have been feeling very much under pressure. This is quite clear from a letter he wrote to John Kenyon which started 'I write in haste. We're beat, almost dead beat. Money, cursed bribery, and intimidation of tenants, have beat us, added to our too great confidence and damned mismanagement.' He bemoans the local politics as the Whig candidate had been 'turned out' and two of the candidates in the election campaign had brought religion into the fight – something Andrew disapproved of and made his views on this known to them very forcibly. Characteristically the letter finishes with 'My experiments at Broomfield go on famously.' In 1834 Andrew hosted a meeting of the Taunton Literary Association at Fyne Court. They met at 2 pm and spent the afternoon fishing, shooting and walking around the grounds, before enjoying a good dinner. This was followed by a discussion on the belief in ghosts. The party left just before midnight.

In 1835 his son Robert was ordained a Deacon, and on the 23 October that year was appointed the Curate to St. Mary and All Saints Church,

Broomfield, where so many members of his family were buried. Robert was to hold the living there until 1846. He lived at Fyne Court, only a few hundred yards from the church, until his marriage in 1837, held not at Broomfield but in Ruishton Church, Somerset. In November that year Andrew had a brush with death which was reported in the *Taunton Courier* of 4 November. He was shooting on Broomfield Hill with a friend, Mr Beadon, when an ox, being driven by a Dorset man, rushed at his friend, who pointed his gun at the beast, which then veered away from him towards Andrew. Although he had a gun he did not wish to shoot the beast which knocked him down and thrust its horns under his body. One horn ripped the sleeve of his shooting jacket, while the other was prevented from inflicting what could well have been a fatal wound, by the providential position of a metal button on his trousers which prevented the tip of the horn penetrating his body. The ox then raced off into a nearby thicket pursued by the drover, leaving a shaken and bruised Andrew to climb to his feet.

The year 1836 was a memorable one for Andrew. There is independent evidence from two families in the form of family tradition, backed up by documentary and circumstantial evidence, that they are descended from an illegitimate son of Andrew Crosse. Andrew seems to have had an affair with Eleanor Ingram, the daughter of John Ingram (c.1766-1866) and Charity (c.1761-1834), both of whom were born and lived locally near Fyne Court all their lives. John Ingram was, according to family tradition, the gardener on the Fyne Court estate, but documentary evidence shows he was simply an agricultural labourer, although this does not preclude the possibility that he also did some work in the gardens. Eleanor, who was born c.1808, was the youngest of five children, and went on to have three children herself, John who was born in 1828 but who died in 1829, Mary born in 1831 and Charles, who was born in 1836. According to the baptismal records for Spaxton, no father is shown for any of the children, so all three were illegitimate and Eleanor never seems to have married.

In addition to the story in both families that they are descended from an illegitimate child of Andrew, it is known that Charles's education at Spaxton School was paid for by Andrew and he is believed to have spent time at

Blundell's School in Tiverton, Devon, which was larger and grander than any other West Country school, with room for one hundred and fifty fee paying scholars. In addition, Eleanor was allowed by Andrew to live in Piertwater Cottage on the edge of Spaxton village, rent free. Spaxton is three miles (4.8 km) north of Broomfield, and the Fyne Court estate owned land and properties there. Piertwater Cottage, a mid-18th century building that today has colour-washed stone elevations under a pitched tiled roof, is named after the nearby Piert Water stream.

Eleanor seems to have occupied the cottage before she had Charles, and he continued to live there after his mother's death, and remained in it until his own death in 1918 when it reverted to the Fyne Court estate. He was also allowed to collect the quarterly rent from Crossmoors Meadow Farm and keep it as 'pocket money'. A family tradition claimed that Charles was Estate Manager at Fyne Court, but on the census records he is shown as 'labourer', providing further evidence that he was favoured by Andrew, and continued to be by the estate after Andrew's death.

When Eleanor had her children Andrew was aged forty-three, forty-six and fifty-one. There seems to be a very strong possibility that Andrew did father her third child Charles, but could her second child, Mary, also be his along with her first child who died? Eleanor was given a rent-free cottage and was not forced to look for a husband to provide for her children. A clue as to whether all three were Andrew's may be in the way they were recorded in the parish baptismal records. In the case of John and Mary, both are described as 'base born' but, in the case of Charles, although Eleanor is described as 'single woman', there is no comment about the child in the final column like his siblings. Could it be that the parish clerk knew who the father was, even if just from local gossip – a well-liked and respected local landowner, Andrew Crosse, so did not want to emphasise the child's illegitimacy? Andrew married Mary Ann Hamilton in 1809 and remained married until her death in 1846, so was married during the period when Eleanor was pregnant with Charles and bringing up her daughter. During this period his wife was often ill, so did Andrew seek comfort elsewhere? One final piece of possible circumstantial evidence: when an engraving of Andrew on the cover of a publication was shown to a member of one of the families descended from Charles, she exclaimed 'Why is Uncle Reg on the cover?' Suggesting Reginald looked just like Andrew!

Andrew was great friends with the Rev. Sydney Smith (1771-1845). Considered a great wit, churches were filled to overflowing when he preached, and he often used humour to bring over serious points. In 1802 he founded *The Edinburgh Review* in which he wrote articles calling for reforms such as Catholic emancipation. He was universally liked, but was ambitious and hoped to have become a Bishop or even Archbishop of Canterbury, but his views on preferment and corruption in the church made him a thorn in the side for the Church of England, although he was eventually appointed Dean of St. Paul's. He was interested in science, and in 1835 gave over seventy of his valuable books to the Taunton Mechanics Institute. On one occasion Andrew was seated opposite Smith at a dinner party held at Wilton House, Taunton, the home of the Kinglakes, when Smith jocularly remarked that he would have bishops in every part of Great Britain and in every island around her shores. 'I would have' he said 'a Bishop of the Flat Holmes, and a Bishop of the Steep Holmes' referring to two small islands in the Bristol Channel visible from the Quantocks on a clear day, one of which, at that time, had just half a dozen houses on it. Andrew immediately replied 'that would be a great advantage Mr. Smith, for they would be surrounded by their sees!' (seas). When Smith was asked if he would bury a Dissenter, as a neighbouring clergyman had refused to do so, he replied 'On the contrary, I should only be too glad to bury them all!'

One morning Smith, accompanied by a Dr Holland, visited Andrew in his laboratory where he showed them one of his favourite demonstrations, which he often performed when talking to local mechanic's institutes and scientific societies. It was based on a discovery by Sir Humphrey Davy who found that mercury could be made to swell to twenty or thirty times its original size in a dilute solution of ammonium carbonate. Andrew had refined this 'trick' by making the mercury, connected to the negative pole of a Voltaic battery, float on the water. The moment the circuit is broken, the mercury shrinks to its original size and sinks to the bottom of the vessel, which invariably impressed the observers, bringing gasps from the ladies.

Andrew was certainly not cut off from the scientific community as he had met and become friends with Professor Adam Sedgwick (1785-1873), one of the founders of modern geology, who proposed the Devonian period of geological time and later the Cambrian period. He was the first to distinguish between stratification, jointing and slatey cleavage. A Fellow of Trinity College, Cambridge, he was appointed Woodwardian Professor of Geology from 1818 until his death. He was to have a long correspondence with Charles Darwin after the publication of *On the Origin of Species* in 1859, as he believed that the different species of organisms originated in a succession of Divine acts over a long period of time. Noted for his loud cheery voice, his bad puns and still worse riddles, he obviously got on well with Andrew. He stayed at Fyne Court on a number of occasions over the years. He recorded that he had 'seen Mr. Crosse's splendid experiments', and he was so impressed that he wrote a letter to William Whewell (1794-1866) describing his visit, light-heartedly referring to Andrew as that 'lightning-monger.' This letter inspired Whewell to visit Andrew.

Whewell was a priest, scientist, philosopher, theologian and historian of science. At a time when researchers had started to specialise, he was one of the last great polymaths. He was appointed a Fellow and Tutor of Trinity College, Cambridge, in 1817, and was elected Master of Trinity College in 1841. He also held the post of Professor of Mineralogy from 1828-38, and from 1838-55 was Knightsbridge Professor of Philosophy. He published works on mechanics, physics, geology, astronomy, economics, the history of architecture and the history of science. He was the author of the *Bridgwater Treatise*, translated Goethe, wrote poetry, sermons and theological tracts. He coined the term 'scientist', and suggested to Faraday the words 'anode' and 'cathode'. He died in Cambridge as a result of a fall from his horse. Unfortunately, his journey to Fyne Court did not turn out to be straightforward.

He arrived at Bridgwater and went to a local inn to hire a horse and get directions to Fyne Court. He set off for what he thought would be a pleasant ride thorough several miles of beautiful countryside. However, he quickly lost his way in the intricacies of Somerset's country lanes, and for quite a while could not find anyone of whom to ask the way. Eventually he saw an agricultural worker, Mr Hodge, and asked him how to get to Broomfield. He was a local hillman, and Whewell was obviously not conversant with the Somerset dialect. After a great deal of somewhat confused discussion the man suddenly explained with a grin 'I'ze warrent ye do waant Squoire Crosse o' Brumwell.' Finally they had some mutual understanding! Dr Whewell received fresh directions and happily turned his horse in the direction indicated. Now confident and relaxed, all was going well until his horse stumbled and threw his rider straight into a bed of gorse! It was glorious with blossom but bristling with very sharp prickles.

One can only imagine the 'comments' he made in the strong Lancashire accent that came out when he was excited. He had a rather overbearing manner and temperament and was not a 'gentleman', having achieved his exulted post and reputation by his skills and hard work. Eventually he arrived at Fyne Court, and was somewhat mollified by the warm welcome he received. Andrew's acquaintances were not confined to scientists. Andrew was in London in June 1838 when he and John Kenyon called on Elizabeth Barrett (1806-61), a cousin of Kenyon, who was one of the most prominent poets of the Victorian period. She had published her first collection of poems in 1826 and also wrote for many magazines. Her work was popular during her lifetime in both Britain and America, and much more was published by her husband after her death, but from the age of twenty she began to battle with a lifelong illness that caused her to be frail and weak.

CHAPTER FIVE

Andrew Stands Before his Fellow Scientists: 1836

In August 1836 the British Association for the Advancement of Science (BAAS) held its annual meeting in Bristol. The British Association was founded in 1831 by scientists who were disillusioned by the elitist and conservative attitude of the Royal Society founded in 1660, although a number of the more eminent members belonged to both. Andrew had never joined the BAAS, although he was Chairman of the Taunton Mechanics Institute and Vice President of the Somerset Archaeological and Natural History Society. Andrew had been engaged on his scientific investigations for many years, but in Somerset had few people with whom to discuss his ideas and results. At Taunton was one of the few other local people interested in science with whom Andrew became friends. This was Dr Standert, a clever surgeon noted for his caustic wit. Andrew's character was such that he was always loath to push himself forward and he had had no real public notice since George Singer had published some results of his observations on atmospheric electricity in 1814, and Andrew had his first paper published in 1815.

He seems to have had little in the way of ambition, but did have an amazing dedication to science, and was not distracted from his passion despite problems with money, the estate and almost constant illness in his family. However, he was in touch with the scientific community. One of the most eminent scientists who visited Fyne Court several times in the early days was Professor Adam Sedgwick. Andrew often went to Bristol and had friends there, but it seems had no plans to attend the BAAS meeting there until his friend Tom Poole strongly urged him to go. Poole was one of the few people locally who could begin to understand the significance of Andrew's research. Besides such poets as Coleridge, Southey, Lamb and the Wordsworths, Poole moved in circles that included various well-known scientists of the day, and he had known Humphrey Davy, who had visited Fyne Court in 1827, for many years.

As Andrew himself said 'I was very uncertain about going for I always shrank from pushing myself forward, and I was but little in spirits for such an occasion, for a constant succession of family illnesses had crushed me almost to the earth.' However, Poole's urgings prevailed, and so Andrew went to Bristol intending only to listen to the papers to be presented, but taking no more active part. He might not have gone on his own, but fortunately Poole was going, so they went together. While at Bristol he dined with a friend and there met Dr John Dalton (1766-1844), a chemist, meteorologist and physicist, best known for his pioneering work on the development of modern atomic theory and research on the cause of colour blindness. Dalton published the first table of relative atomic weights in 1805, and was made a Fellow of the Royal Society in 1822. Andrew was impressed by the fact that Dalton had kept a diary of meteorological observations since 1787 (and kept them until his death), although Sir Humphrey Davy described him as 'a very coarse experimenter'. Despite this he did get good results and published many papers in scientific journals. Over dinner, talk naturally turned to the research each was engaged in, and when Andrew gave an account of his experiments on electro-crystallography the others were fascinated, and urged him to present his results to the meeting. In fact they begged him to do so!

The Rev. Dr William Buckland (1784-1856) was chairing the sessions of the Geological Section of the BAAS meeting. Dr Buckland introduced Andrew, saying that, until yesterday, he had not heard of him, that he was unconnected with any scientific society, (the Somerset Archaeological and Natural History Society, the Electrical Society, and the Taunton Mechanics Institute did not count!), but who had made twenty-four minerals and even crystalline quartz, a statement which was greeted with cries of 'Hear, hear'. Buckland continued that he did not know how Andrew had made them, but said this was a discovery of the highest order. An account of Andrew's talk was published in the *Annals of Electricity, Magnetism & Chemistry*:

We were then surprised by an observation of Dr. Buckland, that he had now to introduce to the section a philosopher who had made great discoveries by the use of a brick with a hole in it, immersed in a pail of water. Mr. Crosse then presented himself, and after laughing at the Doctor's description of his apparatus, began a modest and unprepared account of the results of his experiments on the conversion and production of mineral substances, in which he had been engaged for many years. He stated that he had extensive voltaic batteries at work, by which he had formed quartz, arragonite, malachite, &c.; but that, as such formations were slowly produced, so he had latterly used no acid in his combinations, but only pure water.

He detailed various results of different experiments, some successful and some failures, and in his impassioned descriptions of the latter he created much merriment. The most lively bursts of satisfaction proceeded from all who were present during these details; and Professor Sedgwick then announced his recognition of Mr. Crosse, as an electrician, the magnitude of whose experiments had surprised him during a mineralogical excursion in the Quantock Hills about seventeen years before.

As an example of the length of time electricity was passed through a solution, Andrew had said that in order to produce regularly shaped quartz crystals able to scratch glass, he had passed a current through fluosilicic acid (fluonic acid in which silica is dissolved) from the 8 March to the end of June 1836. He concluded his talk with another of his prophetic statements. That he was fully convinced that it was possible to make artificial diamonds and it would not be too long before such a mineral would be created. He was partly right. While there were many claims that an artificial diamond had been made between 1879 and 1928, on analysis these proved not to be 'real' diamonds. It was not until 1953 that the first true artificial diamond was manufactured. He then extended an invitation, that if any member of the Association wanted to visit him at Fyne Court, even though it was in a 'wild and savage region on the Quantock Hills', he would willingly repeat his experiment in their presence. Andrew sat down to prolonged cheering from the audience.

Professor Sedgwick then said that Andrew's residence was not, as he had described it, in a wild and savage region, but was located among an area which demonstrated the sublime beauties of nature. He went on to describe Andrew's experiment on atmospheric electricity and explained to the members how he had attached electric wires to trees and was using them to conduct streams of lightning, 'even turning them through his house with the dexterity of an able charioteer', a description that was not completely accurate, but which whetted the appetite of the audience. Sedgwick said that the members should congratulate themselves on what they had just heard, and that 'Mr. Crosse may have hitherto concealed himself, but from this time forth he must stand before the world as public property.'

Another account of Andrew's talk was detailed in a letter by E. L. Richard reporting on the meeting, which is interesting as it describes Andrew's physical appearance and gives further information about him. He noted Andrew's talk was preceded by two other speakers. The first was William Hopkins (1793-1866), geologist and mathematician, speaking on dislocations of rocks and their magnetic structure. He was President of the Royal Society in 1851 and President of the British Association in 1853. This was followed by Robert Fox's talk on his experiments on the effects of electro-magnetism on the formation of mineral veins. In this Fox acknowledged Andrew, and said he had been inspired to carry out his research by Andrew's work on crystals, and had known him for some years. Richards then goes on:

It is difficult to give any just notion of the appearance of Mr. Crosse when he first got up to speak; simplicity and a perfect unconsciousness that he had anything extraordinary to communicate, were the prevailing features. In person he is tall, of light complexion with a manner at once frank and open-hearted. His address was not polished; he appeared that which indeed he stated himself to be, the child of seclusion, devoted to scientific pursuit, which had engrossed his mind for nearly thirty years, and forming one of the noblest instances on record of a man of wealth and station dedicating the best period of his life to the development of Nature's mysterious power, with the sole aim of benefiting mankind and doing honour to his country.

Dr Buckland's jocular remark concerning the brick in his introduction suggests he had seen or heard an outline of his work before Andrew presented his talk. In it Andrew referred to one of his experiments in which he kept a piece of scouring brick moistened with 'carbonate of lime' (calcium carbonate, $CaCO_3$) through which he passed an electric current for four or five months. Richards was very far off the mark in describing Andrew as a 'man of wealth'. Andrew was a good speaker, well able to infect his audience with his enthusiasm. During the evening there was a General Meeting of the British Association members, when the Chairmen of the various sections reported the proceedings of their particular section. Andrew had certainly made an impression on the Geological Section. Dr Buckland described Andrew's contribution, saying that his discoveries were entirely new to science, and that 'the patrons of science owed him an obligation for an achievement which would immortalise his name in the annals of geology.' The President of the BAAS, the Marquis of Northampton, said that Mr Crosse had not had any intention of speaking at the meeting, but was led to do so by the discussion he had heard (not quite true!), and that this was 'a very singular and pregnant instance of the advantage derived from this Association.'

The Chairman of the Chemical Section then asked Andrew to speak to his members, and so he addressed them on both 'Some Improvements on the Voltaic battery', and 'Observations on Atmospheric Electricity.' Not having expected to give a talk, Andrew had no notes with him, but relied on his phenomenal memory for the details of the experiments and the results. Despite this lack of preparation and any materials to demonstrate his work, his talk caused much excitement among the hearers and compliments were once again showered on him by this eminent audience. Dr Dalton said that he had never listened to anything so interesting which, coming from such a great chemist, greatly pleased him. Andrew once again showed his natural diffidence, or was it a lack of confidence? The very positive impression he had obviously made on the scientists at his friend's house before the meeting, and his instant fame among so many well-known scientists, and the plaudits, compliments and invitations heaped on him he found overwhelming. In his own words: 'I slipped away out of it all.' Two or three days before the meeting finished Andrew was once again busy working in his laboratory at Fyne Court. However, he could not have failed to have been buoyed up and elated by this visit to Bristol. It was a real turning point in his life, and he had so nearly not gone!

The great impression that this almost unknown man had made on the scientific community was reported in such widely read journals as *The Athenaeum*, which consistently misspelled his name in its reports. On the 3 September 1836 it reported:

> It is impossible to convey an idea of the enthusiasm with which his statement was received by the crowded assembly present. There appeared to be a real electrical effect … as if the interior recesses of Nature had been of a sudden laid open to them, and her processes, which had been conceived as past all mortal ken, submitted to their inspection. Mr. Cross was often interrupted during his address with loud peals of applause, which lasted for several minutes after he sat down.

The very positive impression Andrew made at the Bristol meeting meant that his invitation to welcome people to his home / laboratory was taken up. One of the first to do so was Sir Richard Phillips (1778-1851), a chemist who was elected a Fellow of the Royal Society in 1822. He was, at one time, President of the Chemical Society and Curator of the Museum of Practical Geology. He wrote several books and was later to communicate the results of Andrew's *Acari* experiments to *The Annals of Electricity, Magnetism and Chemistry.* He wrote an account of his visit to Fyne Court which appeared in *The Annals*. This is of great value as it is a detailed description of Andrew's laboratory by a scientist, and written from notes taken during his visit:

> The originality of the circumstances determined me at once to accept his invitation, and the day after that on which the business of the Association was finished, I proceeded to Bridgwater, from which Broomfield is distant about eight miles in the hill country. On reaching the handsome mansion of Mr. Crosse, situated in an undulating park, studded with trees of great bulk and age, I was received with much politeness, and found that I was the first visitor from Bristol. As I was preparing to retain my conveyance, to convey me back to Bridgwater, I was requested to return it, and pressed to stay to dinner and take a bed.

Breakfast being well served, Mr. Crosse then conducted me into a large and lofty apartment, built for a music room, with a capital organ in the gallery; but I could look at nothing but the seven or eight tables which filled the area of the room, covered with extensive voltaic batteries, of all forms, sizes, and extents. They resembled battalions of soldiers in exact rank and file, and seemed innumerable. They were in many forms – some in porcelain troughs of the usual construction; some like the couronnes des tasses; others cylindrical; some in pairs of glass vessels, with double metallic cylinders beside them; others of glass jars, with strips of copper and zinc.

Altogether there were 1,500 voltaic pairs at work in this great room, and in other rooms about 500 more. There were, besides, another 500 ready for new experiments. In all 2,500 pairs. It seemed like a great magazine for voltaic purposes! There are also two large workshops, with furnaces, tools, and implements of all descriptions, as much as would load two or three wagons. In the great room there stands a very large electrical machine, with a 20-inch cylinder, and a smaller one; and in several cases were all the apparatus in perfect condition, which are described in the best books on electricity. The prime conductor stood on glass legs, two feet high, and there was a medical discharger on a glass leg of five feet. Nothing could be in finer order, and no private electrician in the world could, perhaps, show a greater variety, both for experiments and amusement.

Beneath the mahogany cover of a table, on which stood the prime conductor, &c., was enclosed a magnificent battery of 50 jars, combining 73 square feet of coating. Its construction, by Cuthbertson, was in all respects most perfect. To charge it required 230 vigorous turns of the wheel, and its discharge made a report as loud as a blunderbuss. It fuses and disperses wires of various metals: and the walls of the apartment are covered with framed impressions of radiations from the explosion taken at sundry periods. Mr. Crosse struck one as an electrical curiosity and a memento of my visit.

But Mr. Crosse's greatest electrical curiosity was his apparatus for measuring, collecting, and operating with atmospheric electricity. He collects it by wires, the 16th of an inch diameter, extended from poles to poles, or from trees to trees in his grounds and park. The wires are insulated by means of glass tubes well contrived for the purpose. At present he has about a quarter of a mile of wire spread abroad, and in general about a third of a mile. A French gentleman had reported to the section at Bristol that the wires had extended twenty miles, filling the entire neighbourhood with thunder and lightning, to the great terror of the peasantry, who in consequence left Mr. Crosse in the free enjoyment of his game and rabbits. This exaggeration Mr. Crosse laughed at most heartily, though he acknowledged that he knew that no small terror prevailed in regard to him and his experiments.

The wires are connected with an apparatus in a window of his organ gallery, which may be detached at pleasure, when too violent, by simply turning an insulated lever; but in a moderate strength it may be conducted to a ball suspended over a great battery, which being connected with it, is charged rapidly, and is then discharged by means of a universal discharger. He told me that sometimes the current was so great as to charge and discharge the great battery 20 times in a minute, with reports as loud as cannon, which being continuous were so terrible to strangers that they always fled, while everyone expected the destruction of himself and premises. He was, however, he said, used to it, and knew how to manage and control it; but when it got into a passion he coolly turned his insulating lever, and conducted the lightning into the ground. It was a damp day, and we regretted that our courage could not be put to the test.

Everything about this part of Mr. Crosse's apparatus is perfect, and much of it his own contrivance, for he is clever in all mechanical arrangements, and has been unwearied in his application almost night and day, for 30 years past. I learned too, that in the purchase and fitting of his apparatus, he has expended nearly £3,000, although in most cases he is his own manipulator, carpenter, smith, copper-smith, &c.

About 12, Professor Sedgwick arrived, and in the afternoon one or two others, besides seven or eight gentlemen of the neighbourhood, who had been invited to meet us at dinner: Mr. Crosse unites to the rank of Esquire that of a country magistrate, in the duties of which he is respected alike for his humanity to the poor and for his liberal opinions in politics. Mrs. Crosse I had not the pleasure of seeing, one of the sons [John] being ill. Mr. Crosse himself was educated at Oxford, and his second son [Robert] holds the living at Broomfield. He is master of all his father's experiments, and, in spite of the complaints of an Oxford education, I found him to be a very expert mathematician, well read, and variously accomplished. At seven o'clock we enjoyed a dinner as well served as I ever saw in any state dinner in London, and beds being reserved for Professor Sedgwick and myself, we next morning renewed our survey, previous to fresh arrivals, and I took notes of everything connected with his aqueous voltaic batteries, in the following order, errors excepted:-

1. A battery of 100 pairs of 25 square inches, charged like all the rest with water, operating on cups containing 1 oz. of carbonate of barytes and powdered sulphate of alumine, intended to form sulphate of barytes at the positive pole, and crystals of alumine at the negative.

2. A battery of 11 cylindrical pairs, 12 inches by 4. This by operating six months on fluate of silver, had produced large hexahedral crystals at the negative pole, and crystals of silica and chalcedony at the positive.

3. A battery of 100 pairs of four square inches, operating on slate 832, and platina 3, to produce hexagonal crystals at the positive pole.

4. A battery of 100 pairs, 5 inches square, operating on nitrate of silver and copper, to produce malachite at the positive pole; at the negative pole, crystals already appear with decided angles and facets.

5. A battery of 16 pairs, of 2 inches, in small glass jars, acting on a weak solution of nitrate of silver, and already producing a compact vegetation of native silver.

6. A battery, esteemed his best, of 813 pairs, 5 inches, insulated on glass plates on deal bars, coated with cement, and so slightly oxydated by water, as to require cleaning but once or twice a year by pumping on

them. I felt the effect of 458 pairs in careless order and imperfectly liquidated, and they gave only some tinglings of the fingers, but this power in a few weeks produces decided effects on minerals.

7. A battery of 12 pairs, 25 inches zinc and 36 copper, charged two months before with water, and acting on a solution of nitrate of silver, poured on green-bottle glass coarsely powdered. It had already produced a vegetation of silver.

8. A battery of 129 galley-pots, with semi-circular plates of one and a quarter inch radius, placed on glass plates, and acting five months through a small piece of Bridgwater porous brick, on a solution of silex and potash. I saw at the poles small crystals of quartz.

9. A battery of 30 pairs, similar to No. 8 acting since July 27th, on a mixture, in a mortar, of sulphate of lead, of white oxide, of antimony, and sulphate of copper, and green sulphate of iron (205 grains), and three times the whole of green bottle-glass (615 grains). The result has been, in five weeks, a precipitation on the negative wire, of pure copper in two days, and crystallised iron pyrites in four days. It had been expected to produce sulphurets of lead, copper, and antimony, by depriving the sulphates of their oxygen.

10. A battery of 5 jars, with plates of different metals, as two copper and platina, one of lead and lead, and one silver and iron, and one copper and lead – Experimental.

11, 12, and 13. About 200 pairs, in three batteries, working in a dark room, of which I took no note.

It is clear that Sir Richard was very impressed both by the laboratory and by Andrew himself as he was 'deeply penetrated by the view of his labours, and the expense and zeal with which he had prosecuted his experiments.' The 'magnificent battery' and charging device that impressed him was made by John Cuthbertson (1743-1821), the foremost maker of electrical devices, which were used by many of the leading scientists in both Britain and

Europe. This had been a gift to him by his good friend George Singer. They had a deep discussion on galvanism, the possible effect of electricity on geological processes, and atmospheric electricity. Sir Richard explained to Andrew his own ideas of how minerals were formed in the earth, work he had been engaged on for forty years. Both learned from each other. When other people began to arrive he went to Taunton to arrange accommodation before setting off for his home. Sir Richard was impressed by Andrew's hospitality, which is in contrast to comments made by Professor Wheatstone (1802-75) some years later when he stayed at Fyne Court, as he described it as 'the strangest and most uncomfortable house he had ever stayed in.' The visit from a number of members of the British Association to Fyne Court elicited sufficient interest locally to be noted in *The Western Flying Post* of 31 August.

Shortly after his return Andrew received a letter from his friend John Kenyon, whom he had known for forty years. Kenyon had intended to go to the meeting but 'thinking I should meet no very particular friends, I begged off again, though I was at perfect liberty to move: now I could bite off my finger ends, to think I have missed you and Poole.' Apparently he had been travelling for several days, and so had not seen an account of the British Association meeting until Tom Poole had written to inform him of Andrew's triumph, and the extraordinary praise he had received. This letter gives an insight into the Crosse family health problems at this date: 'please God that the family affliction which (perhaps) you are still suffering, in the health of your son Richard, may pass away, and leave you at liberty to give a quickened attention to these things.' It goes on to reveal other interesting insights into Andrew's life:

> I know how desirous you are to see me at Broomfield, but you have a sick house. For many years all your cares, administrative and others, have been there, as you once said to me 'I have a stake through my body which nails me to Quantock.' How could we have believed, forty years ago at Seyer's, conjuror as we called you, that you should be writing with crystal pens of your own making, and I be carrying your autographs about the country.

Well, it has pleased God to try you with much household distress for some years – in your own unsatisfactory health, in the health of Mrs. Crosse, in the health of living children, and of those who are gone, and with other trials to which, more or less, flesh is heir to; but you have also been blest with compensation in a mind (as you once said with your characteristic energy) that, with a magnifying glass, could be happy in a prison, looking at a straw, and in a resisting buoyancy of spirit; and now, after all your furnace-watchings and explosions, whether vinous or electrical, comes at last a deserved reputation in part payment.

Now that Andrew had come to the notice of the scientific community, and following the invitation to visit him at Fyne Court, a variety of people began to make the trek to Broomfield. One who did so was Edward W. Cox in 1836. He was a practising solicitor in Taunton and founded the *Somerset County Gazette*, whose first issue, printed by William Bragg of Taunton, appeared on 31 December 1836. Cox combined his legal practice with being editor until 1845. He was also the founder and owner of *The Law Times* and *The Field*, and founded *The Exchange and Mart* and several other publications. He begins his account by describing his journey to Fyne Court:

If, when you come to the village of Kingston, about three miles from Taunton, you turn upon your right into a dark and narrow lane, you will soon find yourself climbing with a toil a difficult and very steep hill; the road is rough, and the hedges meeting overhead give it an aspect of the profoundest gloom. But by day, in the summer time it is deliciously cool and shady, and a very wilderness of wild flowers. Having conquered this hill, a turn of the road on your left conducts you to a park adorned with many fine beeches, on one side of which you behold a sheet of water, with a shrubbery in the background, whose very aspect invites you to trespass in it. All this you see as you walk under a row of trees that overshadow the road; and if you are a stranger to the place and its owner, you will wonder what can be the meaning of the mast-like poles fixed at the tops of the loftiest trees, by which a line (so it appears) is carried round the park till it is lost in the shrubbery.

Presently you see a mansion, oddly roosted in a hollow, under the ridge of the high ground you are treading, just as if the soil on which it had been built had suddenly sunk on some fine morning; for it is difficult to believe that an architect could have placed it there on purpose. It is a plain building on the outside, but it contains that within which passeth show. Knock fearlessly at the door; the votaries of science are always welcome there. Your name?, your station? your calling?, your property? Trouble not yourself about any of these things, nor hope thus to commend yourself to the inmates. You are a man, you have a mind, you venerate science, even if you know little of it: these are your passports into the mansion. Are you a stranger? You will not be so long. 'One touch of nature makes the whole world kin.'

Cox's detailed account is also of interest as he describes Andrew himself, although he did not know him too well at this stage judging by his comments regarding Andrew's health:

He is now in his velvet jacket, his laboratory costume; his frame is made for activity; light but muscular, having not an ounce of superfluous fat, with a trifling stoop at the shoulders; his face, too, is thin and long, with a fine forehead, grey eyes, bushy brows, a well-shaped nose, and a pointed chin. Its expression is highly intellectual, with an air of seeming melancholy, which is in fact one of thought; but a lengthened gaze discovers in it a lurking propensity for fun, which continually peeps out at the corners of his eyes, and in the curl of his lips. His hair is brown, partially silvered by age, which is betrayed only there, for his gait and countenance have all the liveliness and energy of youth; his step is springy, his voice cheerful, his aspect that of one who enjoys good health and its attendant, good spirits. Such, dimly outlined we must confess, is the personal appearance of Andrew Crosse.

From this time on, Andrew entertained increasing numbers of visitors to his scientific house and was pleased to do so. He had immense patience even with those visitors who did not really understand what he was doing. In October 1836 Andrew also learnt of a fascinating woman who was based in Dorset in a letter he received from John Kenyon, then staying in Teignmouth, Devon. Kenyon starts by regretting he will not have time to visit Fyne Court before returning to London, and continues:

I should like to have spent a day or two with you, if only to ask how the baby crystals are growing, and if their limbs and faces are well defined? I stayed three days at Lyme Regis; when I fossilized with that very interesting person Mary Anning (the discoverer of the Saurian remains in the Blue lias of Lyme)... She has not been very lucky in her finds lately, but the day I was with her she found the jaw of a shark, for which she received five guineas from one of our party...

We don't know if Andrew ever met Mary Anning, but he was certainly in correspondence with yet another eminent scientist in September 1837, Professor Charles Wheatstone who he met for the first time at the Bristol meeting. Wheatstone started as a musical instrument maker in London, and when he took up science his early research was into acoustics and optics. In 1838 he suggested the stereoscope enabling photographs, which had only been produced on paper for the first time in 1835, to be viewed in 3-D. With William Cooke he produced the first practical telegraph one mile (1.6 km) long in 1837. He produced the first printing telegraph in 1841 and the single needle telegraph in 1845. By 1852 more than 4,000 miles (1,609 km) of telegraph line had been laid throughout Britain. Appointed Professor of Experimental Philosophy at King's College, London in 1834, he was knighted in 1868. Another of Andrew's letters to Wheatstone, undated but written in the 1830s when Andrew was staying with friends in London, throws some light on what Wheatstone or researchers at King's College, London, were doing at the time: 'I have a great wish to see the experiments on Animal Magnetism so much talked of and should be extremely obliged to you to inform me in answer when and where I can have a sight of them. I should wish much to have some conversation with you ...'. An indication of Andrew's interest in electricity within the living body.

On one occasion a large party had travelled to Broomfield from some distance, and Andrew was showing them around the house, that was in effect one huge laboratory, and explaining the various equipment and experiments that were going on. At length, they arrived at his main laboratory in the music room and were taken up onto the Gallery. Here stood two enormous Leyden Jars which he charged using the copper 'exploring wire' strung around the trees of the estate to capture atmospheric electricity. An old gentleman in the party looked at the arrangement with a face that reflected stern disapproval, until at last he said 'Mr. Crosse, don't you think it is rather impious to bottle the lightning?' Andrew, with a laugh, said 'Let me answer your question with another. Don't you think sir, it might be considered impious to bottle the rain water?' To which the old gentleman could think of no reply!

With scientific equipment filling the whole house, rows of batteries, vessels 'growing' crystals and all the paraphernalia of a scientist of Natural Philosophy, the house must have been a nightmare for the servants to keep clean, although this did not seem to be high on Andrew's list of priorities. Servants had strict instructions to avoid touching any of the equipment. However, one day a housemaid, a Welsh girl, carrying out her duty of dusting, was in the music room and went up to the gallery. She noticed that the brass cylinder, bearing the prominent engraved sign *Noli me tangere* (Do not touch me), was dusty, and so rubbed it vigourously. This was connected to the 'exploring wire' and, unfortunately for her, that day there was a considerable amount of atmospheric electricity present, and as she dusted it she received a considerable, but luckily not fatal, shock. She ran to Andrew and said, in her strong Welsh accent, 'That nasty thing in the gallery had nearly knocked me down.' He sternly told her 'I thought that I told you never to touch the apparatus.' To which she replied 'Yes, sir; but I thought you had written No Danger on it!' Hopefully, this near miss would have taught Andrew that warning signs had to be in English as not all the household could read Latin! Andrew's head gardener hated it when groups of visitors arrived at Fyne Court as he was sometimes called on to demonstrate that electricity could really be drawn from the air by touching the apparatus and receiving a shock from it!

Andrew's account of his research at the Bristol meeting had been met with great acclaim, but following the meeting there were some who criticised his work, and one who particularly annoyed Andrew was the Rev. Dr William Ritchie (1748-1830) who was present at the meeting and heard him talk. Richie was the first person to produce an electromagnetic motor (in 1833), a machine that produces a rotary motion using an electromagnet. Faraday is often credited with inventing this in 1821, but he merely demonstrated the principle using a wire in a container of mercury. Andrew was quite happy to discuss and defend his results and methods with people who came up with intelligent and reasoned objections, but generally ignored any attacks on him that he regarded as ridiculous or ill-informed. However, he obviously felt that the points made by Ritchie in *The Bristol Atlas* were so inaccurate and misleading, that he could not ignore them and so put pen to paper, something he rarely did to answer critics. One of the main points being made by Ritchie was that Andrew's work on electro-crystallisation was first carried out by Antoine Cesar Becquerel (1788-1878). However, this was certainly not the case.

While Andrew had only publicly presented the results of his electro-crystallisation research in 1836, he had been working in this field since about 1807, and was engaged in numerous experiments on electro-crystallisation from 1817. Becquerel had joined the French army, then engaged in the Peninsula War, as an Engineer-Officer in 1808. He saw action with the Imperial Troops in Spain in 1810-12, and again in France in 1814, the year he decided to resign from the army and devote his life to scientific investigation. While fighting with the army he had no time for experiments on the effect of electricity on minerals (or anything else!) and did not begin this research until after 1814. He was only engaged in this field for a relatively short time in his early days as a scientist before beginning investigations into luminescent phenomena and other fields. He was the first to prepare metallic elements from their ores by electrolysis, and hoped that this would lead to an understanding of the recomposition of crystallised bodies and the processes by which crystals are formed in nature. Andrew had been working on this at least seven years earlier.

In 1825 Becquerel invented a differential galvanometer for the accurate measurement of electrical resistance, and in 1829 invented a constant-current electrochemical cell, which was the forerunner of the Daniel Cell. In 1837 he was made a Fellow of the Royal Society of London, the same year he was awarded the Copley Medal in recognition of his scientific papers on the production of crystals of metallic sulphurets and sulphur by the long continued action of low levels of electricity. Crosse and Becquerel did not know of each other's work until after 1836, but sometime later

Andrew was in correspondence with the French scientist who fully acknowledged the important discoveries that Andrew had made. Andrew's reply to the criticism levelled at him is interesting as it not only answers Dr Ritchie's points, but gives an insight into Andrew himself, his diffidence, and details of his laboratory and the work he was engaged in at that time:

To the Editor of the Atlas
Jan. 31st, 1837.

It is exceedingly disagreeable to me to be compelled to bring the name of so unimportant an individual as myself before the public, and had I not met with such an unfair attack as that of Dr. Ritchie, I should not have presumed to make the following statement. From my boyhood I have detested nothing so much as cant or humbug of any sort; and if I had been disposed to form a high opinion of myself, the very severe lessons I have met with in my passage through life would have been amply sufficient to humble me. It was by mere chance that I attended the meeting of the British Association at Bristol, having only made up my mind so to do on the day previous to the commencement of the business. So far was I from having the least idea of making a communication, that I previously feared lest, from the pressure of the crowd, I should lose the opportunity of hearing what was going on.

Chance led me into conversation with some eminently scientific men, who, having heard some observations of mine, requested me to make them public. To this I assented, and what followed is known. I never attached the least merit to what I had done, nor tacked the word discovery to any of my experiments, but gave a simple statement of what took place. It was for the public to form what opinion they pleased. At the close of my observations before the chemical section, I stated distinctly, that if any one present wished to question me, I would endeavour to answer them to the best of my ability: and Dr. Ritchie, who was present at the Association, and knew what was going on, might have taken an excellent opportunity of exposing my ignorance, face to face. No questions were asked.

M. Becquerel's experiments were then brought forward of which I had not seen any account, although I heard shortly before the meeting of his having formed sulphurets of lead and silver by the electric action. I stated that my experiments were made from the mere love of science, and that I did not wish to detract from or presume to set myself in competition with any one. The only statement I myself published since the meeting, was contained in your paper, in a letter in answer to one received from you. A great many mistakes and exaggerations concerning me have been circulated in different papers at different times; but it is no fault of mine that such things occurred.

In fact, it cannot be expected that those who have not made a particular science their study should be correct in their details concerning such science. It is very true that, in my electrical room, a brass ball connected with an atmospherical conductor is suspended over a battery, so arranged as to be united or disunited at pleasure; but such battery is a common electrical, and most assuredly not a voltaic one. Dr. Ritchie must have known well that the absurd report of having brought into my house streams of lightning as a large as the mast of a ship originated in a joke that fell from the eloquent lips of a distinguished professor who attended the meeting.

Dr. Ritchie, however, in supposing such a miracle possible, compares the inferiority of such an enormous electrical current with the superiority of that manifested by Richman and Romas, the former of whom was unfortunately killed by want of proper precaution, having contrived an apparatus to bring the electric fluid into his house, but apparently without making a due arrangement to carry it out. The latter, by means of a kite, elevated far above the highest of my poles, brought down an amazing quantity of electricity; but such a temporary apparatus as a kite is ill-calculated for scientific purposes, to say nothing of the extreme danger attending it.

I have really no wish to be knocked on the head in aspiring to eclipse my neighbours. Dr. R. next proceeds with something more tangible – my letter to you. He is first offended with the term circular batteries. It is quite clear that plates answer as well as cylinders; but I made use of the latter shape on account of my employing common glass bottles with their necks off as insulators, into which I fitted two zinc and copper cylinders.

He next insinuates that I claim as a discovery the filling the cells with water instead of dilute acid. When did I state this? I may, however, in justice to myself observe, that I have not heard of effects produced by other batteries filled with common water at all equal to what are produced by the arrangements I adopt, and for the truth of this I appeal to those scientific men who witnessed their effects.

Dr. R. then notices my remark on the greater power of these batteries between the hours of seven and ten in the morning, and that such increase of strength was unconnected with any matter whatever. Here he observes that I do not know the properties of the agents used in a voltaic battery, and proceeds to lecture me on the alteration of the conducting power of primary and secondary conductors by the influence of heat, summing up with the inference that the increase of temperature is the cause of the increase of power observed, and that, too, between the hours of seven and ten in the morning! I shall only say, in reply to this, that my batteries are placed in a room with a south aspect, and that every fair day the sun shines full upon them, at which time the shock they give to the human body is decidedly less than at the hours alluded to.

As to my ignorance of the effects of heat, &c., on voltaic batteries, I have tried fluids of all temperatures, and often used boiling water in the cells, which occasions a considerable increase in power. I do not agree with Dr. Ritchie that 800 pairs of plates used in water are equivalent in power to 50 pairs of the same size, and under the same circumstances, used with dilute acid. Of course the former are far superior in intensity, but they are by no means equal in the density of the current.

Dr. R. next finds fault with my stating that an increase of number of plates produces more than a corresponding effect in power; and he averts to his investigations published in 1832. I stated at Bristol that my apparatus was incomplete, and that I was in the midst of a train of experiments. I am so still, and it is most unfair to expect a perfect result during the course of investigation. I have not seen the account of those experiments to which Dr. R. alludes, but if they were performed with batteries each cell of which was not separately and carefully insulated, it would amply account for his failing to produce effects equal to what would otherwise have taken place. To say the truth, I have made a much greater number of experiments in this branch of the science that Dr. R. may be aware of, but am not about to enter at present upon the comparative powers of the simple electric, the decomposing, the fusing, or the magnetic effects produced from differently formed batteries. Opinion to me is but a wind, experiment a rock.

Now comes his attack on my electrical crystallisations of substances. I before stated all I knew concerning M. Becquerel. Had M. Becquerel been the Englishman and I the foreigner, I do believe that gentleman would have received from Dr. R. the censure of myself, as if it were a crime for a countryman hitherto unknown to experimentalise at all.

The next remark on me is: 'According to Mr. Crosse, either pole of the battery will crystallise equally well.' When and where did I state this absurdity? It is the first time that I have heard of it. I have, however, met with some curious and quite unexpected facts which bear on this part of the subject, which neither chemist nor electrician would have expected without previous trial. Then follows: 'The crystallisation of quartz and carbon is still doubtful.' That I have produced the first by the electric action long continued, as also arragonite, I can prove by unimpeachable witnesses; the last (carbon) I have not attempted.

As I never aimed at procuring public applause (although I am deeply sensible of the great kindness I have received from my friends and the public) but have pursued science for its own sake, those shafts of Dr. Ritchie fall powerless against me. I cannot, however, refrain from adding that I would scorn to admit for one instant such a spirit towards another as he has evinced towards me, a stranger to him in all respects, save public report, even for the power of crystallising carbon.

I am, in the meantime, sir,
Yours sincerely,
ANDREW CROSSE.

P.S. I should have sent this answer long since, but have been prevented by severe illness. I must beg in future to decline engaging in scientific warfare with any one, having neither inclination nor time for that kind of amusement.

This did not deter Andrew from his electro-crystallisation research, and in 1837 he began to investigate the effect of light on crystal formation.

CHAPTER SIX
That Notorious Experiment!

Within a few months of attending the meeting of the British Association for the Advancement of Science (BAAS) at Bristol, where Andrew came to the notice of and impressed many eminent scientists, he embarked on a series of experiments that was to bring him to even wider notice, and ensure his name survived forever – as the man who created life! While engaged in one of his electro-crystallisation experiments, attempting to create crystals of silica (quartz), he found, much to his surprise, that small organisms resembling mites appeared. The first person outside the family to hear about these mites was Andrew's friend Robert Southey, whom he had known since 1806. Andrew was out walking on the Quantock Hills considering the strange result of apparently developing living creatures instead of crystals, when he saw Southey toiling up a steep hill behind his carriage. He was on his way to stay with their mutual friend Tom Poole at Nether Stowey. Andrew and Southey greeted each other, and Andrew's thoughts, being full of these mysterious little creatures, regaled him with a detailed account of this strange occurrence. It has been reported that Southey said 'Well, I am the first traveller who has ever been stopped by so extraordinary a statement!'

One of the reasons this unexpected outcome was to become so widely known was because of Andrew's new found fame. Only a few months earlier he had been hailed by Professor William Buckland and others at Bristol as a genius, doing research of the utmost importance for the study of physical geology. The *Athenaeum* report of the meeting which appeared on 3 September 1836 said that one geologist had claimed that Andrew's discoveries 'were of such importance, that had the British Association been of no other service than in bringing them to light, they alone were worth all the pains it had taken for the advancement of science.' This was not surprising as geologists of the time were rapidly becoming convinced that natural electricity played a part in crystallisation, stratification and the formation of mineral veins. Just before Crosse's talk they heard William Hopkins and Robert Fox lecture about these very subjects. Many attending the Geological Section hoped that geology would become a physical science that was capable of experimental research. Adam Sedgwick, Professor of Geology at Cambridge, said that Andrew's work provided one of the most important advances yet made in geology, and stated that 'from this time forth he must stand before the world as public property.' This gave Andrew huge credibility, so that anything he said, or was thought to have said, were the words of a genius endorsed by some of the country's leading scientists. His name was now well enough known to sell newspapers.

The news leaks out

Andrew knew that under certain circumstances these mites appeared, but only if he set up specific conditions. He was not an entomologist or zoologist so did not know if they were a new species or not, and had no theory to account for their appearance. It was all very puzzling. He discussed what had happened with a few friends, 'amongst whom were some highly scientific gentlemen, and they plainly perceived the insect in various states.' However, he had no intention of making the results known more widely, certainly not at this early stage. Towards the end of 1836 Edward Cox published a new newspaper, *The Somerset County Gazette*. He visited Fyne Court early in December and learnt of Andrew's curious discovery of mites appearing in his silica experiments. Ever open and honest, Andrew was perhaps naive in discussing the matter with a newspaper man, but he had known Cox well for some time as he was Secretary of the Taunton Mechanics Institute. This was too good to miss. Deciding that an article on page three would attract readers to his new paper, Cox published a brief description of the experiment on 31 December 1836, under the headline 'EXTRAORDINARY EXPERIMENT, BY ANDREW CROSSE ESQ.'.

Although Cox wrote an outline of the discovery, the article was edited by 'S.G.C.', the paper's only reporter at that time. This outlines, not quite accurately, the experiment with a rock from Mount Vesuvius, and then describes the appearance of the mites. How Andrew noticed small white specks on the stone on the 14th day, which by the 18th day had become oval and which he initially thought were crystals. To his astonishment on the 22nd day he saw they had eight legs projecting from what was then clearly bodies. By the 26th day there was no doubt, they were creatures that looked like a mite. Around eighteen of these appeared, and their movement was clearly visible to the naked eye. The report does not say that Andrew offered any explanation for their appearance. The report goes on to explain the significance of Andrew's discovery in case the readers failed to grasp it:

> But what is that power which has called forth the slumbering spirit of life within them? Clearly, the influence of the electric fluid. The how and why are matters for future investigation. Mr. Crosse has discovered the fact; he leaves to others the explanation of that fact. But a new field of inquiry is opened which, if well investigated, may perhaps lead to the clearing up of many things which have been hitherto mysterious and not merely the ken, but even the hopes, of Philosophers.

The author of the piece also clearly states why he felt it was so important to publish the account of this momentous discovery:

> Already others have stolen many suggestions and experiments and passed them upon the world as their own, for Mr. Crosse conceals nothing of his knowledge, and, for the sake of science, communicates his discoveries, careless of the fame which is his right.

This announcement was not authorised by Andrew, and it concludes by saying that it had been published in order to protect Andrew's priority: 'We trust that by thus early publishing and awarding them to their proper owner, we shall prevent much unfair appropriation of the honour of his brilliant researches by those who have no title to it.' Andrew, wanting to correct errors in the story that had appeared in the *Somerset County Gazette* and elsewhere, wrote a letter to the paper, which was noted in the next edition on 7 January 1837:

To Correspondents.

We have received a very polite note from Mr. Crosse stating that in our description of his singular experiment, although we had given a correct account of the results and the main facts, we had erred in some of the details. We should have shewn him the M.S. before its publication had time permitted, but we purposed only to give a popular and not a scientific account of it, and as most ridiculously erroneous reports had gone abroad respecting it, we thought it desirable to take the earliest opportunity of contradicting them. Mr. C. had previously informed us that he had no objection to the experiment being made public as he himself communicated it to several persons.

This suggests Andrew did expect it to be published in the local paper at some point, and his main concern was with the inaccuracy of the report. However, in a letter Andrew sent to the *Taunton Courier*, published on 4 January 1837, he is not only concerned with accuracy, but suggests he had not given permission for his experiment to be reported:

Dear Sir,

Having seen in a recent publication what is stated to be an account of some experiments of mine in which insects were produced instead of crystals, I take this earliest opportunity of making known, that such an account was published without my knowledge, and that although the main fact is as represented, yet the mode of conducting such experiments is inaccurate. I am the more anxious to correct this statement, as several perfectly erroneous accounts have already appeared in different papers, calculated to produce a false impression of my experiments in the minds of all but scientific men, who can, if they please, readily distinguish an error when they meet one.

I am sorry to observe that a gentleman of high repute [Dr Ritchie] who seems to have forgotten both science and temper on the present occasion, has taken advantage of some misstatements to form a weak foundation for a most illiberal attack on me in the Literary Gazette, which I shall take an early opportunity of replying to as it deserves. I must further request my friends and the public not to give credit to any publication as coming from me unless my name is attached, and as I detest nothing so much as a literary or scientific dispute, I had hoped to have glided through the remainder of my life without provoking the malevolence of the ill-disposed, and more particularly as I am unconscious of having done anything to offend the most captious by presumption or misrepresentation.

The news spreads

The bulk of the initial report of Andrew's findings as given in the *Somerset County Gazette* on 31 December 1836 was repeated in *The Times* on 4 January 1837. On 7 January 1837 *The Times* featured the letter from Andrew that had appeared in *The Taunton Courier* on 4 January 1837. At the same time Andrew sent a fuller account of his discovery to William Stitchbury of the Bristol Institute for the Advancement of Science and Art, founded in 1823, who then forwarded it to *The Bristol Advocate*, which regularly featured the *Proceedings of the Institute*. They published the account on 4 February 1837. Such an amazing discovery from the laboratory of the hero of the British Association was quickly taken up by *The Gentlemans Magazine* in March 1837 and then by hundreds of other newspapers, magazines and journals. Within a few weeks news of Andrew's initial report and his reply had spread across the country. Accounts appeared in a wide range of publications. *The Athenaeum, The Literary Gazette, The Mirror of Literature, Amusements and Instruction, The Magazine of Popular Science,* and *The Mechanics Magazine,* as well as the daily and weekly press right across the United Kingdom which picked up the story. It also appeared in some continental newspapers. Most editors reported the discovery without comment, only a few were more sceptical. The view of the *The Albion* of Liverpool, on 9 January 1837, was 'Credat Judaeus, or 'tell it to the marines, for the sailors won't believe you.' However, *The Western Flying Post* printed a supportive letter concerning Andrew on 12 January 1837:

Andrew Crosse has been made the subject of a severe and ill-natured attack in the Literary Gazette, supposed by Mr. Crosse himself to have been occasioned by some of the incorrect statements of his experiments which have appeared in Newspapers and Magazines. Mr. C. has promised to take an early opportunity of replying to the article as it deserves, and we are quite sure he will fully vindicate himself from the illiberal insinuations thrown out against him, and evince the fairness of his claims to that splendid and honourable report that his indefatigable scientific researches have won for him.

By the end of January 1837 the creation of life by the use of electricity had become an established fact for many of the public, who believed it must be true as it said so in the newspapers! This not only generated great excitement, but brought strong criticism and personal attacks on Andrew and his work. One man wrote to him referring to Andrew as 'a disturber of the peace of families' and 'a reviler of our holy religion.' Another letter, anonymous, in a local paper claimed that the mites were the cause of an agricultural blight which took place at that time. He even received threats of violence. Andrew was very upset by all this publicity and fuss, and said to many people that it was not his intention to raise any questions concerned with either the natural world or religious beliefs. Being of a religious nature himself he said he was 'sorry that the faith of his neighbours could be overturned by the claw of a mite.' However, the story that a local clergyman from Bridgwater conducted a service of exorcism in the hills above Fyne Court, as described in Peter Haines *The Man Who Was Frankenstein*, seems to have originated not in a local folk tale or history, but appeared in a story by 'The Man in Black', read by radio star Valentine Dyall (1949).

He was now besieged by correspondents wanting further details of his experiments, and so was kept busy preparing accounts for newspaper readers. Andrew had informed Dr William Buckland of his findings in writing soon after his discovery. He had met Buckland for the first time at Bristol when he was chairing the meeting of the Geological Section of the British Association to which Andrew had given a talk. Buckland advised him to send some of the mites to Richard Owen (1804-92) a comparative anatomist and palaeontologist, at that time Hunterian Professor of Comparative Anatomy and Physiology at the Royal College of Surgeons, and President of the newly founded Microscopical Society. He was not a specialist in entomology, but few people were in Britain at this time. Contemporary accounts, both by Andrew and others, usually refer to the mites as 'insects', but mites are not insects as they belong to the class *Arachnida* the group of eight legged arthropods that includes ticks, spiders and scorpions. Andrew mounted ten of the mites in Canada balsam, a resin, between two small pieces of glass so they could be examined under the microscope, and sent them to Owen with a covering letter and notes, dated 10 February 1837 (plate 15).

In this he explained that they were living when he placed them in the Canada balsam using a moistened camel hair brush, included two sketches of the mites and details of the experiments in which they appeared. Andrew concludes his letter: 'Not being an entomologist I can give no opinion on the matter. I have only related facts. Many persons have seen the insects and their motion is plainly discernible. Whether electricity has anything to do with their birth or not I cannot say without further experimenting.' That he was thinking of doing more experiments to further investigate his strange findings is also suggested by the final sentence of the letter he sent to Owen: 'I should feel extremely obliged to you for your opinion on the subject and grateful for any hint you may give me respecting any further experiments which it may be desirable to try on this subject.' Owen reached the conclusion that they were common cheese mites (one of several species of *Tyroglyphus casei*), and had shown the specimens to other scientists in London, including William Clift (1775-1849), the museum's Conservator. He was also an expert on comparative anatomy, and agreed with him. Within months this initial assessment of the creatures being a type of *Acarus* was backed up by a respected French naturalist but he said that although it resembled a cheese mite, it was not one.

The Western Flying Post published a letter from Andrew on 30 March 1837, which was the answer to his critics mentioned on 12 January. This would not have given its readers much more information than had already been released, and his caution is obvious:

In respect to these experiments of mine in which insects made their unexpected appearance I have given no opinion whatsoever as to the cause of their production, I have mentioned FACTS not OPINION. Without more data than we at present possess I do not see how it is possible to form an opinion on the matter, or to say whether the electric agency is or is not the secondary cause or acceleration of their birth. Since my first two experiments I have met with eight other results, in which similar insects have appeared. In the cause of my observations I have met with some rather curious phenomena which shall be laid before the public when the train of experiments now in hand, and which must necessarily occupy much time, is completed.

An accurate description of the experiment

In March Andrew sent a more scientific account in the form of a circular letter to some of the scientists he had met at Bristol. A number of these circular letters are in scientific and university archives. The first official notice of the curious outcome of his experiment to come to the attention of the wider scientific community appeared in volume one of *Annals of Electricity, Magnetism and Chemistry* (pp. 242-40). This was published by William Sturgeon (1783-1850) who had also founded the Electrical Society as a way of bringing together the many individual researchers in electricity, a subject being widely explored. Andrew had joined the Society soon after it had been founded. Andrew's submission to the *Annals* consisted of an account of his experiment which Andrew sent to Sir Richard Phillips, presumably for his views on publication, who had immediately sent it on to Sturgeon, editor of the *Annals*. This was accompanied by a covering letter from Sir Richard:

Dear Sir,

This morning I received the enclosed from Mr. Crosse, of Broomfield. Its contents are so novel and interesting that I am persuaded you will, even at this eleventh hour, give it a place in your forthcoming number. With all my best wishes for the success of your valuable Journal.

I am, respectfully,
R.PHILLIPS.

Andrew's communication, from Broomfield, dated 23 March 1837, was entitled 'On the production of Insects by Voltaic Electricity'. He poured a dilute solution of potassium silicate (K_2SiO_3) supersaturated with hydrochloric acid into a bowl above a Wedgwood funnel. A strip of flannel hanging over the edge of the bowl caused the fluid in the bowl to drip into the funnel. It then dripped onto a piece of slightly porous red iron oxide (Fe_2O_3) from Mount Vesuvius which was placed in a funnel. Excess solution was collected in a bottle below, and periodically poured back into the bowl above the first funnel. Two platinum wires, fixed on opposite sides of the rock were connected to the positive and negative poles of a Voltaic battery. This consisted of nineteen pairs of five inch plates in cells filled with 0.3% hydrochloric acid. The rock was kept continually moist and constantly given a low electric charge (plate 14). Then came a most unexpected result:

At the end of fourteen days, two or three very minute white specks or nipples were visible on the surface of the stone, between the two wires, by means of a lens. On the eighteenth day these nipples elongated and were covered with fine filaments. On the twenty-second day their size and elongation increased, and on the twenty-sixth day each figure assumed the form of a perfect insect, standing on a few bristles which formed its tail. On the twenty-eighth day these creatures moved their legs, and in the course of a few days more, detached themselves from the stone, and moved over its surface at pleasure, although in general they appeared adverse to motion, more particularly when first born.

In the course of a few weeks more, about a hundred of these insects made their appearance on the stone. I observed that each of them fixed itself for a considerable time in one place, as far as I could judge appearing to feed by suction; but when a ray of light from the sun was let fall upon it, it seemed much disturbed and finally removed itself to the shaded side of the stone. I ought to state that out of about a hundred insects, not above six or seven were born on the south side of the stone.

I examined some of these insects with the microscope. Their shape was similar to that of the cheese mite, but they seemed to be from twice to eight times the size of that animalcule, and the motion of their legs was occasionally discernible by the naked eye. They had in general eight legs, but there were some with only six; their bodies were covered with bristles which gave some of them the appearance of a little star; the length of the bristles at the tail was considerable, and these when highly magnified appeared spicated.

Instant death followed their removal from the stone, however delicately performed, but in the course of time most of them were washed down into the bottle below, and poured into the basin above, from whence they found their way to the wooden support which was kept moist by the fluid dropping between it and the Wedgwood funnel. On examining this piece of wood I found upwards of forty living insects actively crawling over its surface, and apparently feeding on the silicious matter with which it was impregnated.

There follows details of a second experiment, whose aim seems to have been primarily designed to create silica crystals, not a further investigation in to the appearance of mites (plate 14):

I filled a small glass jar with a concentrated solution of silicate of potash [potassium silicate, K_2SiO_3], and plunged into it a thick iron wire connected with the positive pole of a battery composed of twenty pairs of cylinders in cells filled with common water, and immersed in the same a small coil of fine silver wire connected with the negative pole of the same battery. In the course of a few weeks gelatinous silex [silica derived from flint] was formed in some quantity round the iron wire, and after a longer interval of time, a similar formation, but much less quantity, filled up the silver coil. On examining these wires with a lens, I first observed a similar insect at the negative wire, and some time afterwards I found two more; in the whole, three at the negative, and shortly afterwards I found twelve at the positive; in the whole fifteen.

Each of these insects was well formed, and quite as large as those observed in the first experiment. They were deeply imbedded in the gelatinous silex, with the bristles of the tail projecting. They were in general from half to three quarters of an inch below the surface of the fluid. In this experiment there was neither flannel, wood, volcanic stone, nor acid, consequently the insects appear to have been born in the silex. Not being an entomologist, I can give no opinion on the matter. I have only related facts. Many persons have seen the insects both dead and living.

Whether the electric action has anything to do with their birth or not I cannot say without further experimenting. Perhaps if the experiments were repeated and varied, curious facts might be the result. Since the above, having found that all the insects in the first experiment had died, I poured into the basin an additional quantity of the same fluid, and in the course of two or three weeks I had a second crop of insects upon the volcanic stone.

I have also had two other formations in distinct solutions: 1, a weak solution of oxide of copper [copper oxide, Cu_2O]; 2,3,4,5, in concentrated solutions of green sulphate of iron [iron sulphate, $FeSO_4.7H_2O$)], sulphate of zinc [zinc sulphate, $ZnSO_4$], sulphate of copper [copper sulphate, $CuSO_4$], and nitrate of copper [copper nitrate, $Cu(NO_3)_2$] – in the whole, ten separate formations; five in silicious solutions, and five in solutions of metallic salts &c. – each of which was exposed to a long continued electric action, before any insect made its appearance, still without further experimenting I would not venture an opinion. I hope in the course of time to know something more about this.

Faraday repeats the experiment – not true!

While brief accounts appeared in hundreds of publications, they did not have enough accurate details to allow others to replicate the experiments to check Andrew's results. However, confirmation of his discovery was, according to the popular press, forthcoming almost at once. Towards the end of February 1837 Michael Faraday was reported to have successfully repeated Andrew's experiment using stone from Vesuvius and a silica solution. This was not true. On 17 February 1837 Faraday gave a Discourse, a regular Friday evening event, entitled 'On Dr. Marshall Hall's Reflex Function of the Spinal Marrow'. A lengthy account of this appeared in *The*

Athenaeum on 25 February, *The Literary Gazette*, also on 25 February, and a short piece in *The London Medical Gazette*. Not one account mentions Andrew's *Acari*, as they would certainly have done if Faraday had reported that he had successfully replicated his experiment. As part of this event objects of interest were displayed in the Library, brought along by members and others. The items were not necessarily related to the Discourse. *The Magazine of Popular Science* reported, on 25 February, that examples of Andrew's *Acari* were shown on this occasion by Clift, and it is known that Owen was also present at the meeting.

It is not clear exactly what happened following the Discourse, but these were very popular, particularly when Faraday was speaking, and there would have been many people around. The question of the *Acari* would have come up in conversation, and Faraday probably said something along the lines of 'an interesting result, but I would wish to repeat the experiment before giving an opinion'. The chances are this was misunderstood, misheard or only partially heard by a correspondent of a journal, who added their own embellishments. A report in *The Patriot* of 27 February 1837 reported:

> At the last meeting of the Royal Institution, held on Friday evening, Dr. Faraday delivered a lecture, in which he alluded to the recent discoveries of Mr. Crosse, with respect to the formation or revivification of insects in flint, which, although doubted by many, he knew to be true, inasmuch as, by a continuous voltaic stream from silica of potash, he himself produced living animalculae. He also exhibited some insects obtained from hard polished stone, and which were now, like those of Mr. Crosse, enjoying life after the transition of many thousands of years.

The Patriot may have been repeating verbatim a report in another journal as the reference to 'the last meeting' must refer to that of the 17 February when Faraday spoke and *Acari* are known to have been exhibited. There was a Discourse the following Friday (24 February) but the speaker was Mr Cowper, not Faraday. The other possibility was that this report was held over for a week before being published. This inaccurate report was picked up by several other papers. What was probably a very reasonable statement by Faraday, deferring judgement, was transformed by the popular press into endorsement of Andrew's results. Faraday had not tried to replicate Andrew's experiment, but the erroneous reports that he had done so and had also created mites had a major impact on the next stage of this mystery. The story of the supposed successful Faraday experiment was given blanket coverage all over Britain and beyond, joining the initial report of Andrew's work as a scientific 'fact' that electricity could create living organisms. Faraday quickly took steps to suppress this claim about his involvement, making a formal disclaimer at one of his Friday evening Discourses. It is not known if he sent a disclaimer to *The Patriot*, but he did send letters to *The Literary Gazette* and *The Times* neither of which had carried the inaccurate report. *The Times* carried a letter from Faraday on 4 March 1837:

> I take the liberty of asking whether an erroneous statement which has appeared in several journals may be contradicted, in The Times? I have no right to request this favour, as the error has not appeared in that paper, but do it with the feeling that, if permissible, one correction there will be sufficient for all the mistakes elsewhere. I am reported to have said, that by experiment I have fully confirmed the extraordinary results of Mr. Crosse, who states that he has obtained living insects by the agency of electricity and silica, etc. What I said was almost the reverse of this, for I merely stated, upon the occasion of the insects being shown by Mr. Clift and Mr. Owen at the Royal Institution, that we wished it to be directly understood we had no opinion to give respecting the mode of their production.
>
> My impression is, that the electricity and the silica are merely accidental circumstances in relation to the production of the insects, and not essentials; and I have refrained from experiments because I thought it only just to Mr. Crosse that he should be allowed the opportunity by further trials in close vessels and with other precautions that will easily suggest themselves, either to correct his views, if they need correction, or to add that clear and confirmatory evidence which the subject at present requires.

Faraday's hope that this statement might end the rumours of his having successfully created mites like Andrew was in vain, possibly due to *The Times* having a limited readership in Europe! On 9 July 1837 Christian Friedrich Schöenbein (1799-1867), a German chemist who discovered ozone, guncotton and a specialist in electrochemistry, wrote to Faraday from Basel:

> Some of our continental papers, particularly German ones, have still much to do with Mr. Crosse's insects, said to be manufactured out of siliceous matter by the agency of a current. As these Journals frequently make use of your Name to prove the truth of the pretended discovery and enter in this respect into particulars, such for instance, as to assert, those insects had been exhibited by you at the meetings of the Royal Institution I should be very much obliged to you, if you would have the kindness to tell me, what to think of such reports.

Faraday replied to Schöenbein on 21 September 1837:

> With regard to Mr. Crosse's insects etc. I do not think anybody believes in them here except perhaps himself and the mass of wonder-lovers. I was said in the English papers to have proved the truth of his statement, but I immediately contradicted the matter publicly and should have thought that nobody who could judge in the matter would have suspected me of giving evidence to the thing for a moment. Contradict it in my name as fully as you please. It is but just of me to say that in conversation with Mr. Crosse I was very much pleased with him and with the readiness with which he received my critical remarks. As regards the cristallization supposed as real he was lugged into view and must not be charged with having pressed himself forward. He is in fact a very modest man but has been dragged into an unkind situation.

Faraday was desperate to disassociate himself from the 'electrical mites' as Andrew's apparent results were too close to the question of the origins of life itself, a subject of great sensitivity which impinged on religious views, as well as having political and social implications, as Charles Darwin was to find out some years later. Faraday regarded this question to be beyond the boundary of scientific investigation. The other consideration was that Faraday felt he had a clear understanding that physics dealt with the non-organic world, and that 'life' or its creation did not come within his specialisation. Andrew's apparent discovery threatened to break the clear distinction between the physical sciences and the biological sciences, and blur the distinction between matter and life. So it is not surprising that there was so much excitement, disquiet and disbelief among scientists. For many Christians and conservative clerics Andrew's findings were tantamount to evidence of atheism, something that hit Andrew particularly hard as a devout and committed Christian all his life.

At the end of the year the claim moved from newspapers and periodicals to a standard work of reference, *The Annual Register*, a handbook regarded as an authoritative work detailing that year's most important events. In its Chronicle Section it published the paragraph that had appeared in *The Patriot* on 27 February 1837 without any comment or qualification. This was regarded as a reliable reference work, so Faraday was dismayed to see the erroneous story about him appear in it. Faraday's supposed success in creating mites was also included in Harriet Martineau's *History of England During the Thirty Years Peace, 1816-1846* published in 1849. The account of Andrew's discovery appeared with his permission, but he could not have seen the proofs before publication or he would have corrected the Faraday error, as she informed her readers in volume two that 'At a lecture at the Royal Institution, in 1837, Mr. Faraday avowed his full belief of the facts stated by Mr. Crosse, similar appearances having presented themselves to him.' Faraday was later to contact Martineau to insist a correction should be put in the next edition of her work: 'I feel it a great honour to be borne on your remembrance, but I would not willingly be there in an erroneous point of view.' Martineau replied politely, thanking him for his correction.

This story about Faraday never completely died and appeared as late as 1979 in a serious article about Andrew by N. Roth, 'Bug and blasphemy: Andrew Crosse and the Acarus electricus', in *Medical Instrumentation*, and in a book about Andrew by Peter Haining, *The Man Who was Frankenstein*, the same year. It is also still found as fact on the internet. Despite all the difficulties this misattribution caused Faraday, he and Andrew were to become good friends in time. While the report of Andrew's experiment that appeared in volume one of the *Annals of Electricity, Magnetism and Chemistry* would enable replication by others, there seems to have been no recorded attempt by another researcher to do so in the first few months following the public knowledge of these amazing results. However, it was obvious to those scientists that did not believe Andrew's findings, that the only way to disprove them and stop the ever spreading belief in the power of electricity to create life was by experiment. They could not just ignore his findings or condemn them without themselves testing them by experiment, as this would be unscientific. Their expected negative results would be communicated to the numerous publications that had reported Andrew's initial findings. The results Andrew seemed to have found shook these scientists because, if true, they violated the disciplinary boundaries of science, and it was not long since most specialisations had been classified under the term Natural Philosophy. Andrew's findings were relevant to entomologists, geologists, physicists working with electricity, chemists, physiologists and taxonomists classifying the natural world.

Experiments to refute Andrew's results

The experiments to disprove Andrew's findings were carried out by three notable figures of the scientific world who, between them, had the skills and experience to repeat and assess his experimental method and results. John George Children (1777-1852), elected a Fellow of the Royal Society in 1807, was an expert in mineral chemistry. He built the largest Voltaic battery to date in 1813 and used it for chemical analysis. In 1822 he joined the Department of Natural History at the British Museum, although he never became a professional naturalist. Secretary of the Royal Society in 1826 and 1830-35, he was instrumental in establishing the Entomological Society in 1833, and was its first President. He contributed many papers on mineral chemistry to *The Annals of Philosophy*. A devout Christian, he was noted for his fairness and open minded attitude to science. He was assisted by John Edward Gray (1800-75), the conservative Curator of the British Museum's zoological collection. Noted for his combative character due to many early setbacks in his career, including being black-balled by the Linnean Society in 1822, he became Assistant Keeper of the Zoological Collections of the British Museum. Appointed a Fellow of the Royal Society in 1832, he was a founder member of the Zoological Society in 1826, the

Royal Geological Society in 1830 and the Entomological Society in 1833. By the time he retired he had written 1,100 papers. The third member of the team was Golding Bird (1814-54), an apothecary at the time of this investigation, he was awarded a botany prize in 1836 and granted a licence to practice without examination. He later qualified as a physician and became Lecturer in Natural Philosophy at Guy's Hospital, London.

They performed Andrew's experiment in two different ways, the first exactly as he had done and the second in a closed container. In both cases no mites appeared. Gray decided to present the negative results at the meeting of the BAAS to be held at Liverpool in the Summer of 1837. It was at the British Association meeting at Bristol that Andrew's reputation had been established in 1836, and it was at their next meeting that Gray wanted to destroy it. Gray read a paper to the Natural History Section at the meeting about a giant water lilly, and then launched into an unscheduled, but obviously pre-planned attack, on Andrew's results. He described the negative results obtained by Children and Bird and, it seems, another experimentalist not named. Gray suggested that the mites in Andrew's experiments had hatched in the normal way from eggs that had survived the chemicals and low voltage treatment that he had used. This was reported in *The Athenaeum* on 16 September 1837 which noted that 'a very animated discussion ensued,' and many people attested to the almost indestructible nature of insect eggs. An account of the negative results also appeared in *The Literary Gazette* on 16 September and 21 October 1837. News of the negative results were also widely circulated in a variety of newspapers and periodicals.

However, this campaign against Andrew did not go absolutely smoothly as some publications used it to attack the British Association itself. *The Mechanics Magazine* said it was surprised that 'it has been one of the objects of the Liverpool Meeting to undermine, if not pull down, the very reputation which it was the highest boast of the Bristol meeting to have built up.' It is interesting to note that although Gray and his co-researchers reported their results in the popular press and periodicals, they left it out of the official *Proceedings of the British Association Meeting*, so avoiding giving Andrew's findings any credence within the writings of established science, although this amounted to a form of bias or even censorship. A negative result is as valid scientifically as a positive one. On 10 November 1837 Josiah Wedgwood II (1769-1843) wrote a letter to Charles Darwin (1809-82) in which he mentions Andrew's mites: 'Surely you mean to go and see Mr. Crosse's animals with your own eyes – you see a cargo arrived in London – I think this new fact that though they are born in the acid they are drowned if they tumble in again is the oddest of all – & beats poisoning oil of peppermint hollow.' It is not known whether Darwin did take the opportunity to examine any of Andrew's specimens in the possession of Owen, Sedgwick and a few other people.

A new species of mite?

In the meantime, a report on the mites had been compiled by Pierre Jean Francois Turpin (1775-1840) dated 13 November 1837. This followed a note on the mites, which was read before the Academy of Sciences in Paris on 30 October 1837 by M. Roberton, possibly the English surgeon John Roberton. Turpin was a botanist but had also done work on algae and insects, and was a skilled illustrator of plants, animals, birds, fish and insects, being regarded one of the greatest ever illustrators of natural history. It seems that the Academy initially stated that the subject did not warrant any report at all, although they quickly changed their mind for some reason. Turpin's report was reprinted, translated by J.H. Lang, in volume two of the *Annals of Electricity, Magnetism and Chemistry* in 1837 (pp. 355-60) under the title 'Note on a kind of *Acarus* presented to the Academy', while another, slightly different version but with the same title, also appeared in volume two of the *Annals and Magazine of Natural History* (pp.55-62) the same year.

Turpin's report on the mite (*Acarus*) was a very detailed description of a single specimen preserved in alcohol which he had examined. This had not come directly from Andrew, but had been received from Buckland, to whom Andrew had given several specimens. When Turpin removed it from the alcohol he examined it under a microscope at a magnification of about 280 times. This revealed considerable physical detail of the insect, including an egg. The report noted that it was lucky that this single specimen furnished 'material proof of the manner of reproduction, well known among *Acarians* ...'. After the description of the insect Turpin's report continued: 'The *arachnide* of Mr. Crosse appears to constitute a new species of the *acarus* race. The species described and figured, to which it nearest approaches are those of cheese and meal, and perhaps more particularly the *Acarus dimidaitus* of Hermann ...'. Such a detailed description and Turpin's engraving of the *Acarus* (plate 16) would enable entomologists to determine whether or not it was a newly discovered mite. He then goes on to state his views on its creation:

> From our own knowledge, acquired by a long series of labours, in organisation and physiology, we should say that the means which Mr. Crosse has employed, even supposing them in this case indispensable to the appearance of the animal, have only been simple stimulants, which, like those which excite and favour germination of a grain of wheat, have hastened the hatching of the eggs, similar to those contained by the female individual sent by Mr. Crosse himself; eggs which were lain or brought on the surface of the Vesuvian stones used in the experiment.

> Ignorant of the works written by Mr. Crosse, on the artificial and voluntary production of his Acarus, we do not know whether the animal comes from the experiment in its most complete state, or whether, as would be more in accordance with the law presiding over the developments and metamorphoses we so well known among all species of Acarus. If, in the experiment, it begins by being only a point, then a globule, then an egg, afterwards a young Acarus, having as yet only six claws, and finally a perfect Acarus with eight, male or female, without eggs, or containing some like that in the figure which we have had the honour to show the Academy.

> But in this way of viewing the fabrication of Mr. Crosse's Acarus, there would still remain a very great difficulty – that of knowing where and how these animals, naturally so voracious, would find the nourishment necessary for their development; for organised beings can only increase in size and weight, by taking the nutritive matter which they find about them, and assimilating it themselves, by a mysterious power which belongs to them.

Turpin, in compiling his report, obviously had not seen any of Andrew's descriptions of the development of his mites or the sketches he had sent to Owen in February 1837 which depicted the stage of development at 10, 22, 26 and 28 days, and showed just the normal growth of an *Acarus* that Turpin would have expected. In his report Turpin included a very detailed drawing of the specimen, and captioned it *Acarus horridus turp*. The word *Acarus* refers to the creatures subclass and family, *horridus* refers to its bristly appearance, and *turp*. (short for *turpiniensis* – Turpin Latinised) indicates he was the first person to describe and classify this new mite. Turpin's report made it clear he did think this was a new mite, but doubted that it had been created by the use of electricity.

Andrew's further experiments

The research on the apparent spontaneous generation of life caused by electricity seems to have, not unnaturally, opened a new line of research allied to his main interest in the production of new minerals using electricity. That Andrew continued to do further work on the mites is clear from an article about the experiment published in *The Taunton Courier* on 15 November 1837 which quotes a letter that Andrew sent to *The Morning Post*:

> I send you by my friend a small bottle of spirits of wine, containing about thirty insects, produced in silica of potash under long continued action of voltaic electricity. I am quite as much surprised and as much in the dark about this affair as I was at first. I have had lately several new families of them and have at this present time them growing on a piece of iron wire plunged into silica of potash and a quarter under the surface of the fluid at the positive pole of a battery consisting of 20 pairs of small zinc and copper cylinders. I likewise have them forming on the surface of constantly electrified sulphur of copper at the edge of the fluid and strangely mixed up with crystals of sulphur of copper. In fact I have them in all stages from their earliest formation to full perfect and crawling about pretty nimbly.
>
> Most of these formations take place in the dark. The access of light is very prejudicial to them as far as I have observed. I have hundreds of vessels of

the same water as that used in the solution in the same room and in other rooms, with not the slightest appearance of a similar insect or the germ of one. In one of these experiments the vessel was covered with paper and yet the insects were found as before. Of course I have no merit to claim in the affair, it was pure accident and the looking for artificial minerals that brought them to my notice.

It goes on to note that 'Mr. Crosse states he is preparing an apparatus to repeat the experiments in a more unexceptional manner and until then does not wish to enter into detail on the subject.' Andrew had always seen his scientific research as a relaxation, a way of escaping from the family and financial concerns that troubled him most of his life. His work was to elucidate those mysteries of nature in which he was particularly interested, and while he was always generously willing to impart advice and the results of his work to anyone interested, he did not do this for publicity or self-aggrandisement. In the popular press Andrew was seen as the type of scientific genius who was above all the petty jealousies and squabbling of the relatively few 'professional' scientists, and a man who was in touch with nature. A man of the people, as far as a landowner and member of local Society could be at that time. At odds with this was his republican views, since republicanism, associated with the French Revolution, was feared by many people in all classes of society. Despite Turpin's report of a new *Acari*, this did not clear up the matter as few, if any, British taxonomists seem to have accepted Andrew's discovery as a new type of mite. Over the next few years, in addition to Turpin's name for them, they were also to be referred to as *Acarus crosi*, *Acarus crossii*, *Acarus galvani*, *Acarus galvanicus*, *Acarus galvanici* and *Acarus electricus*. Andrew was irretrievably linked to his 'electric mites'. In a letter from Elizabeth Barrett Browning to H.S. Boyd dated June 1838 she says:' Mr. Crosse the great lion, the insect-making lion, came yesterday with Mr. Kenyon ...', and according to *The Daily News* in 1895, which described Andrew as 'the best abused man of his generation', he himself was jocularly nicknamed 'Acarus Crosse'.

The medical view of the mites

Medical opinion was not united in their view regarding the origin of the

Acari. One of the reasons many medical men were prepared to believe in spontaneous generation, or equivocal generation as it was sometimes referred to, was because of their familiarity with the ongoing problem concerning the origin of internal gut parasites. Before 1851 there was no experimental method available to ascertain how these parasites originated, and it looked very much like spontaneous generation. In Germany there was a very strong belief in the possibility of spontaneous generation in the first three decades of the 19th century, more so than in France and Britain. Although even in these countries the possibility of life arising in that manner was widely accepted. Dr E. J. Hytch, writing from New Court, Carey Street on 8 February 1837, wrote a piece in *The Lancet* entitled 'Mr. Crosse's Revivification of Insects Contained in Flint' which favoured Buckland's initial theory of the electricity activating dormant mites or their eggs in the rock, and he expected such organisms to be found and 'activated' in other minerals. He quotes the method Andrew used as given in the letter to William Stitchbury of the Bristol Institute for the Advancement of Science and Art since he felt it would be of 'interest to your readers.' After giving the method and results of Andrew's experiments, he adds his own comments:

> The vivification of these insects is, doubtless, to be attributed to the agency of the electric fluid; but the species to which they belong, the period of their generation, and the influence which electricity had in developing their existence, are questions which deserve much and deep consideration. Electricity has been too little studied. Its effects on organic life, its agency in supporting animation, and its effects on the nervous system – these things combine to form a field of inquiry which has been too little explored. But inasmuch as electricity is a science which materially affects the constitution of man, it is one which deserves the attentive investigation of every medical practitioner.

The views of geologists

A few geologists also believed that spontaneous generation was a possibility, although the majority vehemently denied this, but some of the leading figures in the field were in a difficult position. They had praised Andrew's work at the Geological Section of the BAAS meeting only the previous year in the highest terms, and had said of his research 'the patrons of science owed him an obligation for an achievement which would immortalise his name in the annals of geology', although they were not referring to his 'discovery' of *Acari*. To avoid embarrassment and loss of face, they came up with an explanation for the origin of his mites, which they could do since the initial news of his discovery in the *Somerset County Gazette* said that Andrew had stated the facts without attempting to account for it. William Buckland, the eminent geologist, suggested a possible method to account for their appearance. Christian Gottfried Ehrenberg (1795-1877), a German geologist, had recently demonstrated that siliceous rocks were composed of *infusoria*, single celled organisms of an extinct group of protozoans, so Buckland suggested that the electricity Andrew had used on his piece of rock may have somehow brought to life the dormant mites or their eggs.

The story of Andrew's discovery in *The Somerset County Gazette* finished with the suggestion as to the possible origin of the mites: 'May not the germs of some of them released from their prison house, and placed in a position favourable to the development of vitality, have sprung to life after a sleep of thousands of years?' This theory, proposed by Buckland, may have been suggested to the author of the article by Andrew who was in correspondence with the famous geologist soon after his discovery. This gained easy acceptance, as about this time it was found that ancient grain and seeds from Egyptian tombs could, in some cases, still be germinated and grown. This explanation was acceptable to religious sensitivities, although it did not last long among many scientists. When Owen and Turpin reported on the physical complexity of the *Acarus* mites, it became clear they were nothing like the very simple forms of *infusoria* that had been discovered by Ehrenberg.

Faraday rebuked the Rev. William Conybere (1787-1857), a noted geologist, at an informal meeting in London for giving too much publicity to Andrew's discovery, and by March 1837 even Buckland, at a meeting of the Ashmolean Society in Oxford, admitted he did not believe that the creatures could have been brought to life after several millennia. He also made a point of correcting the misunderstanding about Faraday's part in the affair which, according to *The Literary Gazette* on 25 March 1837 had been reported in *The Oxford Herald*, which was in turn reporting a communication by Buckland to the Ashmolean Society: 'the animals have been exhibited at the Royal Institution, by Mr. Faraday; whence originated the erroneous report that Mr. Faraday had, by a series of similar experiments, produced the same animals.'

Buckland's initial 'revivification theory' did gain ground in the popular press, and is even found in a children's science book, *The Newtonian Philosophy*, published in 1838, where the lecturer, Tom Telescope, suggests that Buckland's idea was correct for 'the extraordinary discovery of insects by Mr. Crosse, amid his experiments on crystallisation.' That year J. Murray of Hull published 'Considerations on the Vital Principle: with a Description of Mr. Crosse's Experiments.' This refutes Andrew's results. The initial account of Andrew's mite experiments dated 23 March 1837 that had appeared in *The Annals of Electricity, Magnetism and Chemistry*, were followed up by a very much more detailed description by Andrew in 1838 which appeared in the same journal (2, pp.246-57). This was reprinted in January 1839 in *The American Journal of Science and Arts* (35, pp.125-37), spreading news of Andrew's discovery even to the 'New World'. Many people had obviously been asking Andrew for further details of his experimental method after the initial account appeared, and it may well be that they too hoped to take up research on 'electrical mites'. Andrew began his second paper to the *Annals*, dated 27 December 1837:

> My dear Sir, I trust that the gentlemen who compose the Electrical Society will not imagine that I have so long delayed answering their request, to furnish the Society through you, as its organ, with a full account of my electrical experiments, in which a certain insect made its unexpected appearance, that such delay has been occasioned by any desire of withholding what I have to state, from the Society in particular, or the public at large.

Andrew carries out further experiments

Andrew continued to experiment to clarify the origin of the *Acari*, as he stated in a letter he sent to *The Morning Post*, and quoted in *The Taunton*

Courier on 15 November 1837: 'I may state here, that in all my subsequent experiments relative to these insects, I filled the cells of the batteries employed with nothing but common water.' In this account he too dismisses the theory, initially proposed by Buckland, who had abandoned it within a few months:

> I never, for a moment, entertained the idea that the electric fluid had animated the organic remains of insects, or fossil eggs, previously existing in the stone or the silica; and have formed no visionary theory which I would travel out of my way to support.

However, he does, rather diffidently, propose a possible origin for their appearance:

> I have never ventured an opinion as to the cause of their birth, and for a very simple reason – I was unable to form one. The most simple solution of the problem which occurred to me, was that they arose from ova deposited by insects floating in the atmosphere, and that they might possibly be hatched by the electric action. Still, I could not imagine that an ovum could shoot out filaments, and that those filaments would become bristles; and moreover, I could not detect, on the closest examination, any remains of a shell. Again, we have no right to assume that the electric action is necessary to vitality, until such fact shall have been most distinctly proved.

> I next imagined, as others have done, that they might have originated from the water, and consequently made a close examination of several hundred vessels, filled with the same water as that which held in solution the silicate of potassa [potassium silicate, K_2O_3Si], in the same room, which vessels constituted the cells of a large Voltaic battery, used without acid. In none of these vessels could I perceive the trace of an insect of that description. I likewise closely examined the crevices and most dusty parts of the room with no better success. In the course of some months, indeed, these insects so increased, that when they were strong enough to leave their moistened birthplace, they issued out in different directions, I suppose in quest of food; but they generally huddled together under a

card or piece of paper in their neighbourhood, as if to avoid light and disturbance.

Most *Acari* eggs are too small to see without a very good microscope, and it is not known how powerful Andrew's instrument was. Other interesting and intriguing points emerge from this longer and more detailed account, which contains information about further experiments he had carried out to look at the apparent formation of the mites. While the two initial experiments took place in Andrew's main laboratory (the music room) a similar occurrence happened in another room a considerable distance from the first. This time, using clay slate and low voltage electricity for many months, the top of the cylinder was covered with paper to keep out dust. In this case he saw similar mites 'forming around the edge of the fluid within the jar, which, when perfect, crawled about the inner surface of the paper with great activity.' He repeated his first experiment three times with the same apparatus but freshly prepared solutions, and three times the mysterious mites appeared.

Another experiment involved connecting together a series of solutions and passing the same current from one to another. The solutions he used were nitrate of copper [copper nitrate, $Cu(NO_3)_2$], subcarbonate of potassa (the recrystallisation of potassium carbonate from water), sulphate of copper [copper sulphate, $CuSO_4$], green sulphate of iron [iron sulphate, $FeSO_4.7H_2O$], sulphate of zinc [zinc sulphate, $ZnSO_4$], water with a minute portion of hydrochloric acid and water poured on powdered metallic arsenic. After many months Andrew again observed mites at the edge of the fluid in all the solutions except that of the subcarbonate of potasa and the metallic arsenic. At the base of each cylinder containing the solution Andrew had placed a paper label and found a colony of mites under each, but no sign they had been born under their labels.

Another similar experiment produced mites in only one of six different solutions, silicate of potassa [potassium silicate, K_2SiO_3]. Most of the appearances took place from half to three quarters of an inch (13-19 mm) under the surface of the solution. He then repeated these experiments in a third room and found that mites also formed. The room was darkened and the extreme heat of summer or cold of winter 'did not favour their production.' In this second paper to the *Annals*, he summarised his observations to date, and mentioned further research:

1st. I have not observed a formation of the insect, except on a moist and electrified surface, or under an electrified fluid. By this I do not mean to assert that electricity has anything to do with their birth, as I have not made a sufficient number of experiments to prove or disprove it; and besides, I have not taken those necessary precautions which present themselves even to an unscientific view. It is, however, my intention to repeat these experiments, by passing a stream of electricity through cylinders filled with various fluids under a glass receiver inverted over mercury, the greatest possible care being taken to shut out extraneous matter. Should there be those who blame me for not having done this before, to such I answer that, independent of a host of other hindrances, which it is not in my power to put aside, I have been closely pursuing a long train of experiments on the formation of crystalline matters by the electric agency, and now different modifications of the Voltaic battery, in which I am so interested, that none but the ardent can conceive what is not in my power to describe.

2nd. These insects do not appear to have originated from others similar to themselves, as they are formed in all cases with access of moisture, and in some cases 2 inches below the surface of the fluid in which they are born; and if a full grown and perfect insect be let fall into any fluid, it is infallibly drowned.

3rd. I believe they live for many weeks: occasionally I have found them dead in groups, apparently from want of food.

4th. It has been frequently suggested to me to repeat these experiments without using the electric agency; but this would be by no means satisfactory, let the event be what it would. It is well known that saline matters are easily crystallised without subjecting them to the electric action; but it by no means follows that, because artificial electricity is used, such crystals are formed without electric influence. I have made so many experiments on electrical crystallisation, that I am firmly convinced in my own mind, that electric attraction is the cause of formation of every crystal whether artificial electricity be applied or not. I am, however, well aware of the difficulty of getting at the truth in these matters.

Andrew concludes this second account with details of another experiment in which mites appeared. It shows he was thinking very carefully to try and account for the origin of the *Acari*, as he says that the fluo-silicic acid (fluonic acid, Fl-ac, in which silica has been dissolved) in which they appeared was procured from London and therefore made using London water, 'so the idea that their being native to Broomfield water is quite set aside from this result.' Andrew's mites caused problems for those writing textbooks on electricity. William Leithead in his book *Electricity: Its Nature, Operation and Importance in the Phenomena of the Universe,* published in 1837, obviously did not believe in the spontaneous generation of electrical organisms. He gave details of Andrew's method of producing crystals by the use of electricity, and then refers vaguely to electricity 'imparting regular form to bodies'. Andrew carried out an experiment to see if *Acari* appeared if he took all precautions against contamination from either the water used or from the air. In this he again used silica in the form of calcined flints, preparing them hot and throwing them into boiling distilled water. This was poured into a retort, carefully washed with hot alcohol, with two platinum wires passing into it, one via an airtight seal in the neck and the other into the beak of the retort which rested in a cup of mercury, forming a seal at this end. A small Voltaic battery provided electric current to the solution, which liberated oxygen and hydrogen at the electrodes, so displacing atmospheric air and replacing it with a oxyhydrogen atmosphere. Placed in a dark cellar, Andrew found a single *Acarus* on the 140th day. However, he soon lost sight of it and realised he had made a mistake by not including anywhere for the mites to rest. However, he kept this apparatus set up and electrified for a year but saw no further mites. Once again Andrew was puzzled as to how even a single *Acarus* had appeared in a caustic solution in an atmosphere of oxyhydrogen.

Since the *Acari* always seem to have died if they fell back into the liquid, then this was presumably the fate of the single insect that Andrew saw, and any others that occurred in the vessel would have also disappeared for the same reason. This was why Andrew only saw one *Acarus*. Andrew's apparent result of spontaneous generation having been dismissed by most of the scientific community, it could have been expected to die a natural death, at least among scientists if not the public. It was not to be, thanks to a physician from Sandwich in Kent. William Henry Weekes (1790-1850), had qualified as a surgeon, apothecary and man-midwife, but had long been interested in electrical research, particularly its use in medicine. Later his research embraced atmospheric electricity. Not unnaturally he knew of the leading researcher in such work, Andrew Crosse, and made a visit to Fyne Court in 1837. They became great friends, regularly corresponded and sometimes saw each other at meetings of the Electrical Society held at the Adelaide Gallery in Regent Street, London. About 1838 or 1839 Weekes followed Andrew's example by erecting an 'exploring wire' in, or rather over, the town of Sandwich as part of his research into atmospheric electricity.

Andrew's experiment successfully replicated

Towards the end of 1840 Weekes began a series of carefully designed experiments to look into the results that Andrew had obtained during his mite experiments. It is possible that others also repeated or modified Andrew's experiments but did not publish the results, and it would not be surprising to find that his results were also investigated by European researchers, particularly in Germany. The reason for doing so, besides scientific curiosity, is because Weeke's hoped they 'would render nugatory all objections urged against the original experiments of Mr. Crosse.' Andrew had carried out some initial research in isolating the experiment from the outside air, and Weekes, probably after discussion with him, continued and refined this method of investigating the appearance of the mites. In his first paper, dated 4 January 1842 and published in the March edition of *The Proceedings of the Electrical Society*, entitled 'Details of an experiment in which certain Insects, known as the *Acarus crossii*, appeared incident to the long-continued operation of a Voltaic Current upon Silicate of Potass, within a close Atmosphere over Mercury', Weekes makes his views clear on how Andrew's unexpected result was received in some quarters:

… the ungenerous treatment not long since experienced in a very marked degree by one of the most disinterested lovers of truth and scientific enquiry whose labours have graced the annals of modern philosophy; and, I doubt not, it will at once be obvious to all who are conversant with the progress of British science, that my present allusions are directed to the celebrated voltaic experiments of Andrew Crosse, Esq.; one of the incidents of which, in the year 1837, was the appearance of a new species of insect, now denominated the *Acarus crossii,* or *Acarus galvanicus.*

Painful as it must ever be to the genuine lover of science to witness the diligence and research of its votaries assailed by calumny and misrepresentation, I feel assured that no remarks of mine are needed to disengage the Broomfield experiments from the abuse of those who have sought to crush and misinterpret facts which, if carefully investigated, will ultimately conduct us to a more intimate acquaintance with the sublime laws of Creative Wisdom. The experiments, however, which it is the object of this paper to detail, will, I trust, constitute a more powerful appeal to conviction than the most persuasive eloquence could command for the occasion.

Weekes provided a very detailed account of his apparatus, the method he used, and his results. Like Andrew he carefully washed his apparatus and boiled the solutions he used. He then went further in filtering the silica solution. A heated bell jar, wiped carefully inside to remove all dust and any other extraneous material, was placed over the silica solution and stood in a circular groove of mercury. The electrodes of a Voltaic battery passed through airtight seals, while escaping gas also passed through a seal, so making it impossible for outside contaminants to enter the bell jar (plate 17). The whole apparatus was then placed within a screen so it was in complete darkness. The experiment commenced at 'seven o'clock on the evening of the 3 December, 1840.'

The gas evolved from the platinum electrodes escaped only through the sealed orifice designed to vent it, showing that the mercury seal between the bell jar and the base on which it stood was gastight, so no air could enter by this means. Weekes kept a detailed account of his frequent observations of the apparatus. January and February 1841 were very cold, but a stove kept lit in his laboratory prevented the solutions of either the battery or the experiment freezing. On April 12 the silicate solution was found to have assumed a 'turbid and somewhat milky character. A very remarkable appearance has taken place over a considerable extent of the inner surface of the bell-glass, and consists in certain groups or clusters of small greyish-white spots, such as would happen from accidental splashing with a wet brush, or from the operation called sprinkling by book-binders.'

On April 18 the solution had become even more milky, while the negative wire was completely enveloped by a mass of gelatinous silica. Over the next few days the turbidity of the solution increased, the gelatinous matter continued to build up round the negative wire, and a dark grey aggregation built up on the positive electrode. Minute crystals appeared on the inner surface of the bell jar among the 'spots'. Towards the end of October the silica solution had reduced to about two thirds of its original quantity and resembled a milky jelly with a silicious encrustation round the negative wire. Then in the last week of October:

> While applying a microscope very attentively to examine some appearances within the air-bell, I felt convinced that I saw an insect, having the exact character of the *Acarus Crossii,* the figure of which had long been perfectly familiar to me, fall slowly through the atmosphere of the bell, as though it had been accidentally occasioned by the brass mounting. The intense degree of interest excited by this incident, I have no doubt caused an involuntary, as well as an irregular movement of the hand, in consequence of which, the insect was suddenly lost out of the focus of my lens, and, not withstanding my repeated efforts at that period, I could not find the creature again, and therefore refrained from any mention of the circumstance.

The next exciting development occurred four weeks later:

> On the afternoon of the 25th November, while engaged in using a microscope to the groups of spots or splashes as I have hitherto denominated them, and which I now found to consist in an infinitude of

extremely minute pyramidal crystallization's of flinty quartz, I discovered five perfect insects, the exact representatives of those which originally appeared in the Broomfield experiments, crawling freely about on the inner surface of the bell glass: two were full grown, the rest in a less forward state.

Since the last date mentioned, insects of the character in question have been repeatedly seen within the apparatus by myself and others; sometimes in pairs; occasionally three or four (large and small) in a group; but more frequently they have appeared separately; nor have more than four ever been seen at one and the same time since the day on which they were first discovered. In a single instance only, I observed one insect gradually disentangle itself and ascend out of the gelatinous accumulation around the negative wire beneath the surface of the fluid, and, continuing his progress, at leisure, until he got outside of the tumbler, speedily make for a dark recess afforded by the circular mercurial trough formed in the block supporting the bell-glass.

Indeed, as soon as the light is let in, these creatures, in most instances, scamper away, and, apparently, without loss of time, find refuge in some cavity connected with the interior of the apparatus. However, from what I have seen, I am led to imagine that they go down at times to the silicious incrustations in the tumbler, and – it may be – for the purpose of feeding there occasionally; an opinion somewhat strengthened by the fact that when they are found abroad and stationary, their favourite locality seems to be amidst the groups of flinty crystals to which I have before alluded.

Whether, influenced by the circumstances of their situation or otherwise, they sometimes feed upon each other is a question I will not take upon me yet to determine, although I think appearances are certainly in favour of the conclusion. By the aid of my microscope I have several times detected a dead insect adhering to the inner surface of the bell-glass, and, hovering round, or in actual contact with the defunct, a vigorous individual of his species. After a few observations continued from day to day, the dead insect – gradually lessening in bulk from the first – has entirely disappeared.

At the same time that Weekes set up and began this experiment, he also set up another identical arrangement except that the bell jar was filled with pure oxygen rather than atmospheric air. In this the silica solution had become milky, but no mites were observed over the same time period as the other experiment, but he remained confident that they would soon appear. He intended to continue to run the experiments for several more months, and concluded his account:

> I will now merely remark, that it seems quite impossible, in the case before us, for animal life to have entered the bell-glass from without: it must in some way or other have been occasioned by the process within, but, like my predecessor, Andrew Crosse, Esq., I abstain from theorising upon the very surprising phenomena I have witnessed. I have aimed to render a simple detail of facts, and as such I submit this report to men of science, independent of commentary.

> Influenced not merely by my own wishes, but much more so by the kind suggestions of others, it is my intention to continue these experiments, and to adopt even closer investigation, on this interesting and most extraordinary subject. It is of the utmost consequence to science, that the strictest possible caution should be employed. I have been advised by my friend Mr. Cross, with a most scrupulous regard for accuracy of result, to obtain the requisite quantity of mercury for my future experiments, by distillation of its sulphuret, artificially made, &c., &c.; and, in conclusion, I most cordially invite others to join me in working out this mysterious inquiry, subject to the severest restrictions which ingenuity and science can devise for the occasion.

Among the people who saw the mites that had appeared within Weekes's bell jar was Henry Noad, who was inspired to carry out his own research into the electric *Acari*. Weekes wrote to his friend George Newport, who had the letter, containing an account of the experiment and its result, read at a meeting of the Entomological Society in January 1842. One of the people present at this meeting was John Gray, who pointed out to members that Children and Bird had also repeated Andrew's experiments over some months and had got a negative result. What he glossed over, however, was that Weekes had let his experiment run for eleven months before seeing his first *Acarus*, at least twice as long as Children and Bird. The positive results of Weekes's experiment was published in *The Entomologist* in February 1842, but was accompanied by comments from Gray putting the other side of the case and noting the negative result of Children and Bird. Surprisingly, this report did not generate any particular excitement among the readers, presumably due to Gray's input, although James Bladon of Pontypool, Wales, later wrote 'A Note on Acarus horridus', dated 16 February 1842, which was published in *The Entomologist* (1, 307-08). This throws further light on the *Acari* and suggestions as to their origin.

Bladon had not troubled to express any 'remarks upon the absurdity of expecting vitality from chemical action, even when assisted by the electro-galvanic fluid', but he sent in the observations of a Dr Warwick made about 1838 when giving a course of lectures on chemistry in Pontypool. Warwick stated that he had received two perfect adult *Acari* and two 'larvae' from Andrew, and on his return to Exeter his son mentioned these curious organisms to an entomologist living in that city. He wanted to examine them, and when he did so he expressed surprise that it was a great mystery as to their origin: 'I know the *Acarus* very well, and I believe I have some of them at home at the present time. The fact most assuredly is, that Mr. Crosse has a nest of them in his house unknown to himself; and some of them having strayed to his apparatus, and remaining there subject to his inspection, have seduced him into the belief that he had created them.'

Warwick went on to say that up to the time of delivering the lectures at Pontypool, he had found the mites in druggists' shops in every town he had visited during his lecture tour. He had been in correspondence with Andrew and had sent him, from Hereford where he was at that time, a 'supply' of the *Acari* that he had collected from some of the druggists shops in the city. From the tone of the letter, it is obvious that Bladon is under the impression that Andrew was claiming to have 'created' the mites. This note raises another interesting point. What type of *Acari* specifically frequented the shops of druggists? Were these really identical to those that Andrew and Weekes had found? Druggists shops contained a variety of organic materials that were subject to attack by mites. A particular problem they had was with sugar mites (but Andrew's were not these), cheese mites (also not Andrew's) and several types of sp. *Glyciphagus* that attacked the Cantharides that most druggists stocked. Derived from the Common Blister Beetle, an extract, Cantharidin, was given to farm animals to incite them to mate and was used to remove warts without leaving any scarring. We do not know if Andrew compared the *Acari* from the druggists shops with those from Fyne Court.

The new Secretary of the Electrical Society, Charles Walker, sent a notice of Weekes's exciting results to *The Times*, and it was published on 14 March 1842, from where it was picked up by many other publications, so once again the *Acari* were in the public eye throughout Britain. Weekes sent another paper to the Electrical Society, dated 27 February 1842, with the results of the second concurrent experiment he had run with that in his earlier report. The second arrangement was set up like the first but with a water battery giving a low current, and an atmosphere within the bell jar of pure oxygen. His expectations, voiced in his earlier paper had been met. On 26 February 1842 he removed the screen that kept the apparatus dark and, using a lens of moderate power, saw eight or ten fully developed *Acari* in 'vigorous locomotion' on the inner surface of the bell jar and on the outside of the vessel containing the silica solution that had the electric current passed through it. This appearance was 449 days after commencing the experiment, considerably longer than in Andrew's experiment with an oxyhydrogen atmosphere where an *Acarus* appeared after 140 days. He then concludes his account with:

> I will, with your permission, here avail myself of the opportunity to explain that the primary motive for having charged one of the bell-glasses allied to this investigation with pure oxygen gas, was that of providing against a very commonly urged objection, – that the ova of the insects in question might, a priori, be present in the atmosphere in which the experiment took place. Now, unless anybody will undertake to show that the germs of insect life existed in peroxide of manganese, and escaped safely out of a red-hot iron bottle along with the oxygen in its way to the glass receiver, it is clear in this experiment that they could not be present beforehand; and, although we are acquainted with the fact that gaseous matter does actually suffer considerable changes and admixture even when confined in sound glass

vessels, it has never yet been suspected that the ova of insects, however minute, could permeate a vitreous material.

This second paper from Weekes generated questions and discussion, and he wrote a further note, dated 19 March, which was published in *The Proceedings of the Electrical Society*. In this he explains in detail how he generated the oxygen used in the bell jar, and gives the recipe for the linseed oil varnish used to seal the wooden base in which the groove for the mercury was cut to form an airtight seal at the base of the bell jar. The reason for this is that a number of people had suggested that the *Acari* had somehow been present in the materials, particularly the wooden board, used to construct the apparatus.

On 17 May 1842 *The Proceedings of the Electrical Society* published a letter read to members from Weekes at their April meeting. In this he details some of the control experiments he had set up in his *Acari* research, something that Andrew does not seem to have done or even seems to have considered necessary. Curiously, although good scientific practice, it did not occur to Weekes to mention this in his first paper on the subject. As a control he had set up silicate solutions under bell jars exactly like his two main experiments, connected to a Voltaic battery but without applying electricity to the solution. Others were set up under bell jars but inverted over water, and similar setups were placed in various parts of his laboratory, house and 'premises' (presumably an outbuilding). These were carefully examined regularly at intervals by both Weekes and some of his friends, including a Dr C. Brown and other scientists. No *Acari* appeared in any of the control experiments. This stimulated further interest in the subject, and Weekes seems to have received much correspondence on the subject, prompting him to write a letter published in *The Proceedings of the Electrical Society* in May 1842:

My Dear Sir,

I am exceedingly busy, and deeply interested in several new arrangements for carrying out the investigation beyond (I think) the possibility of cavilling. I need not say you shall hear on the subject from time to time.

Weekes obviously hoped his further research would avoid the petty objections ('cavilling'), as he saw it, from various people. The next communication from him, 'Additional Notes On the production of *Acari*, &c., in Close Atmospheres, incident to the operation of Voltaic Currents', was read to members of the Electrical Society and published in the *Proceedings* in September 1842. In this, he still does not commit himself to stating how the mites appeared, but notes, once they have:

> ... it soon became strikingly evident that these creatures were subsequently multiplied also by the ordinary means of generation. Whether the circumstances of their local insulation tended to shorten what would otherwise have been their natural term of life, I cannot take upon me to determine; but attentive daily observation unequivocally demonstrated the disappearance of generation after generation in brief succession, and clearly denoted that the law of order had affixed its usual seal to their singular history.

He goes on to describe how he observed twenty or thirty adult *Acari* on the inner surface of the bell jar, and the inner and outer surface of the vessel containing the silicate solution. This was in the apparatus he set up on 3 December 1840. Also noted on the same surfaces were ova of the *Acari*. These were examined by several naturalists who agreed that this is what they were. The population of *Acari* gradually dwindled over time and by the 20 July Weekes was concerned that all specimens might disappear before they could be retrieved and examined by various people to whom he had promised examples. Shortly afterwards he decided to dismantle the apparatus. Having detached the battery, the bell jar was lifted off its mercury seal and examined internally. Many ova were deposited over the inner surface, but only one living *Acarus* was noted. Placing the bell jar on a sheet of black paper with a watch glass of silica of potass to keep the atmosphere moist, he kept it under observation. Without the electric current the ova gradually dried up or decomposed.

He kept the second apparatus with the oxygen atmosphere going, but the *Acari* were diminishing in numbers. He mentions that the 'new arrangements ... for carrying on these investigations' were progressing well, but gives no further details. The last mention of Weekes's *Acari* appearing is found in *The Proceedings of the Electrical Society* in November 1842 following a note read to members entitled 'Note on the Development of *Acari Galvanici* in Ferro-Cyanuret of Potash'. This notes that a swarm of *Acari* had made their appearance in this solution (potassium ferrocyanate, $K_4(FeCN)_6.3H_2O$) in an experiment set up in May, and he hoped to eventually submit further details of the apparatus and results. He sent fifteen specimens of *Acari* from this experiment, 'being the first *Acari* ever developed from this remarkable electrolyte.' Nothing further was published about these mysterious mites by Weekes.

The publication of the positive results obtained by Weekes inspired other researchers to investigate the mite phenomena, two of whom were well-known and respected electrical scientists. They set up their own experiments to try and replicate Andrew and Weekes' results. One was Henry Noad, who was very highly regarded, having written a standard and widely read text book, *A Course of Eight Lectures on Electricity, Galvanism, Magnetism and Electro-Magnetism*, the first edition of which was published in 1839, although this edition did not mention Andrew's work, followed by three further updated editions. The second of these, in 1844, was dedicated to 'Andrew Crosse, Esq. In this Noad not only included full accounts of the experiments and results of both Andrew and Weekes in the section on electro-crystallography, but stated that he had set up three experiments himself which had been running for sixteen months. Although, at the time of publication, he had not got a positive result, he still remained hopeful.

Alfred Smee replicates the experiments

The other well-known figure to set up experiments on the *Acari* was Alfred Smee (1818-77), a Fellow of the Royal Society and inventor of an improved battery. The apparent appearance of mites due to the action of electricity was particularly exciting for him as his main interest was in the relationship between life and electricity. He visualised the body as a complex series of interconnected batteries, with the central battery being the brain, while the nervous system was a series of 'bio-telegraphs'. He hoped to establish a new scientific discipline, electrophysiology. The results of Andrew and Weekes seemed to point towards the possibility that life might, in some cases, have a physical inorganic basis. Despite trying very hard, he failed to get any positive results, and published no details of his research. However, he regarded this as a temporary set-back caused by his cramped laboratory rather than the implausibility of creating an insect by an electric current. He felt that a lot more research was needed:

> As far as appertains to this subject, I am of the opinion, that the facts should be neither believed nor disbelieved, but kept in abeyance for fresh experiments. The subject has been taken up with much ill-judged acrimony; for the question really resolves itself into this proposition – has, or has not, the Creator endowed inorganic matter with the power of assuming, under the influence of certain forces, an organic form?

Later, in *The Mind of Man: Being a Natural System of Mental Philosophy* (1875), Smee disavowed both Andrew's and Weekes's experiments, as well as his own efforts. No other researchers in the subject obtained positive results, with the exception of Noad with a partial success, or if they did they did not publish them. Another person who may have contemplated investigating Andrew's 'electric mites' was Ada, Countess of Lovelace who, in 1842, was in correspondence with Andrew about his experiments and results. The outcome of both Andrew and Weekes's experiments appeared in *Vestiges of the Natural History of Creation* published anonymously in 1844. This was in fact written by Robert Chambers (1802-71), a popular author and Fellow of the Royal Society of Edinburgh. The work dealt with the formation of the universe, the geological history of the earth and the origin of mankind. Andrew's work was important to Chambers as it supported his theory that, under certain conditions, life might have originated from simple inorganic matter. So miracles were not needed to explain the origin of life. Andrew and Weekes's work featured in later editions of Chambers' book long after they had disappeared from other publications. He was careful, despite doing away with the necessity of miracles, not to exclude God from his theory, something that would have shocked the majority of his readers, not to mention affecting sales of the book! In considering Andrew's results he said:

The experimentalist could never be considered as the author of these creatures except by the most unreasoning ignorance. The utmost that can be claimed for, or imputed to him is that he arranged the natural conditions under which the true creative energy – that of the Divine Author of all things – was pleased to work in that instance. On the hypothesis here brought forward, the Acarus crossii was a type of being ordained from the beginning, and destined to be realised under certain physical conditions.

When a human hand brought these conditions into a proper arrangement, it did an act akin to hundreds of similar ones which we execute every day, and which are followed by natural results; but it did nothing more. The production of an insect, if it did take place as assumed, was as clearly an act of the Almighty himself, as if he had fashioned it with his hands.

William Carpenter (1813-85) a physician, physiologist and invertebrate zoologist, elected a Fellow of the Royal Society in 1844, was still willing to reserve judgement on the apparent creation of mites by electricity. He seems to have been planning his own research on the electrical *Acari*, as he made clear in 1845:

Not entertaining the opinion, which a certain clergyman is reported to have expressed … that 'it was a very dark business, and such as no Christian man ought to engage in', we please ourselves with the hope of being able to throw some light, ere long, upon the history of this interesting creature, by the careful study of the physiological peculiarities of its development; leaving it to those eminent in physical science to investigate the physical conditions under which it is produced. Should the author's views be realised, the Acarus crossii will indeed be worthy to take rank as one of the most – if not the most – physiologically important species of the whole animal creation; affording proof of the possible origin of living beings of complex structure and varied actions, from the combination of particles of inorganic matter under peculiar conditions; and thus outshining, in the eyes of the physiologist, the transcendent merits of frogs, rabbits, dogs, asses, &c. as subjects of experiment.

However, Carpenter did not carry out any experiments as far as is known, since he felt that he was not sufficiently 'eminent in physical science', although he clearly thought the question of spontaneous generation was within the bounds of legitimate science. As a Unitarian, a Christian who rejects formal dogma in favour of a rationalist and inclusive approach to belief, he desired to rid science of miracles and see God acting only through the laws of nature. He helped Chambers revise later editions of *Vestiges* and a sequel published in 1845. That year the eminent geologist Adam Sedgwick, an opponent of spontaneous generation, stated that Andrew had produced nothing more exciting than '*Acarus horridus*', being under the impression, as were others at the time, that this was the Latin name of the common house or furniture mite, which is actually *Glycyphagus domesticus*. He did not realise that Turpin had actually designated Andrew's mite with a taxonomic name as a new species.

The mites cause a difficult time for Andrew

The years following his discovery were a difficult one for Andrew as he had to contend with the increasing frailty of his wife who was often confined to bed, financial problems and the death of his great friend, Tom Poole. So his unlooked for fame, or infamy as it was seen by many people, did not come at a good time. As he said in this second account in the *Annals*:

> I have met with so much virulence and abuse, so much calumny and misrepresentation, in consequence of these experiments, that it seems, in this nineteenth century, as if it were a crime to have made them. For the sake of truth and the science which I follow, I must state that I am neither an atheist, nor a materialist, nor a self-imagined creator, but a humble and lowly reverencer of that Great Being of whose laws my accusers seem to have lost sight. It is my opinion that science is only valuable when employed as a means to a greater end.

The problems the mites caused him lasted for years. In August 1849 Andrew wrote to Harriet Martineau in reply to a request from her to explain certain details of his mite experiments before she included it in her forthcoming book *History of the Thirty Years Peace 1816-36* which was published that year. It is interesting to note from the beginning of Andrew's answer to Martineau how he perceived some people still thought of him:

> Allow me in the first place to state that I have not the slightest objection to your dealing as you please with this answer of mine. You are welcome to publish it if you think proper, or thrust it into the fire, where many of those kind commentators on some of my experiments would gladly have thrust me. It is the bounden duty of philosophical men not to reject or admit as fact, any assertion, without close and fair investigation.

He probably welcomed the chance to once again put his point of view, and he clearly states his position before providing a long and detailed account of the experiments and their puzzling outcome:

> Feeling as I have done the whole of my life, it is not likely that I should plume myself upon any imaginary successful results of a course of experiments, or that I should presume to lay down a theory upon so mystical and perhaps unapproachable a subject as to the origin of animal life.

> As to the appearance of the Acari under long-continued electrical action, I have never in thought, word, or deed, given anyone a right to suppose that I considered them as a creation, or even as a formation, from inorganic matter. To create is to form a something out of a nothing. To annihilate, is to reduce that something to a nothing. Both of these, of course, can only be the attributes of the Almighty. In fact, I can assure you most sacredly that I never dreamed of any theory sufficient to account for their appearance.

Andrew still had at least one medical supporter fourteen years after his original discovery. Dr James Davey, surgeon at the Hanwell Lunatic Asylum and a medical author, wrote in *The Lancet* in 1850 that the 'experiments of Messrs. Crosse and Weekes are conclusive.' *Letters on the Laws of Man's Nature and Development* by Henry George Atkinson and Harriet Martineau was published in 1851. This book took the form of a series of letters between Atkinson who took the part of teacher, and Martineau acting as his pupil asking questions and receiving his replies rapturously. Atkinson maintained that religion was a myth forced upon the common people by a 'puritanical priesthood', so that the study of divinity and religious matters was a waste of time. Atkinson and Martineau referred to the results of Andrew's and Weekes's work as 'those noblest experiments of the age' as they seemed to have broken the distinction between life and inorganic matter, removing God from the origin of living organisms.

The fourth, completely revised edition of Noad's textbook, now entitled *A Manual of Electricity: including Galvanism, Magnetism, Diamagnetism, Electro-Dynamics, Magneto-Electricity and the Electric Telegraph* was published in 1855. This updates Noad's own experiments on *Acari* that he mentioned in the earlier edition of his work, having, at that time, been running the experiment under a sealed bell jar like Weekes for sixteen months. He 'did not succeed in obtaining the insects within the bell jars which covered the solutions undergoing electrolysis, but several, precisely similar to those of Crosse and Weekes, were repeatedly found on, and about, the terminal cells of the battery.' In addition it includes details of Andrew's last encounter with his mysterious mites which occurred in 1854.

Andrew is still finding mites

Andrew was passing a positive current through one piece of sheep's wool and a negative current through another, both of which were suspended in a salt solution. This continued for three weeks. The wool from the positive pot, now impregnated with chlorine, was put into the negatively charged solution and immediately dissolved. This was repeated several times until the water was unable to dissolve any more wool. This solution, yellow in colour and smelling strongly of chlorine, was filtered before being placed in an apparatus to deposit the chemicals that had been extracted from the wool in the form of crystals. Electrodes connected to a battery were placed in this wool solution which was in a glass vessel. To keep dust out of the apparatus a glass jar was inverted over it, the battery wires passing under the edge of this inverted jar. As chlorine was given off it created a chlorine laden atmosphere within the glass jar. This was set up on 10 June 1853. A smell of chlorine was constantly issuing from the small gap under the inverted jar where the battery wires passed under it.

On 27 January 1854, when Andrew was examining the apparatus, he saw a single perfectly formed adult *Acarus*, plus some others in different stages of their life cycle. He carefully examined them with a lens but saw no discernible movement, and drew the mites in their various stages. A week or two later Andrew saw another adult *Acarus*, but again with no sign of movement. Over the next few weeks other *Acari* appeared, all on the inside of the inverted glass jar, and in the strong chlorine atmosphere. Careful observation showed that the limbs of all the adult mites were extended in a natural position just like living examples, but none showed the slightest movement. Some of Andrew's friends who examined them thought they saw some movement, but Andrew put this down to their imagination. He continued to examine them from time to time, and even during the warmer weather of summer they showed no sign of motion. Up to the date of his report, 5 February 1855, they had all remained in their respective positions.

There were a number of different aspects to this that had not been present in earlier mite appearances. This was the first time that these mysterious mites had appeared in cold weather, previously they had always appeared between April and October inclusive. The slightest hint of frost killed them or prevented the appearance of new ones. When the temperature of this apparatus dropped to nearly freezing point there was no discernible change in the mites or their appearance, presumably because they were dead. From this time on references to the experiments and results of Andrew and Weekes start to disappear from serious scientific publications, or at least those claiming to be so. One of the last to mention them is *The Genesis of Organic Forms* by S. Hibberd, published in 1861. In this, in discussing the latest edition of Chamber's *Vestiges of the Natural History of Creation*, he says:

It might be hard to judge 'Vestiges' by the electrical experiments of Mr. Crosse, which men of sober thought and scientific experience agree in considering child's play, but the question must be pressed whence came the primordial germ which serves as the typical seed-plot of all successive generations.

It is a downright pity that Mr. Crosse and Mr. Weekes should have been favoured with *acari*, or mites covered with bristles, instead of primordial cells, because instead of illustrating progressive development, the creation of life by electricity was rather a conformation of Mr. Gosse's plan of prochronism – a bursting into the circle, or line, of the organic scheme, instead of commencement at the beginning. If their experiments were worth the paper on which they were so solemnly recorded, the author would not here repeat, in this new and beautifully illustrated edition that 'we do not present the Crossian experiment, and other alleged cases of primitive generation, as undoubted facts, or as indispensable parts of the present hypothesis … .

However, Andrew and his mysterious organisms never completely disappeared from the popular press. The centenary, or a little after strictly speaking, of the first appearance of Andrew's *Acari* saw many articles once again in publications ranging from *The Times* (29 July 1938) to *Tit-Bits* (3 September 1938) which assured its readers that Andrew had indeed created life:

An English country gentleman puzzled himself by finding something he was not looking for – that which all man can take but which no man can give. No man? He, Andrew Crosse, experimental electrician had done it; he had created life in his own workshop!

Had it happened to-day instead of the year 1837, every radio set in the world would have buzzed with the news that in a vessel of liquid on the littered work bench of a publicity-hating experimenter of Somerset there had appeared live insects whose presence was in direct opposition to all the laws of Nature. For Crosse had accidentally created Life out of a stone. No other explanation was forthcoming to account for the phenomenon.

If the secret of life really had been found it has been lost again this hundred years. Could Andrew Crosse's achievement be repeated today in the light of to-days scientific knowledge combined with enormously improved equipment? The impossible may again happen in some obscure twentieth-century investigator's study – and the creation of Life in the laboratory become an accomplished and awesome fact.

The story in *The Times* contained, as was so often the case in articles about Andrew, inaccuracies, the most glaring of which was the statement that George Singer fully accepted the discovery of *Acari crossii* – which would have been quite amazing as he died nineteen years before Andrew found his first mite! Andrew's story, usually prominently featuring the mistaken belief he inspired Frankenstein, still regularly appears in West Country newspapers and magazines, and the story of his mysterious mites occasionally gets a mention in the national papers and books on 'unsolved mysteries'. However, Weekes's positive results do not feature in most of the more recent accounts or, if they do, only seem to merit only a single line.

The results of Andrew and Weekes raises some intriguing and difficult to answer questions. Where did the mites come from? What species were they? Were they a new species? Could they really have survived in such inhospitable solutions? Could they really have been created from a silica solution by the use of low voltage electricity applied over a long period? The question of where the mites came from is difficult. Contamination is the most obvious answer, but Andrew eliminated the water he used quite early on, although his microscope may not have been powerful enough to spot any eggs, and he looked for similar mites in dust in his laboratory and could not find any. However, dust mites are very small (0.25-0.42 mm) and barely visible with a times twenty magnifying glass, although the female specimen of Andrew's mite examined by Turpin was 0.5 mm long. Andrew also set up an experiment to eliminate contamination from atmospheric air and the solutions he used, and Weekes continued and refined this, and still found *Acari*. Noad only found the mites on the outside of his sealed apparatus, but it is not clear if he checked that these were exactly the same as those Andrew and Weekes had found.

The Big Question: What were they?

It is probably safe to discount the theory put forward by Valentine Dyall in *Unsolved Mysteries* (1954) that they may be of extra-terrestrial origin! Turpin rightly identified Andrew's specimen as an *Acarus*, a taxon of arachnids that also contains ticks. There are a great many *Acari*, and up to the year 2000 some 50,000 species had been identified by entomologists, and it has been estimated that there are up to a million species still living, besides extinct species known from fossils. In the early 19th century the study of the *Acari* was still at a very early stage. So there is every reason to suppose Turpin did indeed identify a species that had not been described up to 1836. He was familiar with the mites that infested cheese and meal, and while it resembled them and the *Acarus dimidiatus*, the adult female specimen examined by Turpin had significant differences which he described. One of its most distinguishing features was the long hairs which covered it, and which inspired Turpin in his choice of name for this mite.

Andrew, despite not knowing much about entomology, did record accurately the typical development of the *Acari* from his careful observations: egg (ova), larvae with six legs, nymph with eight legs and adult (plate 15). Andrew sent some specimens to Richard Owen for his opinion who, in 1856, was appointed as the first Superintendent of the British Museum's Natural History Department, and was a prime mover for the establishment of a separate natural history museum, which did eventually happen. If Owen had given any of the ten specimens of *Acari crossii* that he had to the museum, they cannot now be found. In the species index of the Natural History Museum, London, there is no reference to *Acarus crossii*, but an article published in *The Evening News* on 4 January 1936 mentions that experts at the Natural History Museum had identified the mites as either *Glycyphagus domesticus* (the house mite) or *Tyrophagus longior*. A check on the collections of these species did not reveal any that were supplied by Andrew.

In 2010 staff at the Natural History Museum again considered the problem, and suggested the mite illustrated by Turpin belonged to the family *Glycyphagidae* of the Order *Astigmata*, of which the two most common British species are *Glycyphagus domesticus* which is found in house dust, stored foods and mouldy vegetable fibres, and *Lepidoglyphus destructor*, which occupies the same sort of habitat as *G. domesticus*. Because they are so light they can be carried on air currents and clothing, so could this account for their appearance in the experiments? However, it does not seem likely, particularly in the later experiments that Andrew and Weekes carried out in which they took great care to avoid contamination by using a sealed environment and, despite close observation, no *Acarus* were seen for many months. If introduced during the setting up of the experiments, it would be expected that the mites would have been seen much earlier than they were. *G.domesticus*, at 23-25 degrees C. and 75-90% relative humidity can complete its life cycle in 10-22 days, and females can lay 200-500 eggs in their lifetime. So it is still not certain how they appeared in the various solutions or exactly what species of *Acari* they were. *Lepidoglyphus destructor* and *G. domesticus* do not have an aquatic phase. So the mystery continues. However, three microscope slides on which specimens of Andrew's Acari have been mounted were discovered by Brian Davidson and reported on in the *Quekett Journal of Microscopy* in 2012 (plate 19 and 20). Unfortunately the mites are not in very good condition, and the slides, dated 1838, have comments on the condition of the mites on each one. It is not known whether Andrew himself made the slides or whether the specimens were mounted by someone else, but the labels are not in Andrew's handwriting.

Andrew's 'electric mites' were able to live in various inhospitable environments. In their experiments Andrew and Weekes noted that they were able to survive in solutions of potassium silicate (K_2SiO_3), Copper nitrate ($Cu(NO_3)_2$), copper oxide (Cu_2O), copper sulphate ($CuSO_4$), iron sulphate ($FeSO_4.7H_2O$) and zinc sulphate ($ZnSO_4$). With such a huge number of different species of *Acari* they are found in a wide range of environments, many of which are extreme, ranging from the cold of the Arctic to the very acidic water and environment of bogs. The survival of *Acari* in the solutions in which Andrew found them would depend on their concentration, and the mites developed in what were, presumably, quite weak solutions. Andrew's observation that although the *Acari* developed in the liquid, they drowned if they fell back in, is something that puzzled both him and others, and is specifically mentioned in Wedgwood's letter to Darwin. However, there are a number of species of *Acari* that are aquatic in the laval form, but wholly terrestrial as adults, and would drown if immersed in liquid. So, there is still no definitive answer as to whether Andrew's mites were a new unknown species or something still around today but now known by another name.

The application of electricity to various solutions cannot create complex creatures. However, Chambers was on the right lines when he said in 1844 that he felt that under certain circumstances life might be created from inorganic matter. In the simulation of the most primitive earth conditions by researchers, electricity has featured prominently. In 1953 Stanley Miller at the University of Chicago, USA, circulated methane, ammonia, hydrogen and water, components of earth's primitive atmosphere, past an electric spark. After a week the results were examined and he was amazed to find that the water held a number of organic molecules related to life that had been synthesised. Among them were four of the amino acids commonly found in protein (glycine, alanine, apartic acid and glutamic acid), plus some of the simplest fatty acids and urea. This was successfully repeated by a number of other laboratories. Further experiments simulating flashes of lightning on the primitive atmosphere were also successful, and in only twenty-four hours large deposits of simple organic compounds were produced, along with hydrocarbons and some nitrogenous material – termed the 'primordial soup.' So electricity, in the form of lightning, probably did provide the 'spark of life'.

On 20 May 2010 scientists in the United States announced that they had created synthetic life that was able to reproduce itself. This created world-wide interest and immediate concern about these 'creatures' contaminating the natural world, and that artificial life might replace natural life. The scientists took the DNA sequence out of one bacterium, copied it in a laboratory, and this artificial DNA sequence was put into a different bacteria. This stimulated the bacteria into activity and to reproduce. A leading British scientist stated that this was not actually the creation of life as the DNA sequence was a copy of a natural sequence not a new one. Their work has the possibility of being used to create bacteria for medical use, producing fuel oil and so on. Inaccurate and sensationalist reports of their work appeared in the popular press, providing echoes of the stories of Andrew's mites 174 years earlier.

CHAPTER SEVEN

Increasing Fame or Infamy: 1836–48

Andrew had returned to Fyne Court after the Bristol meeting of 1836 elated with both the positive reaction he had to his research on electro-crystallography and the many contacts he had now made with leading figures in the scientific community. However, domestically, the next three years were to be a great trial to him, not only because of the controversy of his mite experiments, but also his wife's health, fragile for many years, further deteriorated. This tied him to Fyne Court, and he hardly left the estate. In a letter written to Sir Richard Phillips dated 30 November 1836, Andrew said that 'the late hurricane has destroyed 35 of those fine trees which adorn [the] grounds; one of them a beech, containing nine tons of timber, 100 feet high.' One of the last visits that Tom Poole of Nether Stowey received from his old literary friends was from Robert Southey in 1837, and Andrew went over and spent time with both, and this seems to have been the last occasion that Andrew saw Poole before his death. Andrew was very upset when Poole died suddenly of pleurisy on 8 September 1837, and he was one of the pall bearers at his funeral held on 15 September at St. Mary's Church, Nether Stowey. He must have badly missed his old friend and all the fascinating discussions they had over many years on science, poetry, literature and political reform.

However, there was some good news in this period as in 1837 his son Robert married Eliza Mary Mackenzie in Ruishton Church, Somerset. In January 1838 Andrew gave a talk at the anniversary meeting of the Taunton Mechanics Institute where he spoke of the advantages of contact between scientists in both this country and Germany before giving a lecture on electricity with many striking demonstrations. That year also saw the birth of his first grandchild, Matilda Mary Anne, born to Robert and Eliza. In February 1839 Andrew gave one of his most impressive (and dangerous) demonstrations to the Taunton Mechanics Institute. He illuminated four hundred feet (122 m) of iron chain hung in festoons about the room and witnesses described how it was brilliantly lit by the passage through it of a strong electric current from a powerful battery. Everyone was even more amazed when several feet of chain melted!

Unfortunately death also once more visited the Crosse household as in 1839 Andrew's third son, Richard, died aged twenty-five and was buried at Broomfield Church on 9 March. He was named after Andrew's brother Richard, whom Andrew had always been very close to, but unfortunately his brother had also suffered from illness, and by this period was gradually becoming more and more of an invalid. For a number of years it was Andrew's custom to ride over to Hill House that Richard had built about three miles (4.8 km) from Fyne Court to spend Sunday with him. Although Richard and his wife Jane had been married since 1810, they had no children. As so often when they were together, the two brothers discussed Andrew's latest research which was balanced by Richard's deep interest in metaphysics, which was more concerned with the nature of being, the cosmos, and things that exist or may exist. This was a subject on which Andrew, despite years of discussion with his brother, failed to formulate any original ideas, but adopted the views of his brother. Andrew's concerns were with the study of the physical world by experimentation, although he was very keen on poetry and knew a number of the most famous poets of the 19th century, but had not met Coleridge, although Richard had. On one occasion Richard had called on Coleridge, and recalled how he had left after three hours with the poet still talking in the middle of his second sentence! Possibly the poet was under the influence of the opium that he used as a relaxant, analgesic, anti-depressant and possibly for inspiration. He later became addicted, something that became public in 1822.

In 1839 Henry Minchin Noad (1815-77) wrote *A Course of Eight Lectures on Electricity, Galvanism, Magnetism and Electro-Magnetism*. This became a standard and widely read book. Andrew must have been cheered when he saw a copy of Noad's revised 1844 edition, now entitled *Lectures on Electricity, Comprising Galvanism, Magnetism, Electro-magnetism, Magneto-electricity and Thermo-electricity*, and even more pleased when he read the dedication:

> To Andrew Crosse, Esq. of Broomfield, near Taunton, Somersetshire, to whose indefatigable industry for a long period of years, electrical science is indebted for so rich an accumulation of valuable facts: the interesting results of whose electro-chemical researches have taught us the value of patient enquiry: and whose liberal, open, and communicative spirit is not less remarkable than his enthusiastic love of science.

The frontispiece of the 1844 edition shows many items of electrical apparatus, and incorporated within the design are the names of twenty-three leading electrical researchers of the day, including 'Crosse'. It is also of interest that this frontispiece is in the form of an idealised electrical researcher's laboratory. In the centre stands an Armstrong Hydro-electric generator, which is being used to produce the electricity that lights up the title, which is spelled out in a series of tin foil dots placed on a glass sheet. The sparks jump across the numerous gaps that form the letters. Behind the title is a Wheatstone electric clock and the distinctive shape of a Wheatstone and Cooke electromagnetic telegraph. In a basin nearby are some electric eels. Scattered around are batteries, Leyden Jars, magneto-electric devices, a lightning rod, books and manuscripts. Andrew must have met Noad on many occasions at meetings, but there is no documentary evidence for him visiting Fyne Court, although it would be surprising if he had not done so. He too was a Somerset man, being born at Frome, and in 1836 was giving lectures on electricity and chemistry to the Literary and Scientific Societies in Bath and Bristol. Besides writing the standard text book on electricity that inspired many electrical researchers, he wrote many articles on electricity and chemistry in various publications. His research later primarily embraced chemistry and biochemistry.

In July 1840 Andrew's oldest son, John, married Susanna Eliza Bowman at Kelso in Scotland after, apparently, eloping. This marriage seems to have been unexpected and possibly even unknown to Andrew and the rest of the family. His second grandchild, Isabella Francis Crosse, was born to his son Robert and Eliza, and that same year Andrew began to correspond with Dr William Henry Weekes (1790-1850) of Sandwich in Kent. Like Andrew, Weekes was interested in atmospheric electricity and had erected an 'atmospheric exploring wire' sometime before 1840, the year he published an account of it. However, not having an estate, he lived in Sandwich High Street, he suspended his wires between the church towers of St. Peter's and St. Clement's, firmly attached to their respective weather vane spindles, and supported in the centre by a convenient house chimney. By this date Andrew was sufficiently famous to warrant an extended mention in the Broomfield section of the 1840 edition of *The General Directory for the County of Somerset* :

> It has now obtained celebrity as the scene of the singular scientific discoveries of Andrew Crosse Esq., whose residence is in this parish, of which he is the principal landowner. He has fitted up an extensive laboratory, and powerful electrical machines and galvanic batteries. He has also carried a wire round his park on the tops of trees by which he is at all times able to ascertain the electrical condition of the atmosphere, the wire being connected to a conductor in his laboratory.

In a letter to Weekes, dated 17 August 1840, that must have made him envious, Andrew described a weather phenomenon that few have the good luck to see in Britain, particularly in the south:

> On Saturday night last, at twelve o'clock, in walking home from Taunton, I saw a splendid aurora borealis which occupied a tolerably large portion of the atmosphere. The moon was shining brightly in the south-east, and the aurora in the north-west, in the form of a series of pillars of crimson fire, which shone through the dark rolling masses of cloud in a very extraordinary way. It appeared like a series of alternate pillars of flame and dark vapour. Overhead was a very distinct mackerel sky, with a stratum of rolling dark clouds far below. Between these two strata the light of the

aurora struck out all at once in the form of pyramids of pale fire, shooting to the zenith. The pale light of the moon three parts full contrasted, with the electric pyramids and crimson pillars of fire, mixed up with the rolling masses of cloud, gave to the scene a wild and unearthly appearance. I was greatly impressed by it.

The two researchers corresponded for a number of years. An invitation from the Scientific Institution of Bridgwater saw Andrew giving them a talk on electricity in 1841, but the following year he seems to have had another of his depressive periods. Because of family ties and the illness of his wife, he could not escape to London, which seemed to help with these times when he was particularly low. Despite this he took the chair at a meeting of the Bridgwater Literary Association. His third grandchild, John Richard Davy Hamilton Crosse was born to Robert and Eliza that year, but just how fed up he was can be seen in the opening part of a letter he wrote to Weekes on 13 September that year:

I am always much pleased at the sight of your handwriting, morally and scientifically, and I should never allow a post to intervene, without answering your letters, did a kinder fate allow me sufficient time; but alas! this is not the case, as we seem to have little in our power, and are tost [sic] about like withered leaves before the gale. It is only in my power to wish, and I wish you all happiness in this world, and humbly trust we may meet in a better, which I look forward to with not an atom less hope, from the denunciations of those who style themselves orthodox, to such unbelievers as myself.

Despite the fact that his mite experiments had been carried out six years earlier, he was still being castigated by some elements in the church. This would have been deeply wounding as Andrew was always a very religious man who could see God's works all around him. Later in this letter the reasons for his obviously depressed state become obvious, and he sounds like a man who is desperate to get out of the situation he is in:

It is very true that I have serious thoughts of going to the Continent for three years from the time of my starting, which cannot be before the spring of 1843. From the time of my birth to the present hour I have ever been too careless in money transactions, and my love for science has not only led me to considerable expense directly, but has, by calling nearly the whole of my attention elsewhere, prevented me from looking into my affairs with that scrutiny which is absolutely essential in a country establishment, and in the management of landed property.

I have therefore, of course, been cheated tremendously, which I have to thank myself for. My great expense has been in building, and in repairs on farm houses, in which I have suffered immense imposition. Although I am much attached to this place, yet in common prudence, I must quit it for a time, and carry on my experiments on a more limited plan, and in a cheaper country than this. I am happy to say that my family will all be well provided for, and for myself it is of little consequence as to the increase or diminution of a few comforts, as I am very easily satisfied, and my life cannot extend to a much longer term. The income tax has put the finishing stroke to my determination; but still I look forward to returning to my home at the expiration of three years.

His plans to go abroad, leaving his family behind for three years did not materialise, so he remained at Fyne Court with apparently few visits to London at this time. In 1843 Andrew once again gave a talk on Voltaic electricity to the Taunton Mechanics Institute, the same year that his friend, John Gassiot, a wealthy wine merchant and Treasurer of the Electrical Society, hosted an 'Electrical Soirée' to celebrate the visit of the eminent scientist Auguste de la Rive (1801-73). A pharmaceutical chemist with a great interest in electrical research, especially with the theory of the Voltaic cell and electrical discharge in rarified gasses, he described a process for electro-gilding of silver and brass in 1840. This event involved putting on a very impressive display of electric lighting using Grove Cells. Besides the demonstration they also put on an exhibition of electromagnetic machines and specimens of Andrew's notorious mites, *Acarus crossii* as they were often called, along with examples of his electrically produced crystals. Andrew and his family were still having health problems, as he makes clear in a letter, dated 18 January 1844, to Josiah Pyke, Chief Accountant of the Great Western Railway:

I have nothing but sickness in my house since my last letter. Mrs. Crosse and my daughter are at present confined to their rooms and I am much out of order myself, this abominable squashy weather having played the Devil with us.

The summer of 1845 saw Andrew, but not his wife and children, and a group of artistic and literary friends and acquaintances spending a few days in the seaside town of Torquay in Devon. These included his old friend John Kenyon, and the poets Robert Southey, Walter Savage Landor and Elizabeth Barrett who was Kenyon's cousin and was, the following year, to elope and marry Robert Browning in Marylebone Church. She had lived in Torquay for the sake of her health from 1838 to 1840, but returned to London following the drowning of her brother and two of his friends off the resort in July 1840. This left her distraught. So this trip must have brought back some sad memories for her. Also included in the party was Antonio (Anthony) Panizzi (1797-1897) who became a British subject in 1832, and was first Assistant Librarian of the British Museum Library, 1831-37. When he was at Torquay he was Keeper of Printed Books at the British Museum (1837-56). Later he was to become Chief Librarian (1856-66), and was knighted in 1869. There was also a famous artist, Giovanni Aubrey Bezzi, who had discovered a portrait of Dante by Giotto under whitewash in the Cappella del Bragello, Florence. He had restored the painting, although this was not without controversy, which continues to this day.

Other members of the party included Zoe King, a niece of Maria Edgeworth the novelist and children's writer Eliza Warrington a relation of the St. Albyn family of Alfoxton (who was known as 'Airy, fairy Lillian'), Theodosia Garrow (1825-65) who was suffering from tuberculosis and described as small and exotic-looking due to her East Indian and Jewish ancestry. She later met and married Thomas Adolphus Trollope (1810-92), brother of the author Anthony. He too was a prolific writer producing sixty volumes of travel writing, history and fiction, plus a large amount of periodical and journalistic work, spending most of his time in Italy. The group later moved on from Torquay to spend a few days at Ashburton on the edge of Dartmoor, which was a good base for excursions. In Landor's *Miscellaneous Poems* he included several that commemorate this time at Torquay. One of which is entitled 'To Andrew Crosse':

> Altho' with earth and heaven you deal
> As equal, and without appeal,
> And bring beneath your ancient roof
> Records of all they do, and proof,
> No right have you, sequester'd Crosse,
> To make the Muses weep your loss.
> A poet were you long before
> Gems from the struggling air you tore,
> And bade the far-off flashes play
> About your woods, and light your way.
> With languor and disease opprest,
> And years that crush the tuneful breast,
> Southey, the pure of soul, is mute!
> Hoarse whistles Wordsworth's watery flute,
> Which mourn'd, with loud indignant strains,
> The famisht Black in Corsic chains:
> Nor longer do the girls for Moore
> Jilt Horace as they did before;
> He sits contented to have won
> The rose-wreath from Anacreon,
> And bears to see the orbs grow dim
> That shone with blandest light on him.
> Others there are whose future day
> No slender glories shall display;
> But you would think me worse than tame
> To find me stringing name on name:
> And I would rather call aloud
> On Andrew Crosse, then stem the crowd.
> Now chiefly female voices rise
> (And sweet are they) to cheer our skies,
> Suppose you warm these chilly days
> With samples from your fervid lays.
> Come! courage, man! and don't pretend

That every verse cuts off a friend,
And that in simple truth you fain
Would rather not give poets pain.
The lame excuse will never do,
Philosophers can envy too.

A fourth grandchild, Alice Caroline Crosse, was born on 16 June 1845 to Robert and Eliza. Andrew's scientific research continued and he managed to make improvements to the apparatus used to make crystals, speeding up the time to do so and forming carbonates of lime and strontium, along with barium oxide and barium hydroxide. Life continued at Fyne Court with Andrew worrying about the estate, his finances and the health of his wife and brother. In May 1845, in an attempt to improve his financial state, Andrew had the old adit, the horizontal mine tunnel, which he had opened and then closed in the 1820s at Raswell Farm, cleared and a new shaft sunk. This re-opening of the mine was at the suggestion of a Cornishman named Petherick. *The Falmouth Packet* gave a report on the work in the edition of 9 August 1845:

It has long been thought that the Broomfield hills are a copper district and the person who has chiefly directed attention to this highly interesting feature, is Andrew Crosse Esq. A number of men – some of whom are from Cornwall – have been for some weeks at work, sinking, or rather reopening a shaft and driving an adit, which was many years ago commenced by Mr. Crosse. Within these few days the miners have come on a fine copper lode, at the trifling depth of forty feet – a circumstance very unusual, even in Cornwall where better appearances are sometimes not seen at a less depth than 1,000 to 1,200 feet, and there is every indication that the lode will turn out to be a rich ore. It is intended to erect a steam engine and more miners are to be forthwith brought to the place of action, where they work day and night. Should it turn out to be what it promises, it must necessarily add largely to the fortune of Mr. Crosse. The lode is highly impregnated with yellow sulphuret of copper.

Further optimistic expectations were reported in *The Taunton Courier* on 24 September that year:

The specimens of mineral wealth hourly brought to the surface, are of so promising a character, and abound so richly in all the best features of present success and ulterior prosperity, that we cannot but congratulate the respected and successful owner of the soil, and his enterprising and skilful co-adjutor, on the safe results of their intrepid industry.

Further details of this potentially profitable enterprise are found in the *Dorset County Chronicle and Somersetshire Gazette* of 6 December 1845:

With a steam engine of only 12 horse-power and at the depth of no more than 64 feet from the surface of the ground, a ton of capital ore is raised from a very small shaft at every six feet depth of working, and this without pursuing the lode horizontally. As it is well known by scientific geologists and practical miners, that every increased foot of working in depth adds to the proportionate excellence of the ore, both as to quantity and quality, this enterprise promises to be one of extraordinary profit. The lode is near five feet in width. The present engine in work, it is supposed will carry the operations down to 40 fathoms below the adit level, when an engine of augmented power will become necessary. A considerable number of additional miners are about to be engaged, and the undertaking altogether presents the most decisive evidence of ulterior prosperity.

By now Andrew's fame had spread far and wide, and he even sometimes had visitors from America. On one occasion a letter from the United States was delivered to him simply addressed 'Andrew Crosse, Electrician, Quantock Hills, England.' The year 1846 was probably the lowest point in Andrews life, as a stark announcement, under deaths, in the *Taunton Courier* explains:

On Tuesday night, January 27th, at his lodgings in London, Richard Crosse Esq. of Blaxhold in the County of Somerset, in the 60th year of his age, only brother of Andrew Crosse, Esq., of Broomfield, in the said County; and on the following Saturday afternoon, January 31st, Mary Ann Crosse, wife of the said Andrew Crosse, at his home in Broomfield. Both of these deeply lamented relatives are to be interred in the family vault, in Broomfield Church, on the same day.

In his will, Richard left everything to his wife Jane for her lifetime, and after her death everything was to go to Andrew. After the funeral Jane moved back to Minehead where she died in 1851. For some reason she was buried at St. Michael's Church Minehead, where she had married forty-one years earlier, and did not join her husband in the Crosse family vault. Perhaps the family were never really reconciled to their marriage. The loss of the brother to whom he was so close followed by the death of his wife only five days later left Andrew devastated. Both had been ailing for many years, so their demise did not come as a surprise, but this made his shock and loss no less painful and distressing. Richard and Mary Ann were both buried in the family vault in Broomfield Church on 6 February. This left John, Robert and Isabella without a mother, although by this date both boys had married and only Isabella was still living at Fyne Court. Andrew was, not unnaturally, plunged into a deep depression, and went to London, spending much of the next few years away from Fyne Court. Isabella, although twenty-six, was unmarried so presumably went with him to stay at their London house.

All seemed to be going well with the mine according to *The Mining Journal* of 2 August 1846 as they were 'proceeding vigorously with the workings' and were 'endeavouring to lay open the lode east and west, to ascertain if the bunch of ore seen at the 13 fathom level holds down' (i.e. continues downward). However, within a few months of this report and after being worked for fifteen months, the mine was closed down. They raised about ten tons of ore, but it seems that due to a lack of mining experience and inadequate equipment, they had been working on a poor cross vein, and had missed the main lode. So Andrew's dreams of becoming a wealthy mine owner were dashed.

Andrew had never been all that interested in his gardens, and although he liked trees he saw them as a cash crop, and planted many for just this reason. Visitors commented on the size and magnificence of the trees which had been planted by Andrew's great uncle, Andrew (1704-66), when he created the pleasure grounds during the first half of the 18th century. Andrew's second wife, Cornelia, described Fyne Court in the 1850s: 'The house itself is shadowed by lofty trees, through whose branches the winds never cease their sad music. The gigantic limbs and gnarled roots of the old beeches in the avenue strike one with admiration and with melancholy; the still vigorous trees, the growth of centuries, seem to mock at the short life of man; succeeding generations walk under the same shadow.' By the mid-19th century the heyday of the gardens had passed and they had lost their edge, being outshone by those of its neighbours, and were to steadily decline from this date on. Despite his lengthy absences from the estate, some of the more credulous inhabitants of Somerset still held strong views about Andrew to judge by a report in the *Taunton Courier* of 11 September 1847 in which a local farmer said 'Andrew Crosse ought to have been hanged long ago for dealing with the Devil', and continued 'he had raised the Devil four of five times to my certain knowledge.'

It was in 1848 that there were further eminent visitors to Fyne Court. This party consisted of a number of scientists, including Dr Deubeny, Dr Buckland, Baron von Liebig, and his assistant and translator, Lyon Playfair. According to a letter they sent to Andrew later, they all enjoyed their visit despite an incident that occurred on the way. This party of strangers arrived at Bridgwater station, having been to Cheddar to inspect the cheese making process. They ordered a carriage and pair from the hotel to take them to Fyne Court. This was a year when revolutions abroad and Chartist alarms at home were making many people nervous. The innkeeper, on hearing a foreign language spoken, the German being translated by a man with a broad Scottish accent, became alarmed. Fearing that the group might be plotting some mischief with Andrew against church and state, he informed the local police. The Bridgwater police seem to have concluded that they must be dangerous people, and probably Chartists, that is supporters of the People's Charter, drawn up by six MPs and six working men in 1836.

Chartism was a movement for political and social reform in Britain and Ireland between 1838-50. Andrew himself may well have been suspected of being a Chartist, which is not surprising given his views. This was the first working class labour movement that had six aims in its Charter: 1. A vote for every man aged twenty-one or over if of sound mind and not in jail. 2. The ballot. 3. No property qualification for MPs (so anyone could become an MP not just the wealthy). 4. Payment for MPs (so the ordinary working man could become an MP). 5. Equal constituencies. 6. MPs elected to Parliament annually. The police carefully watched them as they passed through Bridgwater, but as this group of scientists had committed no crime they could not arrest them!

This visit again demonstrates the important place that Andrew held in the scientific world that people of this calibre were prepared to travel all the way to Broomfield to visit him. Dr Charles Giles Brindle Daubeny (1795-1867) was a chemist, botanist and geologist. He began studying the volcanoes of the Auvergne region of France in 1819. In 1822 he was elected a Fellow of the Royal Society, the same year he was appointed Professor of Chemistry at Oxford University, a post he held until 1855. He reported some of his results at the inaugural meeting of the British Association for the Advancement of Science (BAAS) in 1831, and was at the Association's Bristol meeting (presenting his research on mineral and thermal waters) in 1836 when Andrew gave his talk. In 1856 he was President of the BAAS.

The Rev. Dr William Buckland (1784-1856) was a geologist and palaeontologist who became a Fellow of the Royal Society in 1818, and President of the Geological Society in 1824. In 1845 he was appointed Dean of Westminster, and a Trustee of the British Museum in 1848. Buckland was the first person to give a full account of a fossil dinosaur, which he named *Megalosaurus*, and was a pioneer in the study of fossilised faeces. He usually carried out his geological fieldwork wearing his academic gown, but one of his more unusual eccentricities was his aim to eat almost every part of the animal kingdom. He consumed, among many other creatures, mole, mouse, crocodile and bluebottle. However, the most shocking item he ate was the relic heart of King Louis XIV. This had been kept in a silver box at Nuneham Courtenay Manor just outside Oxford, where it had been taken after being rescued from St. Denis during the French Revolution. His host was showing it to him, as he did to many visitors, when Sedgwick said 'I have eaten many strange things, but never the heart of a king'. He then grabbed it and popped it into his mouth, hastily chewing the blackened and shrivelled organ before swallowing it, to the horror and disgust of his outraged host.

Baron Justus von Liebig (1803-73) was a German chemist who founded agricultural chemistry and made a major contribution to organic chemistry. In 1824 he was appointed Professor of Chemistry at Giessen and soon made it the most famous chemical school in the world. In 1852 he left to take up the Chair of Chemistry at Munich University until 1865, when he left to take up the Chair of Chemistry at the University of Berlin. He wrote 318 papers and contributed to many others as a collaborator. One of his greatest 'gifts' to mankind was the discovery of chloroform. Lyon Playfair (1818-98) was von Liebig's assistant and translator. After doing art courses at St. Andrew's University, Playfair went on to study chemistry in 1835-37 at the Anderson College in Glasgow. In 1839 he left Scotland to study chemistry under von Liebig at Giessen. On his return to Britain he became manager of the chemical department of a print works, then Professor of Chemistry at the Royal Institution in Manchester. In 1845 he was appointed Chemist to the Geological Survey and Professor of Chemistry in the Government School of Mines. He served on many Government Select Committees and entered Parliament in 1868, spending most of his time on political matters. The visitors were lucky that Andrew was at Fyne Court, although it is probable that the visit was by arrangement as Andrew was spending most of his time in London following his wife's death. Andrew's friend John Sealy of Bridgwater, who was involved in the large pottery industry there and banking (Sealy and Prior Bank), was obviously concerned about him as is clear from a letter that Andrew wrote in reply to him dated 18 July 1848, which gives an insight as to why he had 'abandoned' Fyne Court:

My dear Friend,

Your affectionate letter reached me yesterday morning. You paint very fervidly the beauties of our picturesque county, and seem to wonder at my long stay in this busy and broiling place. I perfectly agree with you as to the glorious magnificence of the scenery of the Quantock Hills; but where are those that rendered it dear to me gone? I feel that I have no home, that I am cast as a weak vessel on the billows of the ocean, and all spots of land are now much the same to me. When I am at Broomfield I have not a soul to speak to, servants excepted. In fact I am quite desolate, and am now thrown on the aids of science, and the companionship of my friends; with the exception of your family, and one or two others, I have no intimacies in the country.

In this huge metropolis, there is a power of selecting one's acquaintances beyond that in any other situation, and moreover I have many old and very tried friends and school fellows here with whom I am on brotherly terms. They rejoice in my successes and grieve with my disappointments, and I fully reciprocate their feelings: nevertheless, I long to breathe, if not for a while, my mountain air, although every breeze of it is full of melancholy associations; and beyond this, I hope to lie in Broomfield churchyard, when it pleases my Maker to remove me from this troublesome world.

However, Andrew was still carrying out his research while in London, and in a letter dated August 1848 he notes that he is engaged in purifying various liquids using electricity. He was also 'superintending' the construction of an apparatus for converting sea water into fresh. This seems to be a larger or more advanced version of something he had already invented, since he had created fresh water at least fourteen months earlier. Andrew had also devised a method of purifying cider without the application of electricity. This involved monitoring the apple juice in a vat, and testing it at intervals with a saccharometer to measure the sugar levels. When it contained the right amount it was racked several times and than a solution of isinglass was added the night before it is purified. The following day the cider was poured through a sieve of calico in which a teacupful of charcoal has been thrown. These multiple sieves were supported on a wooden frame. 'The liquor when thrown into the bags is as foul as thin mud, but in a few minutes it runs out as clear as the finest Bucellas wine.' It was then put in casks and underwent no further fermentation. Andrew was very keen on cider making and gave its production a great deal of thought. He wrote a very full treatise on cider production in *Baxter's Library of Practical Agriculture* (1852), while his purifying technique is also described in *Farming of Somerset* by T.D. Ackland and W. Sturge (1853).

Another of Andrew's friends was John Stringfellow (1799-1883) of Chard, Somerset. He sometimes stayed with him when they spent much of their time discussing mechanics, in which they were both interested, but Stringfellow's other main interest was flying. In 1848 Andrew was fascinated to hear that his friend had achieved the first heavier than air flight with a small plane powered by a steam engine. This took place in a disused lace factory at Chard, where the flying machine, with a ten foot wing span, was launched down an inclined guide wire several yards long before going into free flight. This was twenty years before the Wright brothers' machine took to the air powered by a combustion engine.

CHAPTER EIGHT
Electricity with Everything!

Andrew was investigating how electricity could be used to benefit mankind and explain the works of nature, and his research took a number of different directions. These experiments took place over many years and his techniques were improved and refined as time went on, as was the equipment he used to generate and store electricity.

Electrical Generating Machines

A means of generating electricity by friction had been discovered during the 17th century. This was static electricity, a phenomena demonstrated c.600 BC, by the Greek philosopher and scientist Thales of Miletus who demonstrated the effect of static electricity by picking up small items with an amber rod which had been rubbed with a cloth. However, it was in the 18th century that that the development of electrostatic machines really developed. These used manual power to transform mechanical work into electricity by using moving plates, drums or belts to carry an electric charge to a high potential electrode, hence their name of Friction Machines. Andrew was researching electricity for over fifty years, and during that time probably used or even built a variety of such devices. When Sir Richard Phillips visited Fyne Court in 1836 he noted that Andrew had a large twenty inch (51 cm) machine plus a smaller one. The electric charge generated was stored in what, in modern terms, was a capacitor, one of the most popular being the Leyden Jar, until the development of the Daniell Cell in 1836.

The Leyden Jar

The Leyden Jar is not a battery but a means of storing an electric charge until it is discharged. Unlike a battery which takes minutes or more to totally discharge, the Leyden Jar can discharge its charge in a fraction of a second. It is therefore, in modern terminology, a capacitor. It is one of the earliest pieces of electrical equipment used by Andrew, as he and a school fellow made one to shock their fellows as part of a prank. It was invented by Pieter van Musschenbroek of the University of Leyden in Holland and was independently invented at almost the same time by Ewald Georg von Kleist a German scientist. The earliest jars contained an inner wire electrode in contact with water, mercury or lead shot. The outer electrode was the human hand holding the jar. A further improved version coated the jar inside and outside with separate metal foils with the inner foil connected to a conducting rod which terminated in a conducting sphere. This eliminated the need for a liquid electrolyte.

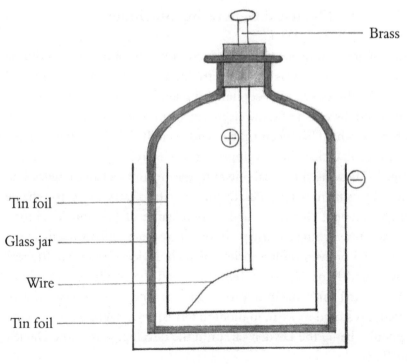

The Leyden Jar.

1. Detail of Fyne Court House and its immediate surroundings on a parish map by I. and H. Clayton dated 1812. This shows the house with its two walled gardens and the serpentine lake.

2. A garden building which formed a feature in the original garden at Fyne Court and was later used for a variety of purposes, including as a laboratory by Andrew Crosse.

3. The only known illustration of Fyne Court House before it was almost totally destroyed by a fire. This photograph shows the building as it was in the 1880s. On the far left can be seen the single-story music room which Andrew Crosse used as his main laboratory, while the library, which also survived the fire, can just be seen on the far right of the photograph.

4. Andrew Crosse, aged about thirty. A drawing by Frederick Lake, which was published in July 1838 by Thomas McLean and Frederick Lake of Taunton. When this was published Andrew was actually fifty-one years old and it was presumably originally issued some years earlier, and re-issued in 1838 since Andrew had come to widespread public notice because of the 'mysterious mites' that had appeared during some of his experiments.

5. Andrew Crosse in his forties in a painting by an unknown artist. This was one of the paintings that was saved from the disastrous fire at Fyne Court in 1894.

6. A piece of the ornate plasterwork from the music room at Fyne Court, used by Andrew as his main laboratory and known to his family and friends as the 'philosophy room'.

7. The music room, used by Andrew as his main laboratory, which escaped the disastrous fire of 1894. His atmospheric 'exploring wire' entered the building on this side through the window on the far left.

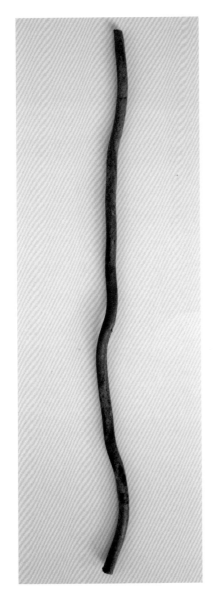

8. A 24 cm long piece of the copper 'exploring wire' used by Andrew to collect atmospheric electricity. Initially one and a quarter miles (2 km) in length, Andrew later reduced it by stages to about nine hundred feet (274 m).

9. One of the many poles supporting Andrew's 'exploring wire' still in place in a tree. The tower of Broomfield church can be seen in the background. Photographed in 1939.

10. Pieces of Daniell Cells used by Andrew in his experiments from the 1840s. Copper crystals can be seen on the pottery which sat in a solution of copper sulphate. The porous ceramic tubes were probably specially made at a Bridgwater pottery.

11. Pieces of wine bottles found at Fyne Court. When Andrew finished a bottle of wine he usually knocked the neck off it so he could use the body to make a battery.

12. A table from Andrew's laboratory. This seems to have been specially commissioned as it incorporates a strip of metal on the top for use in his electrical experiments. Another similar table is to be found at Fyne Court.

13. A table from Andrew Crosse's laboratory incorporating a metal strip. This example is kept at Fyne Court.

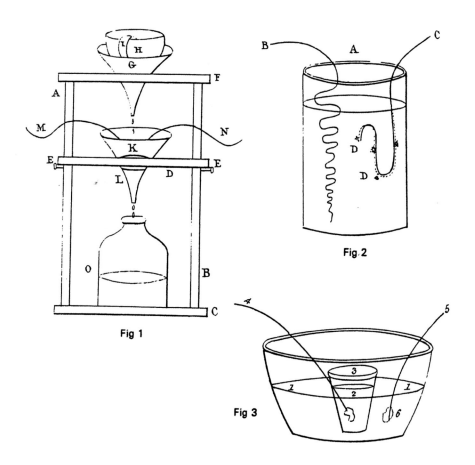

Fig 1

Fig. 2

Fig 3

14. A diagram showing Andrew Crosse's experiments in which mites appeared. FIRST EXPERIMENT (Fig. 1): Basin (H) containing fluid which is covered by a strip of flannel (I) so that it drips into a funnel (G) and on to a volcanic stone (K) in a glass funnel (L). Platina wires (M and N) are connected with opposite poles of a voltaic battery. Mites appeared on the stone. SECOND EXPERIMENT (Fig. 2): Glass vessel containing concentrated solution of silicate of potash. A silver wire (B) attached to the negative pole of the battery, iron wire (C) attached to the positive pole. Mites appeared at points (D) on the negatively charged wire. THIRD EXPERIMENT (Fig. 3): Glass bowl partly filled with fluo-silic acid (1). Porous pot (2) partly filled with the same acid and covered to exclude light and dust. Platina wires (4 and 5) are each twisted around a piece of quartz and an electric current enters through the positive pole (4) and passes out by the negative wire (5). Mites appeared at the negative pole after several months.

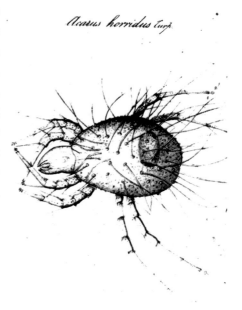

Acarus horridus turp.

15. Andrew's notes concerning the development of the mysterious mites that appeared during a series of experiments he carried out. These were to bring him to much wider notice among both other scientists and the public. These notes were sent to Richard Owen in 1837, one of the few specialists in entomology at that time.

16. A drawing by the French scientist Pierre Jean Francois Turpin whose report on Andrew's mysterious mite said that it '... appears to constitute a new species of the *acarus* race.' He named it *Acarus horridus turp*. This specimen contained an egg.

17. The carefully controlled experiment set up by Henry Weekes who repeated Andrew Crosse's experiment in a sealed environment. He also found that mites appeared.

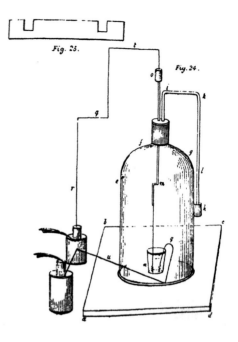

18. A bust of Andrew Crosse, made by J. J. Chadwick of Exeter, showing him in his early fifties.

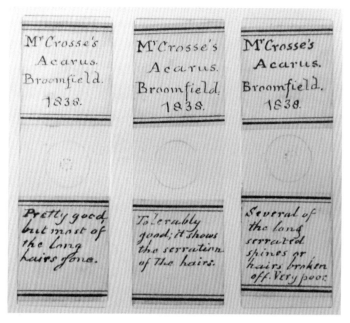

The labels read:

Mr Crosse's
Acarus.
Broomfield.
1838.

Mr Crosse's
Acarus.
Broomfield.
1838.

Mr Crosse's
Acarus.
Broomfield.
1838.

Pretty good,
but most of
the long
hairs gone.

Tolerably
good; it shows
the serration
of the hairs.

Several of
the long
serrated
spines or
hairs broken
off. Very poor.

19. Three microscope slides containing specimens of the mites that appeared during Andrew's experiments. It is not known whether Andrew Crosse himself made the slides or the specimens were mounted by someone else, but the labels, bearing the date 1838, are not in his handwriting.

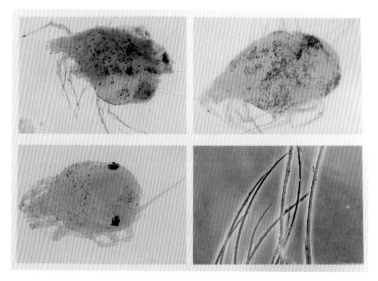

20. Specimens of *Acari crossii*, the mysterious mites that appeared during Andrew Crosse's experiments, with a close-up of their bristles. These were mounted on microscope slides in 1838.

21. The village hall, Broomfield. Originally built in 1854 as the village school, its construction was funded by Andrew Crosse. It remained in use until the school closed in 1933.

22. Ada, Countess of Lovelace. An engraving after a sketch by A.E.Chalon, 1838. A woman with a remarkable mathematical brain, she was to have an affair with Andrew Crosse's oldest son, causing a serious family rift.

23. A miniature painting of Andrew Crosse showing him in his mid-sixties.

24. Cornelia Augusta Hewett Berkley aged twenty-six. Four years earlier, in 1850 and just twenty-two years old, she married Andrew Crosse, then aged sixty-five.

25. A monument to Andrew Crosse erected by his wife Cornelia in the north-east corner of the churchyard of Saint Mary and All Saints, Broomfield.

26. A lump of melted lead 23 x 18 cm which weighs 136 g containing a silver sixpence. Originally part of the roof or guttering of Fyne Court House, it melted in the fire of 1894 and poured onto the ground forming this mass of metal, although it is unclear how the coin got into it.

27. The buildings of Fyne Court that survived the fire of 1894. From left to right: the end of the music room (just in view), the stable and harness room, workshop, the coach house with its double doors, the smithy (originally open-fronted), a storeroom in which some firefighting equipment was kept but was unable to be reached during the fire and, at right angles, the kitchen with library above. The external staircase is a post-fire addition.

28. Fyne Court Cottage, also called the Old Rectory, into which Susanna Hamilton moved following the fire which badly damaged Fyne Court in 1894, and in which she lived until her death in 1916.

The jars work by attracting electrons via the brass top when put into a magnetic field, which is usually provided by an electrostatic generator or even a natural field generated during a thunderstorm. The electrons travel down the brass top and shaft through a dangling wire that touches the tin foil covered bottom of the glass jar. Here the electrons are stored until they are discharged. The tin foil on the outside of the jar is what makes it a capacitor as it keeps the electrons from leaving since it acts as a barrier. The jar holds two equal but opposite charges in equilibrium. Only when the inside metal and outside metal are joined in a circuit will the stored charge be dispelled in the form of a spark or a shock if in contact with a living body.

The Voltaic Pile

Andrew and his friend George Singer were among the first English researchers to make use of the Voltaic Pile, a battery invented by the Italian, Alessandro Volta, and described by him in a letter to the Royal Society of London in 1800. He took small discs of silver, zinc and cardboard soaked in brine, and built them up into a pile keeping to the order silver, zinc, silver and so on. By making connections to the top and bottom of the pile he found that he could obtain electric sparks and could go on getting sparks one after the other without having to do anything to the pile, such as rubbing it.

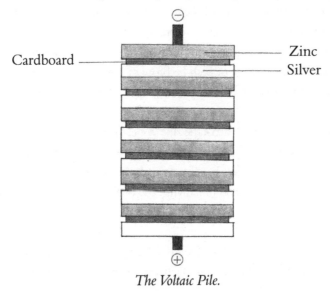

The Voltaic Pile.

Andrew analysed the Voltaic battery and published the results of his study:

1st. I find that a disc of zinc being let fall into water distilled, common, or acidified, being removed with an insulating handle and carefully examined, is in a positive state.

2nd. I find that the fluid from which it has been removed is in a negative state.

3rd. That a disc of platinum being let fall into similar water, and similarly removed, is not electrified, and the fluid from which it has been removed is not electrified.

4th. If a strip of sheet zinc be bent over the edge of the basin containing the above fluid, in such a manner as that one part of the zinc is plunged into the fluid, and the other half is kept outside and dry, while the wet part is positive, the dry part is negative.

5th. If this experiment be repeated with a strip of platinum alone, there is no electricity either within or without the basin.

6th. If both strips, viz., the zinc and platinum, are plunged into the fluid, their wet sides opposing but not touching each other, the wet part of the zinc is positive and its dry outside negative, as before; but in this case the wet part of the platinum is negative, whilst its dry outside is positive: however, no current is produced, till the outside of each be brought into contact or conducting communication with each other. The current will then be as follows:

It commences with the wet part of the zinc alone, from which issues a positive current, electrifying the platinum opposed to it negatively by induction; the positive current from the zinc passing through the negative electricity of the platinum, forming, when combined with the outside of the zinc, a regular voltaic circle, through which a constant electrical current passes.

That the zinc or most oxidable metal is the original motive power, which sets free a portion of the natural electricity of the water, which natural electricity is employed in keeping together the due proportion of oxygen and hydrogen, necessary to form water. The zinc being, as Davy calls it, electro-positive and the oxygen electro-negative, the oxygen passes to the zinc, while its corresponding hydrogen is set free, if zinc alone be employed; but if platinum be opposed, the hydrogen passes to the platinum.

In either case the water is decomposed, and the electricity which was previously locked up is liberated, and goes to the zinc in an accumulated state, but not producing current, without employing the opposite, less oxidable metal, the outer termination of each metal being connected together by a conducting medium, through which the electric current passes. The water thus furnishes the materials for its self-decomposition by the agency of the zinc, and the platinum being merely a conductor. This does away with the contact theory, and also with some others.

The Daniell Cell

Invented by John Frederic Daniell in 1836, Andrew began using these soon after they became generally known, and they proved ideal for his long term crystallography experiments (plate 10). The electrolyte is sulphuric acid or zinc sulphate solution in contact with the zinc plate. A zinc rod dips into the sulphuric acid or zinc sulphate solution contained in a porous pot, which rests in a glazed earthenware jar containing copper sulphate solution. In the space between the jar and the porous pot is a cylindrical sheet of copper. It cannot be left set up for long periods without current being taken from it as the solutions diffuse into each other through the porous pot. If acid is used in the pot, local action will take place at the zinc electrode, but this is avoided by using zinc sulphate solution in place of acid. It works as the zinc dissolves liberating electrons into the external circuit, and at the copper plate Cu++ ions are discharged and no polarisation (bubbles of hydrogen produced at the electrode) takes place. This means that it produces a nearly constant e.m.f. of about 1.07 volts, the precise value depending on the strength of the solutions used. Andrew modified some of the Daniell Cells he was using by replacing the acid with water.

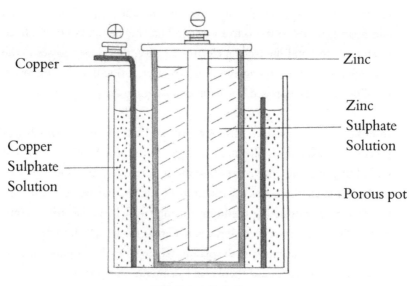

The Daniell Cell.

Later Andrew made a further modification to the 'standard' Daniell Cell which he described in connection with his work on the extraction of metal from its ores. This makes it clear that he always had the economics of his research at the back of his mind:

A battery most available for the extraction of copper from its ores, consists of a certain number of earthen jars (or glass), in each of which a porous pot is placed, commensurate with the size of a jar. In each jar is placed vertically a cylinder of thin sheet copper, which surrounds the porous pot that stands in the centre. In each porous pot a rod or cylinder of stout zinc is placed vertically, the top of which rod is connected by means of a strip of sheet copper with the top of the adjoining copper cylinder.

In order to excite this battery, each zinc rod is first covered or amalgamated with a thin coating of mercury. Next each porous pot is filled with dilute sulphuric acid consisting of one part of acid and nineteen parts of water. Lastly, the earthen or glass jar is filled with dilute sulphuric acid of the same strength with the above. But in the last must be previously dissolved as much powdered sulphate of copper as the fluid will hold in solution;

moreover, a certain quantity of dry powdered sulphate of copper is thrown into the latter solution, to feed or sustain the action of the battery.

This battery is called Daniell's Sustaining Battery; but, for the purpose to which I apply it, it is used with a much less proportion of acid than commonly. The principle expense of this battery is the consumption of the zinc and the acid (the copper being little acted on), and also the consumption of the sulphate of copper. As a set-off against the expense of using this battery, the zinc and copper in solution are both recoverable.

Andrew Crosse's Electrical Research

Crystal Investigations

The formation of crystals was something that particularly fascinated Andrew, and had done so since his first experiments with water taken from Holwell Cave about 1807. He was aware that the form that the crystals took was due to its molecular arrangement, and while he felt that electricity played a part in their formation, this was a secondary cause. To explain that there must be one 'law' that determines crystal formation, he used the following example during a public lecture:

> Light, heat, magnetism, and electricity are qualities of matter which are intimately connected with each other. One great law may regulate them all, and produce them all but as yet we are ignorant of it. I might compare them to four bottles filled with different fluids boiling over a fire, the same cause – the fire – producing the boiling of all.

Not all of Andrew's experiments went as hoped, and he would often be heard muttering '*Ars longa, vita brevis*' ('Art is long, life is short!') but the real motto of his research was rather: 'It is better to follow nature blindfold than art with both eyes open.' He had endless patience, something that was required in large measures for his crystal research. He sometimes had to wait for weeks, months or even years before he got results, making careful observations at regular intervals, while ensuring the set up was tended and maintained. His initial experiments in this field were not always successful due to initially using too high an electric charge. It was perceived wisdom that crystals would only be formed when the fluid from which they were created remained absolutely undisturbed. This was not what Andrew's work showed. In writing about crystal formation he said:

> There are other conditions besides electricity necessary to be observed, such as more or less even temperature, absence of light, and in many cases constant motion of the fluid holding the crystallisable matter in solution, either by dropping from the roof of a cavern, or by water constantly flowing, or by the continual elevation and depression of the surface of the subterranean waters; which surface is for ever varying, low in summer, or more or less overflowing in winter; but constantly in motion. It is this eternal motion that greatly facilitates the growth of crystals.

> This would seem a strange doctrine in the chemical laboratory, where perfect rest is more or less essential to the formation of well-defined saline crystallisations; but such is by no means the case with metallic and earthy matters. I have kept up a constant electrical action, for three successive months, upon fluids in a state of unceasing ebullition, in a sand heat furnace, day and night, without a moment's rest, the evaporated fluid being duly watched in the most careful manner. Yet the crystals formed were as perfectly solid and regular as similar ones taken from a mine, and were much accelerated in their growth, both by the heat employed and by the motion communicated by that heat.

Some of the electro-crystallisation experiments involved heat, and solutions were placed in a sand bath for several weeks at a time. This required care to ensure both the heat was continuously maintained and that the solutions did not evaporate to dryness. Over the course of thirty years Andrew estimated that he had produced about two hundred varieties of minerals, many of which were identical to those found in nature, but a number of which were purely artificial. Andrew was aware there was a wide range of minerals that could not be made by man at that time since they were formed by volcanic action or immense pressure found only deep in the earth. He was convinced that natural electric action played a part in crystal formation, and suggested this could be caused in one of four ways:

1. Permanent magnetic action within the earth.
2. Electric currents created by strata of dissimilar rocks in contact with subterranean water – creating a natural battery.

3. Electrical currents created by volcanic heat.

4. Local electrical action.

He carried out an experiment to verify the 'local electrical action' theory. On a visit to Weymouth, Dorset, he had noticed some rounded limestone pebbles and sea shells embedded in the clay of a small cliff. Each stone and shell was covered with crystals of calcium sulphate ($CaSO_4$) also called gypsum, selenite or more commonly Plaster of Paris. With Andrew's interest in crystals, this naturally attracted his attention, so he began to investigate the reason why they had formed. He observed a strata of decomposing sulphuret of iron (iron sulphide, FeS) running horizontally at the top of the cliff just below the soil. This suggested to him that rain water penetrated the soil, moistened the sulphuret of iron and decomposed it, the oxygen of the water converting it into the sulphate form. The sulphate, being a soluble salt, passed into the clay where it came into contact with the surface of the limestone pebbles and shells (calcium carbonate, $CaCO_3$). He suggested this caused a local electric current to be set up in which the limestone pebbles and sea shells was negative, while the upper stratum of sulphuret of iron was positive. The calcium sulphate and calcium carbonate each decomposed and calcium sulphate was deposited on the surface of the pebbles and shells in the form of crystals. During this process carbon dioxide gas was liberated so the iron, being derived of its sulphuric acid, absorbed oxygen and was converted into red iron oxide (Fe_2O_3) which Andrew found precipitated in large amounts around the crystals in the form of a powder. To confirm his theory he carried out an experiment.

> On my return home I took a large basin, half filled it with pipe-clay, which
> I kneaded up with water to the consistence of moist putty, and embedded

in the clay some pieces of limestone and some sea-shells. I next formed a stratum upon the clay of powdered sulphuret of iron, and then filled the basin with common water, and put it aside in a dark cupboard for a twelvemonth. At the end of that period I brought it into the light and examined it with no small anxiety; but was delighted to find that every piece of limestone and sea-shell which had been embedded in the clay, when taken out, washed, and dried was covered with prismatic crystals of calcium sulphate exactly similar to those found in the cliff at Weymouth; but of course they were small, though perfect. Such are the effects of local electricity. Observe that here no battery was used, nor metal in a metallic state. It was simply a close imitation of nature, but followed out only for a year; whereas nature has at her command unlimited time and resources.

Andrew had arrived at the modern understanding of how crystals are formed, as he thought that 'what is termed chemical affinity is nothing but a greater or less electrical attraction …', which it is, but at the atomic level, and is also dependent on water, temperature, pressure and chemical composition. Over many years Andrew investigated the use of electricity in a wide range of contexts. It was only by such wide ranging exploration that the early scientists were not only able to make new discoveries, but discover those that were to lead to commercial exploitation and continue the industrial revolution. However, many early discoveries were either not appreciated or were unable to be exploited until many years later. Andrew often carried out a particular piece of research over a long period or returned to it at intervals. Because of his phenomenal memory he was able to remember all the details of his experiments, even when carried out years earlier, although his note taking was not very good, which went against most scientific views that all methods and observations should be recorded. Because of this it is not always possible to arrange Andrew's research in exact chronological order. However, by looking at his various experiments his range of interests is clear.

Improving the Tanning Process

Andrew used a low electrical current to speed up the tanning of leather which, in some cases, can take up to three years particularly when using oak bark in the process. His work considerably reduced the time needed and tanners in Bristol got to hear about it. They were so intrigued by this that a group of them walked all the way from Bristol to Fyne Court to discuss it with Andrew. This was in the days before the railway came to Taunton. Such artisan visitors were always welcomed and treated as hospitably as if they had been Fellows of the Royal Society.

The Purification of Fluids by Electricity

One of Andrew's experiments looked at the possibility of purifying sea water. To do this the water had to be distilled once when it was found to be suitable for washing, but could not be drunk. However, if he placed a simple electrical arrangement in the cask or cistern of distilled sea water he found that the water became 'wholesome to the taste' within twenty-four hours. It would also remain sweet in open vessels for an indefinite period. Andrew also purified brackish water using this technique. The electrical apparatus he used consisted of two cylinders of dissimilar metals, usually sheet zinc and sheet iron, which were placed in two porous earthenware tubes, open at the top and closed at the bottom. The two metal cylinders are connected by a strip of copper. The porous tubes, with the metal cylinders inverted in them, are filled with water and placed in the liquid that was to be purified. The electrical action then begins and the liquid is purified. Andrew also found that the liquid becomes antiseptic after a few hours.

Such a technique would have been of great interest to the Royal Navy, which spent a lot of time in the early 19th century blockading ships in their ports, which necessitated long periods of patrolling at sea. In 1847 *The Mining Journal* reported that 'Mr. Crosse has succeeded in obtaining pure water from that of sea by means of some procedure of electricity. He has been occupied in explaining this to the Admiralty.' This was a time when very long exploratory and mapping voyages were being undertaken. If fresh water could be produced at sea it would have greatly facilitated these tasks. Following his work on sea water Andrew used the same electric apparatus to improve wine and brandy. In the case of wine it softened the acidity present in some wines by removing the predominance of potassium bitartrate, a natural crystalline acid that is deposited inside the wine barrels. Andrew had some very good results with a spirit distilled in imitation of French brandy. In one experiment Andrew took two gallons (9 l) of the very worst (and cheapest) English brandy and electrified it for three weeks. It was visibly improved. The water in the positive porous tube had become intensely acid while the negative tube was filled with a green thick and turbid oily substance. It not only looked good but now tasted good too! He applied a similar technique to stopping the fermentation of cider. An enthusiastic account of this technique appeared in *The Taunton Courier* on 13 October 1847:

> Electricity recently applied to the purification of spirituous liquids, cider, beer, impure and sea water. This practical application of scientific skill to useful purposes of life, like other important discoveries by the same gentleman owes its origin to the enlightened zeal and talent of our respected neighbour Mr. Andrew Crosse ... The application of the discovery, which is patented, among other social and manufacturing advantages will prove invaluable to the wine merchant and brewer.

Cider was a major industry in Somerset at that time, and many cider makers visited Andrew to see how he was arresting the fermentation of the cider, and the ever patient Andrew would clearly explain the technique to them and show them the apparatus. He wrote a very full account on cider making in *The Library of Practical Agriculture*, published by John Baxter in two volumes (1852). Charles Campon, a cider maker at Bridgwater said that the improvement to one hogshead of cider (52.5 gal / 229.5 l) equalled the entire cost of Andrew's apparatus. It is believed that one of Andrew's cider improving batteries was in use on a Somerset farm well into the 1900s. It is interesting that Andrew regarded the electrified water as being antiseptic. This led him into a new field – food preservation and improvement. He claimed that not only could the water be preserved for years and remain clear and fresh, but could restore the most putrid substances to sweetness! He took pieces of rancid meat and the skins of animals that had started to putrefy, and put them into electrified water, and in a few hours, he noted, they were 'rendered inodorous', but not necessarily edible! He also kept milk fresh for three weeks in the middle of summer by applying low voltage electricity to it.

On one occasion Andrew kept a pair of soles in 'electrified water' for three months. At the end of that time he sent the fish as a gift to a friend who knew nothing of the experiment. Before his cook dressed them her master asked her if she thought they were fresh, as he had a few doubts – perhaps he knew Andrew too well! She apparently replied that she was sure they were fresh, and even said she would swear 'they had been alive yesterday.' When they were served up they looked just like ordinary fish, but when the family attempted to eat them they were found to be completely tasteless. It seems that the prolonged low voltage to which they had been exposed had destroyed all the essential oils. However, by only using electrified water for ten or fourteen days, fish and meat could be kept fresh and edible. This work led him to speculate whether 'electrified antiseptic water' might be useful for medical purposes. He suggested it might be drunk in the case of typhus (common and often fatal at that time) and other fevers, and used for bathing to cure other ailments.

Experiments in the Perforation and Breaking up of Non-conducting Materials by Electricity

Andrew carried out a series of experiments using a 'common electrical machine' to pass a current between two platinum wires just touching the same side of a piece of glass immersed in an inch of water (2.5 cm), the ends being about a tenth of an inch (3 mm) apart. The wires were connected to the negative and positive conductors of an electric generating machine which was given 200 to 300 turns, after which a small, perfectly circular hole was found in the glass between the two wires and at right angles to the flow of the current. Since the tungsten carbide drill was not invented until the 1940s this technique looked as if it could have had a commercial application for putting holes in glass. This experiment was repeated in a number of different ways. However, when the water barely covered the glass a fountain of water above the electrode gap was thrown more than a foot into the air. When the glass was placed face down with the electrodes on the lower surface and the water scarcely covering the glass, turning the machine's handle caused very minute pieces to be displaced from the glass immediately above the space between the two wires, and a small jet of glass particles was thrown up as was the water previously.

When thicker glass was used it produced a hole in the glass between the two electrodes on the underside, but had no effect of the upper surface. It became obvious that with the thinner glass a series of minute vibrations was being set up that displaced the glass particles. A similar series of experiments was carried out on quartz crystals, and Andrew was able to bore a depression in these. In further work on the technique Andrew found he was able to break certain non-conducting materials into pieces, again by the setting up minute vibrations in the material.

Andrew's discovery is very similar to the Spark Erosion or Electro-Discharge machine invented by the Russian brothers B.R. and N.I. Lazarenko in 1943. The work piece and the tool are immersed in a bath of electrolyte. A high frequency pulsating voltage is generated which creates a spark across the gap between the work piece and tool which vaporises the metal of the work piece in the vicinity of the tool. What is also interesting is that Andrew's technique inspired Dr George Robinson, Lecturer on Medicine at the Newcastle-upon-Tyne College of Practical Science, to send a paper to the Royal Society on 13 June 1854 entitled 'On the Disintegration of Urinary Calculi by the Lateral Disruptive Force of the Electrical Discharge', which was read before its members. In this paper he discusses the possibility of using electricity to break up bladder stones in humans. If it could be done it would avoid 'the dangerous operation of lithotomy.' He felt that the science of electricity had progressed to the point when the intensity of the discharge could be accurately regulated. The bigger problem was the mechanical difficulty of bringing the bladder stone into contact with the electrical discharge.

However, Dr Robinson had read an account of Andrew's experiments in using electricity to break up non-conducting materials, such as glass and quartz in Lardner's *Cabinet Cyclopaedia* published monthly between 1829-49, which had made him wonder if this technique might have a medical application. He quotes in full Andrew's method of passing a discharge between two platinum wires and breaking up non-conducting materials, and then Dr Robinson goes on to describe a series of experiments he had carried out using human bladder stones. His apparatus consisted of two copper wires with platinum wire soldered to their end. Both wires were passed through a fine gutta percha tube which was warmed and pressed together to form a bougie, a thin flexible instrument for exploring or dilating a passage in the body. Gutta percha is a thermoplastic substance obtained from the latex of some Malaysian trees. The platinum wires projected beyond the gutta percha sheaf one eighth of an inch (3 mm) and were one tenth of an inch (3 mm) apart, and connected to a Leyden Jar.

In his first experiment a large stone was placed in a bladder nearly filled with water and the bougie was introduced so that the wires were brought into contact with the stone. The Leyden Jar was given a single discharge after which the bladder was opened and the stone found to have broken into many fragments. A second experiment was carried out using a very hard and smooth bladder stone. After six discharges it broke into at least twenty fragments which, on being pressed between finger and thumb, readily broke down further. A third experiment on a very large stone produced a small cavity on the surface and separated many fine sand grain like fragments but did not break it down. A fourth experiment using a bladder stone from a young boy was witnessed by three Newcastle surgeons and was successful. From this Dr Robinson concluded that it was feasible to break up bladder stones in humans by introducing the wire via the urethra and bringing it into contact with the stone. The patient was in no danger from the electrical discharge since the body did not form any part of the circuit, and Dr Robinson finishes: 'as regards simplicity and security, the electrical apparatus certainly appears preferable to the instruments used for crushing the stone by ordinary mechanical force', a technique introduced c.1834 and popular from the 1880s-1970s. So Andrew's work had inspired the idea of using an electrical methods to treat this condition well over a century before cystolitholapaxy, which utilises ultrasound waves, was developed.

Experiments on Electro-vegetation

Andrew held the view that there must be a connection between the growth of plants and natural electric forces. Specifically that electricity was the reason that minerals were carried into plants, and so would account for an insoluble mineral such as silica being found in grass, cereals and other plants. Soluble silica is taken up from the soil when roots absorb groundwater and some of the silica is deposited in the plant in the form of silicon dioxide. Professor John Quekett (1815-61), microscopist and Professor of Histology, who founded the Royal Microscopical Society in 1839, enlarged and adopted this view in his *Lectures on Histology* (1851):

> The process of dissolving the silica and taking it up to be deposited in the tissues, as is done by the grasses, is probably an electrical one; and in a recent visit to Somersetshire I witnessed the following most striking experiment in the laboratory of Mr. Crosse, a true philosopher, of whom doubtless you have heard as being so celebrated for his experiments in voltaic electricity. In a common tumbler filled with distilled water, were placed, on opposite sides, a portion of silver – if I recollect rightly, a sixpence [actually it was a piece of chemically pure silver] – and a piece of slate; one was connected with a positive and the other with a negative pole of a Voltaic battery ... by this means slow electric action was kept up, and the silver on the one side was actually dissolved by the water, carried across, and deposited in a crystalline form upon the slate on the opposite side of the tumbler. Had a piece of flint occupied the place of the silver, the same effect in all probability would have been produced. It occurred to me immediately that it might be by an electrical agency that the silica, lime, and other inorganic materials were dissolved and assimilated by plants.

Andrew investigated whether low voltages of electricity could improve the growth of plants. One, not successful, experiment involved potatoes. He planted two potatoes in identical soil and kept in identical conditions, but one was in positively charged earth the other in negatively charged earth. After a while the 'negative potato' became diseased, began to decompose and emitted the fetid smell of the rotting potato. On examining the 'positive potato' it had not rotted, but nor did it grow. It had put out no roots or shoots but was still solid, although in appearance it resembled a shrivelled apple. However, other experiments with plants were more successful, although the outcome was that negative electricity was injurious to plants but positive electricity was good (except in the case of potatoes). One of the experiments that clearly demonstrated this was done with two rose branches. They were as identical as possible with the same number and size of buds and so on. Negative electricity was passed though one and positive through the other. Within a few hours the negative branch drooped and died, while the positive branch continued fresh for two weeks, and the buds expanded and flowered. In a letter to John Boyes of Margate in Kent, dated 1 February 1847, Andrew described how to undertake an experiment to test the possible advantages of applying electricity to growing vines:

> I should provide a copper wire with a termination of platinum wire, which termination I should stick between the roots of the vine about twenty inches deep, connecting the copper end with the positive pole of a small battery under an adjacent shed, and making use of a simple copper wire to connect the earth with the negative pole – such wire being about twenty inches deep into the ground, at the distance of about four feet or two yards from the platinum wire. There would be a mutual interchange of elements; and such vine might be compared with a vine under the same circumstances, but not electrified. The electrified vine should be kept well watered, to form a good conducting communication between the two wires, and the unelectrified vine should be equally watered, so as to form a fair test, the battery made use of should be Daniell's Sustaining Battery, about eight pairs of plates excited by sulphate of copper in the negative cells, and water alone in the positive.

Boyes carried out the experiment Andrew suggested and wrote to him on 29 July 1847 to inform him of the results. However, he carried out the experiment on vines grown in pots rather than the ground, applying electricity to one from 30 March to the 30 June. Otherwise it was as Andrew had suggested. Boyes detailed the results:

> The electrified vine shot 74 inches.
> The unelectrified vine shot 31¼ inches.
> Each bore a bunch of white Dutch grapes, the electrified bunch being about $1/_3$ larger than the unelectrified bunch.

The electrified stem is the largest in girth and it has (on this day) twenty-nine ripened joints, whilst the unelectrified has only nine, and in all other appearances the electrified is decidedly the best.

Andrew suggested that the following season Boyes should electrify the vine that was not electrified the first season to confirm that the results were not due to a difference in the health of the plant or some other factor. This he did. The result of this was that the vine that was electrified in the first year and grew 74 inches, only put on a further 68 inches in the second year when no electricity was applied to it. The second vine, that was unelectrified in the first year and grew to 31½ inches, put on a further 60 inches in the second when electricity was applied. Despite the apparent success with a single or very small number of plants, Andrew could not see that it would have a realistic commercial application because of the difficulty of supplying enough electricity for a larger number. The application of electricity to encourage plant growth was tried again in 1918 when the Ministry of Agriculture appointed an Electro-culture Committee, which investigated the matter, using electric current passed through wires above the crop, until wound up in 1937. While they had got positive results, it proved too technically difficult to implement commercially. Experiments were carried out on cereals in India in the 1930s and on various crops in the Soviet Union in the 1970s. The Long Ashton Plant Research Station found that low levels of electricity produced increased linear growth and yield in tomatoes, but was too costly for commercial use, just as Andrew had said!

In 2000 researchers under the European Commission's FAIR programme found that applying pulses of electricity (15 kilojoules per kilogramme) to fruit opens up the cell walls and allows 10 to 12 per cent more juice to be extracted, and up to 30 per cent in the case of vegetables such as carrots. One curiosity Andrew noticed during the course of this series of experiments, was that while the negative electricity was injurious to plants and positive was beneficial, the reverse applied to fungi. Positive electricity entirely checked the appearance of any fungus. Andrew often found fungi growing in his copper and other acid solutions, and Cornelia described seeing the surface of an electrified fluid covered, or nearly so, by a thick flesh-like fungus that was strong enough to bear a considerable weight, and proved so tough it was difficult to tear it.

A New Method of Making Impressions on Marble

Another experiment Andrew carried out was to place a gold sovereign on a piece of white marble in a container of concentrated potassium nitrate, and held down by a glass rod. A platinum wire, connected to the positive pole of a battery, was placed between the rod and the surface of the coin, and a coil of wire placed round the marble, but not touching it, and connected to the battery's negative pole. Nitric acid was generated between the coin and the marble, and at the end of three days the experiment was stopped. The coin was embedded in the marble, and when it was inverted the coin fell out leaving a perfect impression in the marble of the coin.

Marbling of Plaster of Paris

By passing an electric current through ordinary Plaster of Paris (calcium sulphate, $CaSO_4$) it became hardened and crystallised. The external surface looked as if it had been polished, and the hardness was so complete that the Plaster of Paris became as hard as marble. This had potential for the manufacture of artificial marble ornaments.

Keeping Blood Liquid

Among the last experiments that Andrew carried out was an investigation into a method of keeping blood liquid. Two ounces (57 g) of pig's blood was kept electrified between February 1854 and February 1856 when Cornelia discontinued it, Andrew having died seven months earlier. Apparently it remained liquid with its colour unaltered right to the end. Was he thinking of blood transfusions? The first tentative attempts at transferring blood go back as far as the mid-17th century, but the first successful transfusion occurred in 1818 and was reported in 1819. There was much discussion about the advantages and disadvantages of blood transfusions between 1830-50, but it was still rare. Between 1819 and 1849 there are only forty-eight recorded cases of blood transfusions, not all successful. The biggest problem being encountered was the clotting of the blood, and Andrew was presumably trying to solve this problem.

The Mine in a Garden Pot Experiment

One of Andrew's interests was in the formation of fissures in rocks, and to explore whether their formation involved natural earth electricity, so he set up a series of experiments to explore this possibility. This involved forming an artificial 'landscape' with water in porous vessels, and various minerals in porous pots. These 'landscapes' were electrified with a weak Voltaic battery over long periods ranging from 'some months' to up to two years. He got some interesting results from this. The 'negative electricity' created fissures lined with minerals as in nature, and to prove it was not caused by capillary attraction, Andrew reversed the electric current and the effect did not occur. His work on the motion of water through porous material using low voltage electricity, has been commercially developed into electro-osmosis damp proofing in houses.

The Separation of Metals from their Ores

Andrew had been interested and actively involved in mining operations for many years, although he was never successful in actually making any money from it. However, in the 1850s he was looking at ways of using electricity to economically extract various metals from their ores, and in the last few months before his death was conducting experiments on the extraction of gold. While he was generally successful in extracting gold from Californian gold ore, it was a long and complex process and he concluded that it was 'too slow for use.' Another series of experiments involved the extraction of copper from its ore. This was considerably more successful as the process was relatively simple and the result was that pure copper was deposited in a negatively charged receiving cup. This had such potential that he patented the system in the hope it would have a commercial application. There is no doubt of its commercial possibilities, and James Elkington, who owned an electro-plating factory in Birmingham, not only patented a similar method for extracting copper from copper salts, but established the first electrolytic refining plant at Pembury in Wales in 1869.

The only drawback to Andrew's system was the expense of the battery and lack of power for industrial scale processing as he was using Daniell Sustaining Batteries. Like many early scientific discoveries, it needed something that had not then been developed or invented, a powerful and continuous electric current. Andrew once said that if he could only invent a battery at once cheap, powerful, and durable, he might say like Archimedes 'that he could move the world.' As early as the 1830s Andrew had predicted that the time would come when ores were extracted by electricity. Today very reactive metals, such as aluminium, are extracted using electricity.

CHAPTER NINE
Cornelia Berkeley becomes Crosse: 1849–50

In 1849 Andrew spent most of the year in London at his house, 15 Charles Street, Marylebone. He had his dog, Greg, with him, an animal of which he was very fond. In August he had received a letter from Harriet Martineau asking some questions about his 'mite experiments' before she published an account of them in *The History of the Thirty Years Peace 1816-36* (1849). Harriet Martineau (1802-76) was a writer and philosopher, a political economist, a feminist, the first female socialist and the first female journalist in England. She was a controversial figure, suggesting radical ideas such as every working man should be entitled to a vote. She produced many articles, pamphlets and novels. She was a friend of Charles Darwin who on one occasion, presumably before they became friends, said 'I was astonished to see how ugly she is' and on another occasion 'She is overwhelmed with her own projects, her own thoughts and abilities.' Later she was also to become a firm friend of Andrew and his second wife.

Andrew's reply to Martineau, stating that he had no objection to using it in whatever way she pleased, was very detailed, and he welcomed the opportunity to put his side of the story and correct many misunderstandings. The 'mites' were a controversial and sensitive subject for Andrew, although the initial controversy over the results of his experiments in 1836 had died down, he was still associated with them, and was still reviled by some because of his findings. The year 1849 saw the death of Queen Adelaide, the wife of King William IV. Andrew mentions this in one of his letters written from his London house which, reading between the lines, shows that he remained a republican at heart:

The day of Queen Adelaide's funeral was a very gloomy one here – the shops shut, the bells tolling in all the churches, including the deep roar of St. Paul's, heavy guns thundering through the streets, and all the et-ceteras of royal pomp, telling the tale of the death of one poor exalted creature, while the destruction of tens of thousands who pass unnoticed from the earth, one in every second, is not dreamed of. Such is the world! a dream of vanities, fripperies, and nonsense! The late queen was, however, a very good but not a great minded woman. I am not about to find fault with her, nor any other of my unfortunate species.

It was also in 1849 that he was fortunate to meet a young lady, Cornelia Augusta Hewett Berkeley (plate 24). Born in 1827 at Ambleside, Westmorland, in the Lake District, she later moved to the West Country, as the 1841 census shows she is resident at 96 St. Sidwell Street, Exeter in Devon. Cornelia recalled how the first time she met Andrew it was at a dinner party given by a mutual friend. She seems to have had a serious interest in science, particularly electrical science, from a young age, very unusual at that time for a female. She already knew of Andrew and his work as she had made a scrap book of articles about him cut from the newspapers. So it was with some excitement that she met the man whose power in manipulating that mysterious agent, electricity, had so excited her imagination. Cornelia, then only twenty-one, was not only a confident socialite but was described as a great beauty. She was even more excited to find herself sitting opposite Andrew at the dinner table, and listened eagerly as he spoke on the subjects that were the talk of the day, but was disappointed to find that the one subject he did not mention was electricity. She later remarked that perhaps he was hungry! After the company had risen from the table and retired to a drawing room, Cornelia found herself drawn to a group of people listening attentively to an individual. That individual was Andrew. Something in the conversation had reminded him that he had written some verses on the subject being discussed, and he was reciting one of his poems.

In her own words: 'He was reciting some lines of his own poetry; but it was not recitation, it was rather the emphatic utterance of a torrent of thoughts, that fell in rhythm. How his words stirred one's heart, as he changed from the deepest pathos to a burst of earnest patriotism; or, in language simple as the wild flowers, whose scents and hues he summoned round him, he led you in fancy to those wild hills, his home, and yours, for the time, for while you listened you felt what he felt. I had expected to find what I reverenced – a follower of science: I found what I worshipped – a poet.' It seems that despite her scrapbook about Andrew, she had not known he wrote poetry, which was one of the great passions of her life. It was at this point that the twenty-one year old Cornelia fell in love with Andrew, then sixty-four years old and a widower for four years (plate 23).

She was not the only one among this group of listeners on whom Andrew made an impression. He had always been an earnest and enthusiastic speaker once he got under way, particularly concerning those subjects so dear to his heart, science and poetry. He had a way of enthusing his listeners, whether an audience at a scientific meeting or guests at a dinner party, but was able to discourse on a wide range of subjects. We don't know the exact circumstances, or how Cornelia managed it, but the next time she saw Andrew was in his own London house in Charles Street. Did she make such an impression on Andrew that he invited her, or did she go along as part of a group he invited. We don't know. She describes how at home he was the genial host, the country gentleman and the scientist. He had always placed great importance on hospitality, and often used to say that 'I think hospitality so essential, that I don't call it a virtue, but I do call the absence of it a great vice.' His firmly held liberal views also meant that he did not harbour grudges. Concerning this, another of his favourite sayings was: 'If my greatest enemy was to come to my house, I would ask him to dinner, and call him out afterwards.' This was in jest since even under severe provocation he never seemed to lose his temper or seek to hurt others, so 'calling someone out', that is challenging them to a duel, illegal since 1843, is something that would have been unthinkable to him. This ability to remain calm even when others were getting upset was obviously a good thing as far as he was concerned, as he tended to be outspoken and impetuous in passing comment. This could easily lead to misunderstandings by those who did not know of his tendency to speak with disarming honesty without any guile.

The friendship between Cornelia and Andrew developed during 1849, although Cornelia's book *Memorials, Scientific and Literary of Andrew Crosse the Electrician* makes no mention of this. In the Autumn of that year Cornelia seems to have made her first visit to Fyne Court. The house had been suffering from neglect as Andrew spent a lot of time in London after the death of his wife Mary Ann in 1846, and Cornelia described how in a storm, quite a common occurrence high in the hills, the 'slates of the roof seemed as if positively electrified, and flew right and left in mutual repulsion.' Andrew seems to have become concerned at the house's poor condition since, at the time she visited, it was besieged by an army of masons and carpenters. The music room, long known as the philosophical room to friends and family, and Andrew's main laboratory, had just been rebuilt as it had developed some major structural problems, not because of Andrew's experiments but due to a bad architect and a dishonest builder.

Despite the major building work going on, there were batteries in almost every room of the house. In the darkness of the cellar more batteries were connected to apparatus that was 'growing' a variety of crystals, the only sound being the dripping of water in imitation of the way nature formed minerals. Cornelia's description of the house and its domestic arrangements are detailed. Was she considering marriage at this time and so taking it on as mistress and the wife of its owner? It could well have discouraged anyone less deeply in love with its owner, as she seems to have been:

At Fyne Court Mr. Crosse was surrounded by a perfect chaos of apparatus. Certainly the old house had more a philosophic than a domestic air about it. The family plate was occasionally called on to make contributions to the crucible, which, with the aid of the laboratory furnace, converted tea-pots, tankards, and old-fashioned spoons into chemically pure silver in a very short space of time. A great deal of the glass and china of the house was not suffered to remain in vulgar use, but was dedicated to nobler purposes, and was formed into batteries or other electrical arrangements. The rooms generally seemed in a process of resolving themselves into laboratories or other kinds of scientific dens. You were perfectly comfortable, perfectly at home, under the hospitable roof; but, to speak in geological language, the house appeared to be in a transition state.

Cornelia was confronted by a bewildering array of apparatus and materials which, at this point were a puzzle to her, but as Andrew was conducting her round what was to eventually become her new home, his patient and clear explanations meant she began to understand the significance of what she was looking at. Andrew made much of the scientific equipment himself, both to save money and because it was not available for purchase. He had a well-equipped workshop containing, among other items, a lathe, and was an expert turner of both brass and ivory. He recalled how one day some friends were watching him turning an item on the lathe, when one of them remarked on how beautifully he turned. To which another of his friends, John Eagles said, not inaccurately, 'Crosse can turn anything but a penny!' Although there were instrument makers where items of electrical equipment could be purchased such as machines for generating static electrical charges, purpose-made Leyden Jars and even small electrical generators used to give mild shocks for health purposes, along with microscopes and other items, these all cost money and Andrew required large amounts of apparatus, much of which was not available anyway. This visit did not alter Cornelia's feelings for Andrew. By December Andrew was back at his London house. Could there be a hint in a letter, dated 4 December 1849, by him that romance was in his thoughts:

> Your most welcome communication reached me yesterday. Did you ever observe in the early summer sunrise, just before that glorious orb made his appearance, a stratum of sky above the horizon of a pellucid, unearthly golden green hue? I feel surrounded by a similar kind of halo – a mixture of the earthly with the unearthly; such is my waking dream:- all sorts of real and unreal things pass before me, and I feel as though [I am] living in the days and country of the Caliph Haroun al Raschid. I fear I have far too much romance in my unfortunate composition for the stern realities of these frigid times.

However, later in the same letter, after discussing music, his thoughts seem to become darker:

> Alas! I look back upon my own mind, so full of all imperfections. I would be what I am not: I would grasp all the good, and flee from the evil; but here they are inseparable. I would express to you what I feel, but I am

struck down to the ground; a clod! I am called away by worldly but necessary matters, and I must wind up this tiresome scrawl ... .

No mention of love, marriage or Cornelia. December 1849 was a busy month for Andrew as he makes clear in a letter to a friend dated 16 December sent from his London house:

I will state my proposed movements as far as I can at present. In the first place I have engaged, on my return to the west, to pay a visit to your father; from thence I shall go to Winslade [House, near Exeter], to stay a short time with my good cousin Henry Porter. I have also partly engaged to stay with some friends in Somersetshire, and I must visit my old home at Broomfield, to mark a great quantity of young trees there, as they are occasioning great injury to the more valuable trees which they oppress with their branches. After this roundabout I must fly back here, to attend to the scientific experiments which I am carrying on in London. You ask about my health: on the whole I am moderately well, but have suffered much since I have been here; the drizzling fogs, continued rain, with steaming heat and a host of disagreeables have much annoyed me.

If he was in love or contemplating marriage, there is also no hint of it in this, another of his long and chatty letters, and remember he felt no qualms, as can be clearly seen in his letters and poems, about putting his feelings in writing. The overall tone does not suggest he was a man in love:

I look around, and find myself an isolated animal, – my best and dearest friends gone, myself standing all but alone in the gap, ready to be carried off by the next discharge of our common foe, – I feel that I have little to do in this world, but to brace my mind to submit humbly to the fate which my wise Maker may ordain for me.

Andrew himself recognised the duality of his character, as is clear from this letter:

You say that my character is 'very peculiar.' I am aware of it; though, like my own species, I know myself but little. Still I know or believe that I am composed of two extremes in most things. I do feel most strongly, too strongly sometimes for my own comfort; but this is somewhat balanced by a power of reflection (I speak humbly) that enables me after a time, I hope, by God's aid, to correct and control any exuberance of wild thoughts which might otherwise carry me away. I believe I am capable of friendship, and perhaps to a somewhat unusual extent; but to be called forth it must be reciprocal. Indeed, where I have been traduced and abused by those who do not know me, I console myself with the reflection, that I have been too often, far too often praised, and I let the excess of the one contend with the exuberance of the other.

And later in this same letter: 'Alas! I have nothing to boast of but misfortune.' There is little doubt that he was 'low' at this time. Was it thoughts of the approaching Christmas without his wife and beloved brother that was causing this mood? His sons had married, Robert in 1837 and John in 1840, and had their own families (although in John's case Andrew may not have been aware of this). Isabella was full of thoughts of her impending marriage in May 1850 and would soon be leaving home. Andrew would then really be alone. Despite this the 1850s were an exciting time scientifically as far as Andrew was concerned as so much scientific research was now coming to practical fruition. Wheatstone and others had developed a working telegraph system so that Andrew's prophecy of 1816 that 'by means of the electric agency, we shall be enabled to communicate our thoughts instantaneously with the uttermost ends of the earth' was coming true. In January 1850 Andrew was at his London house and still going out into society. On 10 January he was at a ball given by the editor of *The Examiner*, and then went on to a party 'filled with wild and talented people' and on the following day went to yet another party.

At one of these he met John Watkins Brett and his brother, who had founded the Anglo-French Telegraph Company in 1845, which must have been a very satisfying meeting as far as Andrew was concerned as they were just about to lay the first submarine cable. In 1847 they had got a concession from the French to put a telegraph cable between England and France. In 1850 they did lay a cable, but it quickly failed. The following year another cable was successfully laid between Dover and Calais, and in 1852 telegraph cables were laid between Britain and Ireland, and London and Paris, while in 1857 the first attempt was made to lay a transatlantic cable, just two years after Andrew died. In Britain the rapidly expanding railway network was linking even the most isolated parts of the country, but Andrew was not to live to see one of the greatest revolutions in both science, theology and the views of ordinary people, the publication of Darwin's *On the Origin of Species* in 1859, which caused a controversy far greater even than Andrew's mysterious *Acari.*

The next occasion that Cornelia saw Andrew was early in 1850 when he was staying at the house of some of her relatives. A party of gentlemen, some of whom she described as 'men of science' had been invited to meet him, while the others in the party were all interested in the subject. She recalled how he was discussing some cylindrical arrangement of Voltaic batteries, using a rolled up piece of paper to demonstrate what he was talking about, when one of the party mentioned the theory, of which Andrew had long been a believer, that electricity was the basis of all matter, of life and the even the universe. As was usually the case, his face lit up with enthusiasm as he held forth on this subject, one that was obviously close to his heart, since he attributed so much of the world around him to electric forces. This is something now much more understood to be true, certainly at the atomic level. The human body, along with most organic life, relies on electricity to work. Brain, heart and muscles all rely on electrical impulses, which are generated by changing chemical concentrations of potassium and sodium ions which causes a charge in the cell. In 1863, H.L.F. von Helmholtz compared the electrical impulses passing down nerves to the electric telegraph. However, this is not accurate as in a wire electrons flow down it, but in a nerve the charge jumps from one cell to another. Andrew's study of geology then led him to contemplate the ever changing nature of the world, and its never-ending cyclic nature to his listeners:

> Whether we contemplate miles of rock teeming with organic remains, or regard the changes in the vegetable kingdom, still are we filled with wonder and with awe. Mighty forests are hurled upon their native soil; centuries pass away, they are covered with mould, and blacken in their tombs; thousands of years succeed, and the buried trees are mineralised, and

become vast strata of coal; the coal is consumed to create steam, and that which was once a seed lends its aid in impelling mighty ships across the ocean. Its carbon is given to the atmosphere, and again becomes a component part of new forests. This is the language of the Deity. That Great One has ordained that nothing should be lost … .

After this outburst of eloquence and the vastness of the subject he paused and, looking around him, became aware that the whole party had been listening with rapt attention to every word he said. He immediately looked disconcerted as his characteristic humility asserted itself, and he returned, in a more subdued voice, to his original subject of the Voltaic battery. This was the same pattern he showed in public speaking. He would start hesitantly then, when he got going, enthusiasm would carry him and his listeners forward, until he finished, upon which his diffidence would reassert itself. There are many accounts of his skill at draughtsmanship when he drew diagrams and illustrations of the apparatus and experiments he was talking about. A letter from Andrew, dated 8 January 1850, which may have been written after Cornelia saw him again, showed he was once again suffering from his 'nerves'. Could this have been because of an increasing feeling about a young lady? After he details his physical and mental anguish the letter seems to end on a note of hope:

I am suffering much from nervous attacks, which I have had at times, more or less, ever since the age of fifteen. When about the age of thirty, I consulted Sir Anthony Carlisle; his answer was, 'It is mostly indigestion; eat dry biscuits, and drink water alone.' I did so, and became vastly better; but at intervals they come back. The most agonising toothache (from which I have suffered much) is a very great pleasure when compared to them. What I have endured from them is only inferior to what I have suffered from the death of my nearest and dearest relatives; and then, during those overwhelming afflictions, I have given myself up entirely, as a useless incumbrance upon earth, and bowed to my Maker, mentally speaking, in dust and ashes.

I hope, however, that something good may be gleaned from all this as I am taught by my own feelings to pity all my fellow creatures, and to wish them well. I was going to add free from pain; but no – not quite free; with only enough to refine them from the grossness of humanity, and fit them for a purer and happier condition. God grant that this may be my case! It is very strange that, with the exemption of this terrible feeling of nervous attacks, I hardly ever was better or stronger in my life: 'but what can't be cured, must be endured.'

Sir Anthony Carlisle FRCS, FRS, was an eminent physician, but Andrew must either have already known him or one of his electrical friends may have recommended that Andrew consult him as Sir Anthony had been an electrical researcher. In 1800 Sir Anthony and William Nicholson had discovered electrolysis by passing a Voltaic current through water and decomposing it into its constituent elements of hydrogen and oxygen. Andrew spent most of the spring and early summer of 1850 in London, where he was involved with much of the scientific and literary society of the time. His daughter Isabella married Thomas Campbell Foster on 28 May 1850. Andrew and Cornelia must have spent more and more time together. Was Andrew in love with Cornelia? It is impossible to say. Cornelia was undoubtedly in love with him. Was he merely flattered by her interest in him and saw her as a companion who understood his love of science, as quite clearly she did, or was there more to it? She was an intelligent young lady who quickly understood his work and, moreover, was willing to take on the running of what, without exaggeration, must have been a uniquely chaotic household. Whatever Andrew's exact feelings for Cornelia, they were married in St. Mary's Church, Marylebone, the parish in which his London house was situated, on 22 July 1850.

After the marriage, they spent a few weeks at Fyne Court. Cornelia described the house: 'It is an Elizabethan structure of moderate size, and was built in 1629 by one Andrew Crosse; but it has been so enlarged and altered by succeeding possessors, that it can boast only of its antiquity and irregularity.' While not in fact Elizabethan in date, the early house, whose actual date of construction is uncertain, may have resembled the 'E' shape of many Elizabethan houses. They then left for a belated honeymoon in the Lake District, Cornelia's childhood home where they spent some weeks. She presumably still had relatives in the area, but they certainly had friends there. They stayed with Dr John Davy, the brother of Sir Humphrey Davy, and while there they met the brother of Maria Edgeworth, an Anglo-Irish novelist and children's writer who had died the previous year, and her niece Zoe King who was one of Andrew's friends from the West Country. The area was the haunt of artists, writers and poets, some of whom Andrew knew. Poetry played a large part in the lives of both Andrew and Cornelia, and Scott, Shelley, Wilson, Coleridge and de Quincey, had all spent time there, giving rise to the nickname for the area of 'the Poets Corner'. They toured the countryside, spending some time at the Swan Inn at Grasmere, mentioned by Wordsworth in his poem 'The Waggoner'.

Andrew had loved the Quantock Hills of Somerset since he was a child, and this was his first visit to another, even more impressive range. With their familiarity with the works of the Lakeland poets, many of the vistas of rocky hills and deep brooding lakes recalled lines in the poems they loved and knew so well. Andrew was delighted with the scenery and, bearing in mind his interests, was very excited by the storms, a phenomenon that scared many travellers to the area but which delighted Andrew and his new wife. He explained the mechanism of its formation and action to Cornelia, but the poet in him also appreciated its grandeur in poetical terms. On one occasion it caused him to interrupt his technical explanation by quoting from *Childe Harold* by Byron on a similar, but distant land that his neighbour Charles Tynte had invited him to visit with him in the early 1830s, but which he had declined: 'And Jura from her misty shroud / Back to the joyous Alps that call to her aloud.' Andrew was also excited by the variety of minerals to be found, and they never went for a walk without his geological hammer and a strong bag with which to carry back specimens for his collection. No quarry or mine escaped his note, and the opportunity to talk to the workers and miners provided a further pleasure and specimens for his enquiring mind.

They went to visit Harriet Martineau, who had published an account of Andrew's mite experiment in 1849, but she was away from her Lake District house at that time. They had more luck with several other of their London friends, who had gone up to enjoy what was then fashionably popular, the 'picturesque'. Many people were able by this time to appreciate this type of landscape without being intimidated by a wilderness inhabited only by the distinctive Swaledale sheep and buzzards that soared over the rocky crags, the wild rushing streams and the vast expanses of brooding water. As both enjoyed society, they spent many happy hours relaxing and talking with their friends on subjects that were both interesting and amusing, covering the newest theories of the season and discussing the latest advances that science had made.

They lingered on the romantic shores of Lake Windermere and Ullswater, where the scenery deeply impressed Andrew. However, he told Cornelia that the poet in him felt that even this was insufficient to fulfil his poet's imagination of his 'Ideal of beauty.' Cornelia said that in that case he should visit the Alps and the Apennine Mountains where he would really see the magnificence of nature's landscape, which might fulfil his imagined ideal. Andrew replied that 'the same feeling would exist. The mind of man carries him beyond the material beauty of this world, which is but the shadow of what his soul would grasp.' Then taking up his pen he wrote a poem entitled 'Change', which describes the natural beauty of the rocks and cliffs, of mountains that rise grandly in 'cloud-capp'd magnificence', of forests, of unruffled lakes, the sky, the sun, moon and stars, and much else.

They continued their tour through the beautiful landscape of the Lakes until they realised that the evenings were drawing in, and autumn had begun, so it was time to return home to Broomfield before the onset of winter. So it was with great reluctance that they left Cornelia's childhood locality, which she now described as 'twice hallowed'. They came back via London and made an afternoon visit to one of Andrew's old friends, Michael Faraday and his wife Sarah at the Royal Institution in Albermarle Street where he lived as well as worked. Faraday (1791-1867) had had only the most basic education before being apprenticed to a bookbinder, giving him the opportunity to read lots of books. He attended many of the public lectures by famous scientists of the day and wrote copious notes. He showed these to Humphrey Davy, who was so impressed he took him on as an assistant in 1813. He made many new discoveries in electromagnetism and electrochemistry, and was appointed a professor in 1833. The importance of his work was acknowledged by the British government who granted him a pension.

This was the first occasion that Andrew's new wife had met the famous scientist, and Cornelia described how a feeling of awe overcame her as they climbed the stairs leading to the upper chambers of that famous building. Reaching the Faraday's apartment she seemed surprised that the door had an ordinary knocker on it. They were welcomed by Mrs Faraday who led them through the outer sitting room to an inner sanctum, and there was Faraday, half reclining on a sofa. Surrounding him was a heap of novels borrowed from a circulating library, some of which he had rejected and thrown carelessly on the floor, but as they entered his eyes were glued to one which was obviously more riveting. Mrs Faraday later told Cornelia that he read a great many novels 'and it is very good for him to divert his mind.' Cornelia's feelings of apprehension and awe were quickly dispelled by this homely sight, particularly when Faraday rose and greeted them in his vivacious and ever cheery voice, putting aside his book, but not before, Cornelia noticed, placing a bookmark in the novel.

The reason for calling on them was to invite Faraday and his wife to visit them at Fyne Court the following summer, as the winter was a busy time for Faraday with a heavy programme of lectures and his ongoing research work. The discussion began with considerations of the novels of Charles James Lever who wrote about Irish life, and social and political works, and Anthony Trollope, best known for his *Barchester Chronicles* and the Palliser novels. However, it was not long before talk turned to science. The two scientists shared a love of thunderstorms, and Andrew said he hoped that there would be a 'rattling good storm to welcome them to the Quantock Hills', but added 'I am sorry to say that we are not unfrequently disappointed, owing to that abominable Bridgwater river which carries off some of our best storms.'

This lighthearted remark led them on to a discussion about the electric attraction of river systems, and how it may affect the distribution of rain. They also discussed the recent research of Dr C. F. Schonbein on ozone. Faraday asked Andrew about his recent work on the transferring power of electricity in relation to the deposition of metallic ores in nature, and agreed with him this was a strong possibility for the formation of these mineral deposits. When the two scientists began to discuss the allotropic condition of the atmosphere, Sarah Faraday drew Cornelia aside and told her honestly and kindly, that their house was the last place where she would permit her husband to spend his holiday. She was well aware that Fyne Court House, with its laboratories and foundries, was stuffed with electrical apparatus from garret to basement, and foresaw that Faraday, instead of resting both physically and mentally, would spend all day talking science – not much of a holiday!

Cornelia hastened to reassure Mrs Faraday that her new husband was not one of the 'dry as dust school', but often showed the ebullient spirits of a schoolboy, was still fond of his practical jokes, and could talk the most humorous and delightful nonsense. Last and not least he was guilty of perpetrating the most execrable puns! She made this point as Faraday was also known for making bad puns. After an enjoyable few hours and a cup of tea, Andrew and Cornelia were preparing to take their leave, when Faraday offered to show them over his 'workshops' as he referred to his laboratory at the Royal Institution. Cornelia was delighted for this chance to see the place where so many important historic discoveries had been made. They descended to the basement passing through several rooms, until they came to the Old Laboratory where Sir Humphrey Davy had done much of his work. Cornelia and Andrew were aware that this was the very spot on which the science of electrochemistry had been founded. Talking about Davy's achievements, Andrew remarked about the Swedish chemist Berzelius who had belittled his achievements by saying 'It was I, Berzelius, who opened the door and Davy walked in.' There was some basis for this as Davy did claim the credit for a number of discoveries that had already been made by others. Even the famous Safety Lamp he invented in 1816 was almost identical to the design of a safety lamp invented by railway pioneer George Stephenson in 1815. Davy was incensed that he could be upstaged by Stephenson, who was a self-taught working class engineer. No doubt Andrew remembered his delight when Davy visited him at Fyne Court in 1827, just a few years before he died.

Faraday, who had been appointed as Davy's Secretary in 1812, and as his Chemistry Assistant in 1813, described him as a 'truly great man', which was very generous of him as Davy had treated him badly when he accompanied him on a tour of the continent in 1813-15 when he was also made to act as Davy's valet. As Faraday wasn't a 'gentleman', he was not allowed to ride inside the coach, had to eat with the servants, and suffered further from the bad temper of Lady Davy. At one point he got so unhappy that he seriously considered returning to England and giving up science. Fortunately he did not do so, and the trip gave him access to some of the most eminent European scientists, and provided him with stimulating new ideas. Even when Faraday left Davy's employ and started on his own dazzling career, Davy resented him, and when Faraday was proposed as a Fellow of the Royal Society in 1824 Davy vehemently opposed his election, on the basis that he was not the 'right' class.

Before leaving the Old Laboratory Faraday showed them the Froggery, a dismal room in which, so tradition maintained, frogs were kept in the 18th century to repeat Galvani's experiments on animal electricity. They then went in to the New Laboratory where they saw Charles Anderson, Faraday's assistant, busy with the furnaces. Anderson was a retired soldier, having been a sergeant in the Royal Artillery, and was chosen because 'he was never in the way and never out of the way.' Faraday did not expect an assistant to think or reason for himself, and Anderson was at all Faraday's lectures producing the right piece of apparatus or material at the right moment. As they were about to leave the laboratory Faraday turned to him to give him some instructions, and Cornelia commented on his kind tone of voice in giving his orders. This, she felt, revealed that Faraday, the son of a blacksmith, was a natural gentleman. Next Faraday took them to the Royal Institution's lecture theatre, then unoccupied.

This was Cornelia's first visit, but she was subsequently to visit it many times to hear Faraday's regular Friday evening talks. When he was on the programme the theatre would be packed with people from all ranks of society, so popular was he with both British and foreign scientists, and the public. Faraday was explaining to Andrew some new apparatus for demonstrating certain experiments, when he turned to Cornelia and said, with a mischievous smile: 'in the good old days the ladies were kept well out of the way, up there in the gallery; but even poor philosophers must submit to the inevitable, and they have come down amongst us.' To which Cornelia replied 'I hope they are not a disturbing influence!' Faraday laughed, patted her shoulder and said 'We will not talk of that now.' Conversation then turned to lines of magnetic force and Cornelia could not follow the discussion. However, she did recall that at one point Faraday said that he regretted not being a mathematician, and if he could live his life over again he would study the subject, but it was too late now. Andrew remarked that 'an electrician should be a jack-of-all trades', a trait he clearly demonstrated in his own work.

Faraday often quickly changed his expression depending on what he was talking or thinking about. He referred to his early days as a bookbinder's apprentice before he became involved with science, and Cornelia said he must be very happy in his present position and to have elevated himself above all the 'meaner aspects and lower aims of common life.' To her surprise, he shook his head, his countenance took on a look of sadness and he replied 'When I quitted business and took to science as a career, I thought I had left behind me all the petty meanesses and small jealousies which hinder man in his moral progress; but I found myself raised into another sphere, only to find poor human nature just the same everywhere, subject to the same weaknesses and the same self-seeking, however exalted the intellect.' They left the Faradays, and Cornelia must have been elated to have met the man who had been referred to as the best experimentalist in the history of science, and to have got on so well with the couple.

Faraday's discoveries and inventions in the fields of electricity, magnetism and chemistry were enormous. Among these he discovered electromagnetic induction, diamagnetism, the magnetic field round a conductor, and formulated the Law of Electrolysis. His demonstration of electromagnetic rotary devices formed the basis for electric motor technology. He popularised terms such as anode, cathode, electrode and ion. He invented an early form of bunsen burner, and discovered a number of new chemicals such as benzene. He was appointed first Fullerian Professor of Chemistry at the Royal Institution, a post to which he was appointed for life, and was awarded several medals and other honours. The S.I. unit of capacitance, the Farad, is named after him, and he is commemorated in the Faraday Constant (the charge on a mole of electrons – c. 96,485 coulombs), while Faraday's Law of Induction states that a magnetic field changing in time creates a proportional electromotive force.

In the Autumn of 1850 Cornelia and Andrew received an invitation to dine with the poet Walter Savage Landor (1775-1864) in Bath, following a letter she had sent to him:

Dear Mrs. Crosse,

No visit in this world or from another could give me greater pleasure than that which you promise me on Monday, the 14th. Come early; time is precious to me, especially such time. Can you dine at the old-fashioned hour of three? I enjoy the feast of reason; but the feast of nonsense and abandon is a better thing. If you do not keep your husband in order, I shall perhaps tempt him into a little of his epicurism. Talk of Plato! the fellow is what Carlyle would call a sham and a humbug. For dialogue and for style, too, Crosse, I venture to affirm, prefers Galileo.

Ever truly yours,
W.S.Landor.

Andrew had known Landor for some years, and the poet was among the group that Andrew had spent some days with at Torquay in 1845. On arrival at Bath, on a bright sunny day, Andrew and Cornelia found their host waiting for them in the drawing room of his lodgings in 3 River Street. The table was already laid. It was his only sitting room, and Landor lived very simply, doing his own catering, but despite this provided them with a good dinner. They had never seen a room so full of paintings, even the doors on both sides were hung with framed oil paintings. The impression was of a Bath of Sheridan's time, and in fact Landor, who was then seventy-six, knew the city in the last decade of the 18th century. He possessed few books, and those he did occupied a single shelf beside the fireplace. He had a charming smile which gave him a noble and handsome appearance, while his expressive eyes reflected his mood, whether fun, happiness or sadness. He had a very loud laugh, almost overwhelming in that small room, particularly when his dog, Pomero, barked in chorus. He and Andrew had always got on well as Landor was a republican, but his republican views were those of the 17th century. He often praised the Americans, and had many American friends, but said he could never live there as they had no cathedrals or stained glass windows!

A love of poetry was something else they had in common, and Landor was impressed that Andrew was also a prolific poet, although he decried his own efforts as usual. Landor was a very famous writer and poet, who received much critical acclaim, although this was not matched by public popularity. During his long life he produced a considerable output of work in prose, lyric poetry, political writing and epigrams in Latin. He wrote for many journals on a variety of topics. He had a headstrong and hot-headed nature, which had led him to be thrown out of Rugby School, Oxford University and, from time to time, the family home! However, he was also described as the 'kindest and gentlest of men.'

The couple often visited Landor when they stayed in a Bath hotel as they had many friends in the neighbourhood of the city. After Andrew's second marriage Landor would sometimes stay with them at Fyne Court. The winter of 1850-51 was spent at Fyne Court with Cornelia getting used to the house and working out how best to run it, while Andrew continued with his researches and began to get used to the ways of his new young bride. Those first few months at Fyne Court were difficult for Cornelia as she was used to company and attending many parties and soirées. She now found herself rather socially isolated. As she said 'the Quantock range is at once picturesque and almost uninhabited, and Taunton, the nearest town, is six miles distant. A person might walk from Broomfield, over the hills, for eleven miles, without even seeing a house or cottage, excepting dotted here and there in the distant vale.'

Another invitation to dine that Autumn came from Andrew's close friend and near neighbour Colonel Tynte of Halswell Park and his widowed daughter, Lady Cooper. It was here that Cornelia encountered an old custom, much to her surprise, which Tynte, who was eighty, liked to keep.

They dined formally at seven o'clock with 'servants more numerous than guests.' They then retired to the drawing room but at ten o'clock two footmen entered carrying a table which could seat six people. Then, almost like a theatrical scene, came two more servants carrying a dainty hot supper. The supper was announced ready and Tynte pressed his guests to partake of supper and for the gentlemen to have a stirrup cup. However, as all the guests had partaken of a very good, substantial dinner only a short time before, they all declined. Tynte did not seem surprised that this supplementary meal was declined, but was determined to maintain this tradition which dated to an earlier century.

Cornelia learned to enjoy walking, something that Andrew had always indulged in. It was during this first winter that Andrew took her for what she described as a 'very romantic walk'. They walked to the port of Minehead on the north Somerset coast, a distance of eighteen miles (29 km) from Fyne Court. Setting out early in the morning, by noon they reached a point just below Will's Neck, the highest point in the Quantocks at 1,260 feet. (384 m). There they sat and enjoyed the picnic that Cornelia had carried in a small basket and enjoyed the magnificent views of Bridgwater, Glastonbury Tor, the Bristol Channel and, to the west, the fastness of Exmoor. It was here that Samuel Taylor Coleridge and John Thelwall, a notorious republican and French sympathiser, had sat in 1797 watching the sun set. Coleridge turned to Thelwall and said 'Citizen John, this is a fine place to talk treason in.' 'Nay, citizen Samuel' said Thelwall, 'it is rather a place to make a man forget that there is any necessity for treason.' This was in their 'setting up their own Republic' period, an idea Coleridge had first dreamed up with Southey and Poole around the end of the 18th century. This had worried the government, who had heard about them via Dr Lysons of Bath who had overheard his servants, who came from the area, discussing them. Lord Portland, the Home Secretary, sent down an agent, James Walsh, to check them out in 1798.

He had a budget of twenty pounds, but after three weeks he was able to report they were neither French or spies, even if they did unsettle the locals! No doubt his inquiries locally would have disclosed the nearby owner of Fyne Court's republican views, so Richard, Andrew's father, probably also featured in Walsh's report to the government. Although Andrew had been a great friend of Tom Poole, who Walsh regarded as a dangerous man since his Men's Friendly Society gave him the 'intire command of 150 poor men', he had never met Coleridge, whose last visit to Somerset had been in 1807. As they sat there enjoying the winter sun, Andrew and Cornelia too talked of revolution, not of the political kind, but the major changes and revolutions that science and industry in Britain were undergoing at that time. That first day they walked twelve miles (19.3 km) as far as the small port of Watchet, with its narrow winding streets, fishermen's cottages and a pier built to protect the quay in 1801. This was the harbour from which Coleridge's ill-fated 'ancient mariner' sailed ('below the kirk, below the hill') a poem which, so it is believed, he began writing in the Bell Inn in Watchet's Market Street. Andrew was carrying a brass telescope and a knapsack on his back, and in his hand a long handled geological hammer.

Night was falling when Andrew and Cornelia finally reached Watchet since they had got lost several times on the intricacies of the sheep paths which were the only 'roadways' over the hills. By the time they reached the port both were dishevelled and must have presented a notable sight as they came down from the hills. It was here that they spent the night, tired but happy. After a hearty breakfast they set off once again, Andrew pointing out to Cornelia the unusual strata of alabaster rock to be found at Blue Anchor Bay, which was used to make monuments in local churches. After an easier and more level walk than the previous day, they reached Minehead, a further six miles (9.6 km). This had recently had several new houses built, and many cottages were let to visitors during the summer. A contemporary guide book notes that 'here and there an attempt at improvement has been made, and during the Summer Season visitors, in search of health, begin to appear from Bristol, Cheltenham, Wales and even London.' The young Cornelia had managed the walk without difficulty, and it had proved no obstacle to Andrew, despite his age. He often used to walk from Fyne Court to Minehead before breakfast. By rising at three o'clock in the morning he was, by nine o'clock, sitting down for breakfast in Minehead!

Andrew and Cornelia settled into life at Fyne Court. The builders had dealt with many of the problems in the house that had developed during the previous few years when Andrew was spending much of his time in London following the death of his first wife. So at least the house was more comfortable than it had been for a good few years. Andrew spent the mornings on estate business, marking and inspecting trees, and superintending the many other tasks required. The afternoons were devoted to the great love of his life, science. If the weather was bad he had fires lit in his laboratory, which had two fireplaces, and there were always things to do. Cornelia quickly became involved in his research, and far from the days dragging, as she had at first feared because of the limited social life, she found the days were not long enough!

Batteries had to be taken apart or renewed, there were the zinc rods to be cast for the Daniell batteries and copper cylinders fitted into up to 150 bottles which, with their broken necks, were used as battery jars. At this point Andrew was using both Voltaic Piles in series to form batteries and Daniell batteries. Vessels used to produce crystals had to be regularly checked and the batteries refreshed or renewed. Andrew was still constructing items of apparatus, and there seemed to be no diminution in his interest in the mysteries of the natural world. However, money was tight, and Andrew, with his tendency to look for the latest developments in science and industry, was always trying out new techniques in agriculture or mining with which he had long been involved, on and off, not only to save money, but in the optimistic hopes of actually making some. Around this time an account of Andrew and his work appeared in an American publication. In this it says that 'Crosse is a retired country gentleman, and has spent twelve thousand dollars on his apparatus.' It goes on to explain that he is 'living in a republican style of simplicity.' In reality this was due, at least in part, to economic necessity!

This was not the first time that Andrew had come to the notice of American scientists, since *The American Journal of Science & Arts* had reprinted an account of his mite experiments in January 1839 that had appeared in *The Annals of Electricity, Magnetism & Chemistry* (1838). Cornelia estimated that his scientific equipment had cost him between three and four thousand pounds, which today would equate to £300,000 – £375,000. He often used to say that if ever he became immensely rich he would use the money to build a national scientific institution, and give it a rich endowment for educational purposes. However, he would refuse to accept a huge fortune if it was offered to him on condition that he had to keep a great retinue of servants and live the fashionable life.

For whatever reasons this twenty-two year old girl and a sixty-five year old gentlemen scientist married, it was not for money, as was so often the case in those days, as neither of them was particularly wealthy. While they only shared their lives for a relatively short time, it was to be a happy and rewarding experience for both, and gave Andrew a new lease of life. An interesting insight into how Andrew seems to have viewed Cornelia can be found in an undated letter, which must date to 1853, to his friend John Eagles: 'My own health is surprisingly good, far better than I expected, or deserved. I have indeed much to thank my Maker for, who has raised up to me in my latter days (after a life of repeat trials, such as few have been called on them to suffer) the kindest, most affectionate, and truest friend I have ever met with.'

CHAPTER TEN

The Best of Times, the Worst of Times: 1851–55

The year 1851 saw the birth of Andrew's sixth grandchild, Mary Hamilton Crosse born to John and Susanna. Andrew had sent a poem to Walter Savage Landor that year and received a letter in reply:

Dear Crosse,

Let me thank you for your spirited lines, and rejoice in your perfect happiness. In return for your poem, I can only send you the one I wrote last. Next week another will appear in the Examiner more worthy of your notice, because it refers to the greatest and purest of all public men, your countryman and neighbour, Blake.

Landor several times urged Andrew to publish a volume of his poems, but he declined to do so as he did not think they were worthy of a wider audience beyond his family and friends. That year also saw Andrew and Cornelia back in London, staying at their house in Charles Street for three weeks. This was not only to continue their active social life there, but to enable Andrew to go to numerous scientific meetings and lectures, some of which Cornelia also attended. Andrew had the opportunity to meet a number of foreign scientists, of which there seemed to be many in London that year. It was during this period that someone remarked to him that he was 'really a citizen of the world.' The other reason for going to London that year was to visit one of the greatest events of the age, the Great Exhibition held inside the Crystal Palace, built over and around the trees in Hyde Park. It was opened by Queen Victoria on the 1 May. The couple spent the morning at the British Museum and found themselves almost alone in the building as most people had gone to the Crystal Palace. Both were fascinated by the Egyptian rooms and they spent time studying the Assyrian marbles from Nineveh. Andrew had always been interested in items of antiquity, having the view that these artefacts were the symbols of civilisations that had passed into history, and so demonstrated that nothing would last, but at the same time showing how mankind was able to progress.

They spent the afternoon at the Great Exhibition, but they must have visited it more than once, as did many of the five to six million visitors. The Crystal Palace was open for 140 days and occupied a site of twenty-six acres (10.5 ha), forming a showcase for British industry, crafts and arts, along with wonders of the Empire. Queen Victoria visited every other day for three months, although there is no indication that Andrew and Cornelia saw her. However, with his views on royalty, Andrew would not have made any particular effort to do so. With 13,000 exhibitors in nearly a mile of galleries it covered a million square feet (92,00 sq m) of floor space. During this trip Andrew and Cornelia went to an art exhibition, but he does not seem to have been particularly impressed with what he saw. In a letter to John Eagles he noted 'when at the Exhibition of pictures, we heard the most extravagant praises of all that least resembled nature, and the greatest abuse lavished on all that had the misfortune to approach it.' In this letter he also expresses another opinion: 'I must confess, however, that in my opinion the intellect of my fellow creatures is much lowered within the last few years. What with spirit-rapping, mesmerisms, table-turning, &c. – an acceptation of all that is absurd and vile, and a rejection of all that is sublime and noble.' Interest in spiritualism, which originated with ghostly rapping heard by Margaret and Kate Fox in the United States in 1848, rapidly spread.

Within a few years there were thousands of disciples of Spiritualism, as this new movement was called, in America, Britain and Europe, all hoping to get messages from the dead. It was popular in London in the 1850s and one of the most common methods of communicating with the departed at that time was 'table turning', the spirit communicating its message by movements of a table. At the height of this craze Andrew and Cornelia were at a dinner party with Richard Cobden (1804-65) and John Bright (1811-

89). Both were famous politicians and had jointly founded the Anti-Corn Law League in 1839 to oppose the duties on imported corn, which raised the price of food to the benefit of landowners but the disadvantage of ordinary people. Cobden was also a passionate anti-war campaigner since he believed prosperity needed peace. Bright was one of the greatest orators of the 19th century. He entered Parliament in 1843 and was a minister three times in Gladstone's Cabinet. A Quaker, he was an active campaigner for free trade and political reform, and wanted to establish equality for both individuals and peoples.

When dinner was over and the gentlemen joined the ladies in the drawing room, Bright proposed that they should try table turning. The party arranged themselves around a table and placing both their hands on it palm down, waited eagerly for a manifestation. They waited and waited, but nothing happened, and people were growing restless. Bright urged them to have patience. Cobden, who was sitting next to Cornelia gave her a mischievous glance, which she rightly interpreted, and they both began to move the table by subtle movements of their hands assisted by their feet against the table legs. 'It's going, it's going' cried Bright in triumph, and looking round the company saw that Cornelia and Cobden were laughing, and suddenly realised what they had done. He cried 'Oh, it's all a trick; I see Mrs. Crosse and Cobden are in league.' To which Cornelia replied 'Of course I am in the League, as the wife of a free-trader is bound to be.'

Cornelia often heard the poems of Elizabeth Barrett Browning (1806-61) praised by both Landor and John Kenyon. While Andrew had known her for many years, Cornelia had not met her. She thought that Elizabeth's work was much better than that of her husband Robert Browning. So she was very pleased in 1851 to receive an invitation to dinner from John Kenyon specially to meet her. The guests only numbered fourteen as Kenyon 'disliked a crowded dinner table.' Only Elizabeth was present as her husband was otherwise engaged, although Cornelia was later to meet him. However, the mental picture of this famous poetess that Cornelia had conceived from her writings was to be shattered, and obviously Andrew had not clearly described Elizabeth to her. Cornelia wrote:

In reality, at least to my finding, she had a distinctly hard-featured, non-sympathetic aspect; the brow was a noble soul-case, and the eyes were dark and penetrating, but the mouth was hard and immobile for any play of expression, while the lower jaw showed something of the strength of obstinacy. She wore her hair in ringlets, which, falling very much over her face, and when seen in profile, suggested the unpleasing idea of blinkers, that harshly cut across the graceful curves of brow and cheek. It was this style of arranging her dark hair that made Mrs. Browning look, not old fashioned – for that would have given a touch of sentiment – but strangely out of fashion.

Her slight pretty figure was rather disguised than set off by garments that fell lopping round her; but thank Heaven! she was entirely and utterly free from the bad taste of the self-styled clever women, who acknowledge themselves to be failures, as women, by apeing masculine style of dress and address. In conversation Mrs. Browning seemed reserved, with a certain proud aloofness of manner; at the same time there was a listening reticence in her attitude that did not help the playful tossing to and fro of talk.

At other dinner parties they met Mrs Milliner Gibson, as that 'somewhat overdressed lady was called, with her magic bracelet of amber beads' as Cornelia described her. They also met Dr John Ashburner of Wimpole Street, who had phials of 'mesmerised water', in which, so he claimed, if you looked long enough, you could see all your past life. In 1867 he published *Notes and Studies on Animal Magnetism and Spiritualism*. This was a period when many new discoveries were being made in such 'mysterious forces' (at least to the general public) as electricity and magnetism. Many people thought that the spirits were communicating using some form of energy, commonly thought to be a type of electricity, and Michael Faraday was pestered by many people writing to him asking him to explain this 'new force' scientifically.

One day, when discussing this craze with Andrew, he said that 'poor electricity is made accountable for half the follies of the age.' So to prove to himself that spiritualism was in no way scientific he resolved to go to a seance and invited Andrew to accompany him. At this seance a young female clairvoyant was supposed to go into a clairvoyant state when the apex of a rock crystal was pointed at her. She would then give a message from those who had 'passed over'. It was obvious to the pair that, despite her glazed appearance, the girl could see the movements of the crystal. So when Faraday was invited to move the crystal, Andrew handed his hat to Faraday who used it as a screen so the clairvoyant could not see it. He had no sooner done this when the girl completely failed to respond to the movements of the now (to her) invisible crystal. Andrew and Faraday were not impressed! The pair attended other seances and were equally unimpressed, and both felt this whole line of investigation was a fiasco and unworthy of serious consideration by scientists. Faraday wrote to his friend Dr Christian Schonbein:

> I have not been at work except in turning the tables upon the table-turners, nor should I have done that, but that so many inquiries poured in upon me, that I thought it better to stop the inpouring flood by letting all know, at once, what my views and thoughts were. What a weak, credulous, incredulous, unbelieving, superstitious, bold, frightened – what a ridiculous world ours is, as far as [it] concerns the mind of man! How full of inconsistencies, contradictions, and absurdities it is!

However, such views did not stop the growing popularity of Spiritualism, which increased markedly when photographs of 'spirits' began to appear from the 1860s. Back in Somerset, there was hardly anyone who was interested in experimental science except for Andrew's second son Robert, who had become curate of Broomfield Church in 1835. He married in 1837 and moved to Kingston St. Mary, but this was less than two miles (3.3 km) from Broomfield, so he was still in close contact with his father. It was almost only Robert and a friend of his, Dr Edward Draper, an apothecary of Middle Street, Taunton, who had an interest in chemistry, that Andrew was able to hold scientific discussions with. Andrew and his wife were certainly not alone at Fyne Court as is clear from the 1851 census, which shows that not only were he and his wife present but so was his mother-in-law, Cornelia Elizabeth Berkeley, and one of his wife's other sisters, the fourteen year old Ellen. In addition, Edward Cox, a solicitor and owner of *The Somerset County Gazette,* along with his wife and daughter, was also staying at Fyne Court. Also listed are two house servants, Ann Barrudy (twenty-nine) and Eliza Wiltshire (twenty-three).

Unfortunately, Andrew lost the company of Robert when he moved early in 1852 to take up the post of Rector in the parish of Ockham in Surrey, a living that had been offered to him by Lord Lovelace. Friends from London and other parts of the country, both scientists and those from the world of literature, frequently travelled to and stayed at Fyne Court. Andrew enjoyed playing the genial host, and these were happy and interesting occasions for all involved, consisting not only of serious intellectual discussion but amusing chat and the playing of parlour games. One summer Andrew and Cornelia had several American friends staying at Fyne Court and celebrated, with their guidance, the fourth of July with all due ceremony. Another notable visitor to Fyne Court, who stayed with them on several occasions, was John Gassiot (1797-1877), the largest importer of port wine at that time. He was an ardent electrician and spent huge amounts on buying every novel electrical apparatus invented in Britain and abroad. He spent a lot of time on improving the Voltaic battery and invented a delicate apparatus for testing the presence of electricity. He wrote a number of papers and spoke at meetings of the British Association for the Advancement of Science (BAAS).

While at Fyne Court Gassiot often enjoyed a 'superb cider mellowed by electricity' as Andrew had perfected a method of stopping the fermentation of cider at the optimum point. In October, after Andrew and Cornelia had returned to Fyne Court following their visits to the Great Exhibition, a group of friends came to stay, but unfortunately Landor was unable to join them due to illness. A letter from him explained that he was furious at being laid up with whooping cough, which he had as a child, and thought he had done with seventy-two years earlier! This group, which included his two old school friends, John Eagles and John Kenyon, spent a week at Fyne Court, having a particularly happy and enjoyable time. Eagles reduced Andrew and the others to tears of laughter by reading out part of a letter he had recently received from his estate manager. It had been a very wet season and he gave a dismal account of everything. The hay was spoilt, the meadows were under water, the sheep had foot rot and he concluded by saying 'Tis wet everywhere – everything wet – except the cow, and she's dry!' Eagles, wrote an account of this visit, entitled 'Letter to Eusebius about Many Things', which was published in *Blackwood's Magazine* in January 1853. Extracts from this are enlightening as it describes Fyne Court at this period and shows some recent changes Andrew had made, having taken a new interest in the estate since his recent marriage to Cornelia:

> 5 o'clock. Just come in from a walk with the philosopher and our mutual friend [John Kenyon]; and before I dress for dinner, sit down to realise on paper this place and its improvements since I last saw it. It is a situation of singular retirement, amid the hills, yet at the head of a valley lengthening into some distance, sufficient for those various atmospheric perspectives which are the breath of beauty. Its character is pastoral. There is nothing dressed here, not even immediately about the house; but there are beautiful trees. The beeches prevail, whose silver stems so gracefully make a light in the deep wood shades.

> The large pond above the house has now an accessible path, where before there was a hedge; and as you ascend to it, the trees look very high and their large stems imposing. This is an improvement. I could wish the solitary swan had a companion. Poor bird he has lost his mate, and sails now gracefully up to greet every visitor. Philosopher should do as he would be done by; he is happy now no solitary bird; blessed be his nest! As we skirted the valley by the upland, the extent opened before us. The long hill-sides, heathery and of wood, not continuous, but with outstretching and receding patches, that slightly broke without destroying the unity, give a great air of a wild untouched freedom to the whole valley.

On 5 February 1852 Isabella gave birth to Andrew's seventh grandchild, who was named Alice Hamilton Foster, and Cornelia gave birth to Andrew's first child of his second marriage on 31 May that year. He was named Andrew Frederick and baptised in Broomfield Church on 11 July. On 11 August the following year Isabella gave birth to Andrew's eighth grandchild, John Davy Hamilton Foster. From comments in various letters of the period 1851-53 it seems that Cornelia often seems to have been ill, although its nature is unspecified. One possible reason for illness among certain people at this time may have been because vegetables were not regarded as a source of nourishment by the upper class, and fruit was regarded as positively harmful for young children, while large amounts of meat were consumed. Despite these bouts of illness she was still very active at Fyne Court and she and Andrew also regularly went to London where they pursued an active social life.

They met Elizabeth and Robert Barrett Browning when dining at Kenyon's house in Wimbledon in 1852. In a letter to Dr Brittan dated 7 May 1854, things seem to have taken a turn for the better as Andrew says 'We are all well here, my wife is much better than she has been for many years.' One wonders if Andrew was just unlucky with the health of his family or whether it was because Fyne Court, being located so high in the Quantocks, is generally two degrees colder than at the base of the hills and is very damp. Even in dry weather the grass remains green because of the damp night air. Could this have contributed to his family's frequent illnesses? The parish doctor lived at Bridgwater, a long way from Broomfield and the more isolated cottages on the hills, which was particularly difficult if the patient or their family's only means of transport was walking. There was a hospital at Taunton, and as early as 1810 Andrew is noted in *The Taunton Courier* as giving a donation to it.

So Cornelia felt it was her duty to establish a dispensary for the poor of the district at Fyne Court. This was mostly run by Cornelia, but in more serious or difficult cases she would consult Andrew. She had to get to know the local terms for some ailments. One day a young woman came to her dispensary and said 'Pleaas, marm, father's amoist mazed and muddled wi' the information in his head.' She was not implying that her father had learnt too much, but that he had an inflammation (information or sometimes infloration). Somewhat optimistically the young lady had brought along a pint bottle for a 'little small drop of brandy.' Brandy was considered a sure remedy for all cases of inflammation! In the case of rheumatism and the occasional case of partial paralysis, Andrew used his medical electrical device, often with successful results. Other terms Cornelia had to learn would have been brown titis or brown kitties (bronchitis), interjections (indigestion), pewmoaner (pneumonia) and screwmaticks or screws (rheumatism). Like most parts of the country at that time, it was sometimes visited by quack doctors, often to be found at the local fairs selling remedies to treat every complaint, often in the form of a single 'magic remedy' for all ills – something that Andrew, as a scientist, heartily disapproved of.

On the whole Andrew's tenants and neighbours high up in the hills kept in fair health, but this certainly did not apply to Andrew's own family! The area had long been known for the longevity of its inhabitants, with many exceeding the three score years and ten. One of the Crosse's old nurses lived to be nearly a hundred. Possibly by luck, as she was fond of saying that people should 'take their meals regular' and would point out that all her life she had eaten 'a dew bit, and breakfast, a stay bit, and dinner, a nommet and crummet, and a bit after supper.' This makes eight meals a day! This was in the days when medicines were often black draughts, Croton Oil (a foul-smelling oil used as a purgative) and Epsom Salts. She was in the habit of mixing together all the doctor's medicine left after any illness on the basis that what had cost money should not be wasted!

Andrew and Cornelia enjoyed entertaining at Fyne Court. Landor was a regular visitor and Cornelia often corresponded with him. He got on well with Andrew and seemed to be entranced by the beautiful young Cornelia. He was fond of children and was always interested in the progress of their, then, only child, Andrew. In a letter written early in 1853 discussing, among other things, a forthcoming visit he was planning to Fyne Court, he went on: 'I am not too old to be a playfellow to your little boy, but I suspect he will look at me with more gravity than I at him. Two years hence we shall be nearer of a match …'. Unfortunately age was catching up with Landor, and in a letter written later that year to Cornelia he says: 'Alas!, my dear kind friend, in a very few days I shall enter my seventy-ninth year. Your commands ought always to be obeyed; but there is a commander-in-chief who may direct my march to other quarters than the pleasant ones at Fyne Court … Greatly do I doubt whether I shall ever move again from Bath … To-day I feel passably well again. You and Crosse will complete my recovery by coming and dining with me …'.

When in London Andrew and Cornelia often dined with their friend Dr John Percy (1817-89) and his wife Grace. Percy was a physician who had carried out research in physiology before completely changing direction when he began to study minerals and later founded the Metropolitan School of Science in London. In 1846 he worked with David Forbes (1828-76) a geologist, chemist and mining engineer, who had spent ten years as a mining superintendent in Norway; and Professor William Miller (1801-80), Professor of Mineralogy at Cambridge University on the crystallisation of slags. In 1840 Miller went to work for Professor von Liebig, who had visited Andrew at Fyne Court in 1848, at his Giessen laboratory. In 1845 he was appointed Professor of Chemistry at King's College, and in 1848 developed a method of extracting silver from its ore. In 1851 he became the first Professor of Metallurgy at the Government School of Mines in London, and put together a collection of metallurgical specimens that numbered 4,000 on his death, when it was donated to the British Museum's zoological department. He was 'possessed of ample means' and had wide ranging literary and artistic interests, so that the dinner parties at his house in Craven Hill, Bayswater, London, were attended by a very mixed group.

Andrew and Cornelia made many new acquaintances from people such as Edwin Landseer (1802-73) and his family. Landseer was one of the most famous artists of the day, known for his paintings of horses, dogs and stags. Among his best known sculptures were the lions in Trafalgar Square. Among other artists, they knew John Leech (1817-64), an illustrator and cartoonist for *Punch Magazine*, who produced over 2,000 cartoons from 1841 to his death, and Solomon Hart (1806-81), the most famous Jewish artist working in England during the 19th century. He was the first Jewish member of the Royal Academy, where he was Professor of Painting between 1854-63. They also knew Sir William Boxall (1800-79) who was a professional portrait artist, and appointed the second Director of the National Gallery in 1866 as successor to Charles Eastlake. Another famous artist they met was Susan Durant (1827-73), a well-known sculptress. One of her works, the Forsaken Shepherdess, was placed in the Mansion House in London, the first sculptured public work ever commissioned from a female artist in England. She also exhibited works at the Great Exhibition in 1851, and shocked society by having a child by the French sculptor, Baron Henri de Triqueti.

Andrew and Cornelia also got to know members of the acting profession such as Douglas William Jerrold (1803-57) who was a dramatist and playwright, and contributed articles to *Blackwood's Magazine*, *The New Monthly*, *The Athenaeum* and *Punch* from its second issue in 1841 to his death. He had a reputation as a brilliant wit and conversationalist. Among other notable members of society Andrew and Cornelia met was Alfred Elmore (1815-81) an Irish born British painter, Charles Knight (1791-1873) who published many editions of Shakespeare's works, including an illustrated version in eight volumes between 1839-42, and Mr Ferguson, author of *The History of Architecture*. Percy asked Andrew and Cornelia to accompany him and his wife on an expedition to the Pyrenees, but it this never came about. Probably a disappointment for Cornelia who had said on their honeymoon that she would like to take Andrew to a really impressive mountain range.

In 1853 Andrew, was once again short of money, and had to sell off part of his mother's estate that had come to him on the death of his brother Richard in 1846. He sold a significant part of this inheritance including the former Blaxhold Manor to Meshach Brittan of Bristol. However, ever optimistic as far as trying to find a way to improve his finances, he turned once again to the Broomfield mine which had been opened and abandoned in 1825 and again in 1845. This time he was not alone in the enterprise and, according to *The Somerset County Herald* of 2 April 1853, 'Operations are about to be commenced on a portion of the Quantock Hills, which bid fair to create a mining district of no mean importance.' This time Andrew had partners, Colonel Hamilton, Colonel Kemys-Tynte, John Mayo and Henry Howard Molyneux Herbert, the 4th Earl of Carnarvon, who owned Tetton House, near Kingston St. Mary, which became a secondary house of the family when an Acland heiress married the second Lord Carnarvon. It was the younger sons of the Carnarvons who occupied the property. Andrew sold the land to raise money to invest in the mine. The Broomfield mine was now deepened and a new adit dug to drain water. This had three shafts, one of which, Wheal Cornelia, was named after Andrew's wife.

They set up the Broomfield Consols Copper and Silver-lead Mining Company with registered offices at 32 Moorgate Street, London and in East Reach, Taunton. The capital was £12,000 in one pound shares. Meetings of the proprietors were held every two months to review progress and audit the accounts so the mine would be 'kept free from debt and the shareholders secured from liability.' Shares could be purchased in Taunton, London, Exeter and Leeds. Hopes were high, and *The Somerset County Gazette* reported in April that year that: 'Most sanguine expectations are entertained that a perpetual source of immense wealth be opened with the Broomfield mines.' On 9 April an exciting announcement appeared in *The Mining Journal* headed 'Another Gold Discovery at Home':

> It would appear that within the past few days, gold has been discovered in the sett which, according to our informant, has been handed about. The matter seems to have excited some interest, and we hope, on an early occasion, to report further on the golden regions of England.

However, this was not confirmed, and either some had been planted to encourage investors, or perhaps it was a case of mistaken identity and it was iron pyrites, otherwise known as Fool's Gold, although this seems an unlikely mistake for experienced miners. Interestingly, an article on 'Quantock Minerals and Metals' published in 1855 stated that veins of gossan containing a notable portion of gold were frequently found in Broomfield. So perhaps gold was discovered, but too little to be worth extracting. It may also be significant that at this date Andrew was researching the extraction of both copper and gold from its ore by the use of electricity, so he must have had gold ore in his laboratory! *The Mining Journal* of 10 April reported that lead ore from the Broomfield mine had been assayed and found to contain 30 ounces of silver per ton. A further report in *The Mining Journal* of 14 May 1853 makes no further mention of gold:

> ... reported on by Captains J.H. Williams and W. Brice, and also by Messrs. George Henwood and H. English, from whose testimonies it appears evident that numerous lodes exist, on one of which, opened in depth to only 10 fathoms, it was found to be 4½ feet wide, and a fine course of ore was cut. ... A deep adit is now being driven, which will cross-cut all the lodes in one part of the sett, and give backs [working heights] of 25 to 40 fathoms; and it is recommended to erect a 50 ins. cylinder engine, which it is believed will take the mine down to a depth to pay good dividends.

This new deep adit, one mile (1.6 km) in extent from east to west, was situated below that driven by Petherick in 1845, and designed to intersect the lodes at a depth of 30 fathoms. On 17 September, William Trethevey, probably the Manager of the Broomfield mine, noted that 'at present we have six men driving the adit end, and I hope, as the ground is more favourable than it has been, that we shall cut the lode in the course of three weeks, or it may be before.' All seemed to be going well, and no doubt Andrew must have been pleased with progress. Late in 1853 John Kenyon and John Eagles came to stay at Fyne Court for a few days. One evening they were sitting in the music room / laboratory and Andrew remarked 'I have often thought that this world is a place of punishment, where we are called upon to suffer for sins committed in some former state. But we know nothing of the past, of the present, of the future, except relatively; we can only pray.' Following this statement there was a thoughtful silence, when suddenly the room was lit by a flash of light followed by a loud detonation, making them all jump. This came from the organ gallery. Before anyone could say anything there came another blinding flash and crack, a few seconds of darkness, then another series of flashes and cracks every few seconds.

The party was spellbound by this display, but soon the discharges became weaker and the intervals between them longer. In the meantime Andrew had opened a window and, peering out, saw that snowflakes were gently falling, and already the ground was being covered with a white blanket. All was absolutely still and silent outside, and all present were awed at this display of nature's hidden power, only revealed by Andrew's scientific equipment. On examination it was found that the receiving balls connected to his 'exploring wire' had accidentally been left about seven inches apart, a distance that caused the flash that would otherwise have occurred noiselessly. This was to be the last time that all three of the old school fellows were to be together at Fyne Court.

On one occasion, when Andrew and Cornelia were Landor's guests, having visited him on their way to Wimbledon to stay with John Kenyon, they had a spirited discussion about Shakespeare and Milton. Andrew maintained that Shakespeare and Milton were on an equal footing, something that

Cornelia completely disagreed with. He teased Cornelia by saying that her sex was angry with the author of *Paradise Lost* as he had described their mother Eve as 'of outward form elaborate, of inward less exact.' Landor's view was that Milton was 'among the least witty of mankind, and seldom attempts a witticism unless he is angry.' Andrew was Vice President of the Somerset Archaeological and Natural History Society, and attended as many of their meetings as he could. One would expect that such gatherings would be sedate and peaceful affairs, but this was certainly not the case on one occasion. The meeting was held at Glastonbury, whose main fame rests on its ruined abbey where strong local tradition and written accounts dating back to the 12th century say that King Arthur was buried. The first paper was by Mr Jones about the finding of the king's body by medieval monks and its mode of reburial. Many local people had come to hear the talk and all were happy with what this learned man and said about their local hero.

However, during discussion following the talk Mr Freeman, an historian who had a tendency to bully those more ignorant than himself, made a fierce attack on King Arthur's historic authenticity, at which a collective growl rose from the many locals in the audience. Despite this he went on tearing into the beliefs of local people, and told them it was crass stupidity to talk about the burial place of a hero whose existence had never been proved. A dozen leapt to their feet shouting out their reasons for believing in the King's existence, the meeting now beginning to resemble a rowdy political meeting. Several people stormed out of the meeting and it took Andrew some time to calm the situation so the remaining members could hear Mr Warre give his less controversial talk on the ancient Cangi tribe and their cattle stations.

Andrew and Cornelia regularly stayed in London, and often went to dine with John Kenyon, where they continued to meet such notable people as Sir Charles and Lady Lyell. Sir Charles was the most renowned geologist of the day, and his book *Principles of Geology* (1829), was incredibly influential. Another of his very influential works was *Elements of Geology* (1837). He was both a popular and a controversial figure as he maintained that geologists should work on the basis that the visible causes of change are the same kind and of the same intensity as those that have always acted.

This made a big impact on Charles Darwin, who knew Lyell when he was at university. Lyell also stressed the importance of field work, and was the first person to discuss metamorphic rocks and their age. Other people they met at Kenyons included, the Longman brothers, Thomas (1804-79) and William (1813-77), who ran the famous Longman's publishing house that had been founded in 1754, and the surviving members of the Wordsworth and Coleridge families.

Someone whom Andrew found he had something in common with that he met at the Kenyons was Sir Charles Eastlake. Sir Charles (1793-1865) was a painter, gallery owner, writer and collector, and one subject that he and Andrew undoubtedly discussed was Napoleon. One of his most well-known works was 'Napoleon on Board the *Bellerophon* in Plymouth Sound', painted in 1815 and now in the National Maritime Museum, Greenwich. He had hired a boat when the former Emperor was on board the naval vessel off Plymouth, and had sketched him from the boat, so he and Andrew must both have been on the water at the same time as he too had also gone to Plymouth to see the former Emperor. Sir Charles became the first Keeper of the National Gallery in 1843, was President of the Royal Academy, and was knighted in 1850. In 1853 he became first President of the Photographic Society, and first Director of the National Gallery in 1855.

Charles Babbage (1791-1871), who Andrew had met on a number of occasions, was also a regular attendee at Kenyon's dinners. A mathematician, philosopher, inventor and mechanical engineer, he went to Trinity College, Cambridge, but disliked the way they taught mathematics so transferred to Peterhouse College in 1812, the same year he founded the Analytical Society. He was a founding member of the Royal Astronomical Society in 1820 and the Statistical Society in 1834. He achieved fame for his design of a programmable computer, which he first proposed in a letter to Sir Humphrey Davy in 1822, the year he began constructing his device. However, it was not completed because of financial problems and personality clashes. Although mechanical, his machine is very similar to a modern computer. The data and program memory were separated, the operations were instruction based, the control unit could make conditional jumps, and the machine had a separate 1 / 0 unit.

Ada, Countess of Lovelace, a friend of Andrew and of his oldest son, John, designed a way of writing programs for his computer. He later designed an improved version, the Difference Engine No. 2, which he tinkered with until his death, but which was not fully built until 1989-91 by staff at the Science Museum in London. Cornelia regarded Babbage as being very interesting but an egotistical talker. He told her that he had predicted as long ago as 1839 that steam ships would sail to America in seven days, and the subject of his calculating machine was an endless monologue. He was also very fond of talking about Ada, who was a frequent visitor to Fyne Court, which is where Kenyon had first met her, but regarded her as a woman of remarkable intellect but too mathematical for his taste.

They also met there William Macready (1793-1873) actor, manager and diarist. He was a leading figure in the development of acting and production techniques of the 19th century, which made possible the art of the modern theatre. He retired from the stage in 1851. The last part he played being Macbeth, his favourite. It must have been interesting dining with him as he was described as having 'startling mannerisms'. Andrew and Cornelia went, with Dr Percy and his wife, to the first night of the revival of 'Sardanapalus' by Lord Byron at the Prince's Theatre on 13 June 1853. Macready had starred in the original play in 1834, but the revival starred Charles Keene as Sardanapalus, King of the Assyrians. They may also have wanted to see it as they not only knew Macready but Byron's daughter, Ada. Andrew was impressed with the production as it was performed with close attention to historically correct detail. No sooner had they taken their seats when someone behind touched Andrew on the shoulder and said 'Ah, I am very glad to see you here.' They recognised the voice of Michael Faraday. This meeting added greatly to their enjoyment of the evening, especially as they had a good discussion about the play after the performance. Cornelia was impressed at Faraday's ability to discuss so many subjects outside science. After they parted Dr Percy told them that he often met Faraday at exhibitions and plays in London.

While dining with other friends, the Spences, they were introduced to other well-known scientists. Among the foreign scientists they met were Adolphe Quetelet (1796-1874) an astronomer and statistician, who founded and was the first Director of the Royal Observatory in Brussels. Cornelia described him as a 'noble looking man, whose conversation was full of grave interest.' Also Henri-Etienne Sainte-Claire Deville (1818-81) who discovered aluminium in 1827, and was convinced that aluminium could be produced so cheaply it would replace iron pots and pans and even the roofs of houses would be covered with it. He was appointed Professor of Chemistry at the Ecole Normale Superieure, Paris in 1851. However, the extraction of aluminium from its ore was not a commercial proposition until 1886. They also met the eminent French chemist Jean-Baptiste Dumas (1800-84), who made many valuable contributions to organic chemistry. One of life's irritations, as far as he was concerned, was to share the same surname as the author of the famous novel, *The Count of Monte Cristo,* and he was often mistaken for the writer. In France he was known as Dumas le savant, while the novelist jocularly referred to himself as Dumas l'ignorant.

The Broomfield mine, of which Andrew had so much hope after all the initial high expectations of profits for all concerned, proved a disappointment to him for the third time. There is only one more reference to the mine in *The Mining Journal*. On 4 February 1854 an announcement, from 32 Moorgate Street, London announced:

The Broomfield Consols Copper and Silver-Lead Mining Company

A General Meeting of the above Company will be held at these offices on Thursday, the ninth day of February next, at two o'clock, for the purpose of taking into consideration the report of Captain Nicholas Vivian, and the continuance of the works at the mine – By Order of the Committee.'

The report by the Mine Captain was unfavourable, and the mine soon closed, never to be reopened. Andrew, and the others involved, probably lost money on the enterprise, and it is telling that Andrew's wife, Cornelia, in her book *Memoirs Scientific and Literary of Andrew Crosse the Electrician,* makes no mention of the mining operation at all. The year 1854 also proved to be a mixture of happiness and deep sadness for Andrew regarding family matters. On 3 April his eighth grandchild, John Davy Hamilton

Foster, the son of Isabella and Thomas, died aged eight months. Happiness because Andrew and Cornelia's second son was born in late April or early May. Named Landor Richard, he was baptised in Broomfield Church on 14 May. Walter Savage Landor must have been overjoyed that Andrew and Cornelia had named their child after him. The child's second name was presumably after Andrew's brother Richard, although his third son by his first wife was also called Richard, but he had died at the age of twenty-five in 1839.

As a family orientated man, he must have been very happy at this addition to his new family, but this was soon to be tinged with sadness since, on 8 June 1854, Andrew's third grandchild, John Richard Davy Hamilton Crosse, the son of Robert and Eliza, died aged twelve. However, more births occurred that year as John and Susanna gave birth to Andrew's ninth grandchild, Susan Hamilton Crosse, and his daughter Isabella gave birth to his tenth grandchild, Robert Davy Hamilton Foster on 17 November. Like Andrew and his first wife in 1819, this was in the same year that she had lost a child. The Autumn of 1854 was a busy one for both Andrew and Cornelia, as he makes clear in a letter, dated 30 September 1854, written to Theresa, Cornelia's unmarried sister:

> My dear Theresa,
> Thanks for your letter, which I now reply to. In the first place you may wish to know what has taken place here since your absence. Our little Babo was, you know, thin and puny; he is now grown strong and fat, and quite well. Big Babo is quite well, stout, and happy.
>
> On Monday the 11th Mr. and Mrs. Henry Philipps and their niece arrived here. On Tuesday we started for Taunton, to be present at the anniversary meeting of the Somerset Archaeological and Natural History Society. We all met at the Assembly Room, Mr. Labouchere, the member for Taunton, being in the chair. Four different papers were read, some of them interesting. After this we adjourned to the London Inn, where there was a public dinner. Cornelia was led into the room by Mr. Labouchere, who was President, and all our party sat on his right hand, and did justice to a capital dinner.

In the evening there was another meeting; I read a paper with some difficulty, for the room was so scantily lighted. The next morning the Bailiffs of the town of Taunton gave a public breakfast; but we could not attend, as we had invited the whole party to a one o'clock luncheon at our own house. Accordingly, a little before that hour, more than fifty carriages drove up to Broomfield Green; and after inspecting the church, the whole party, consisting of more than two hundred persons came down to Fyne Court.

I had prepared some experiments in the electrical room, and covered my electrical table in the music room, with a variety of choice minerals from the Quantock Hills. All these matters called forth great curiosity, and I was half killed with answering questions. Mr. Calcott, son of the eminent composer, played on the organ, and the whole was the gayest scene possible. People from very distant parts of the kingdom joined our party. We had not such a gathering since the inauguration meeting, when poor Dr. Buckland was present – almost his last appearance in public.

One of the party visiting the church asked the churchwarden to whom it was dedicated. To which he promptly replied 'To Squire Crosse.' 'Little Babo' was the five month old Landor Richard, while 'Big Babo' was the sixteen month old Andrew Frederick. Six days later, on the 19 October, Andrew and Cornelia took the train to Liverpool to attend the meeting of the British Association for the Advancement of Science (BAAS). Presumably Theresa had returned to Fyne Court by then to look after the children. She was either living at Fyne Court or was spending a lot of time there looking after her sister's children, particularly when Cornelia and Andrew were away. They were the guests of Joseph Brook Yates (1780-1855), a merchant and Fellow of the Antiquarian Society, of West Dingle Park, an area of south Liverpool. They did not know Yates and his daughter before they went to Liverpool, but Andrew had been great friends for many years with his brother, James Yates (1789-1871) of Lauderdale House, Highgate, London. James, a Fellow of the Royal Society and Fellow of the Geological Society, was well-known for his efforts to advance the use of the decimal system, which eventually did become the main system of measurement in the field of science, although not in everyday life. With

Andrew's late brother Richard being such a committed advocate of the decimal system, they must both have been friends with him.

Arriving at West Dingle Park Andrew and Cornelia found an assembly of scientists, including the great Sir Roderick Murchison (1789-1871). A geologist, he was the first to describe the Silurian system of rocks, but also did work on the geology of the South of England, Scotland, the volcanic region of the Auvergne, the south of France, the Tyrol, North Italy and Switzerland. In 1855 he was appointed Director General of the British Geological Survey and, at various times, was Director of the Royal School of Mines and the Museum of Practical Geology. Also staying were Dr William Whewell and William Hopkins, a renowned Cambridge mathematician, who used mathematics to clarify questions about the motions of glaciers, rock cleavage, the porosity of metals and the thickness of the earth's crust. He was a good addition to this lively party of scientists as he was a charming companion, had a great fund of anecdotes, and was able to talk on any subject in general or branch of science, with the exception of physiology which he thought distasteful! He had been elected President of the BAAS in 1853.

In conversation with Murchison, Andrew mentioned, in passing, an experiment he had carried out. He had placed a gold sovereign on a piece of marble with the positive terminal put between it and the coin in a dilute solution of sulphuric acid in which the negative pole was immersed. After passing a current through it, he found that carbon dioxide gas was released from the marble (lime carbonate, $CaCO_3$), and that the gold coin broke into pieces, apparently by a mechanical action. This was an additional and unexpected outcome of some of his research on making impressions in marble using gold coins and electricity. Murchison was struck by the potential of this research to account for some unexplained natural geological phenomena, and urged Andrew to write up the full details of the experiment and present them to the Chemical Section.

The formal meeting of the BAAS opened with Hopkins, as outgoing President, handing the chair to the new President, the Earl of Harrowby. Andrew had taken Murchison's advice and gave an account of his research to the Chemical Section meeting in the Sheriff's Court, entitling it 'On the Apparent Mechanical Action Accompanying Electric Transfer'. He presented in detail the experiments which he had carried out in different ways, and found that small pieces of gold from the coin had broken off. However, Professor Miller, Hopkins and a few others disagreed with Andrew's conclusion. They felt that the reason the coin broke up was because the copper in it was affected by the sulphuric acid. As a coin the gold was alloyed with copper, since pure gold would have been too soft for practical use. They suggested that if he had used pure gold then he would not have got the same result.

Andrew replied that he was quite willing to repeat the experiment with a piece of pure gold, but felt he would get the same result as it was the carbon dioxide gas that was causing the effect on the gold. In support of this Andrew produced a piece of marble which bore a dark mark on it. Professor Miller examined it and thought it was caused by the presence of copper. Andrew maintained it was the purple oxide of gold, pointing out that had the acid attacked the copper, it would have been deposited at the negative pole of the battery, and this was not the case. He was determined to pursue further investigation into this matter when he returned home. Andrew also exhibited a number of his electrically formed crystals, being well-known as an expert in electro-crystallisation, which aroused intense interest among the members.

The house party was entertained at dinner each evening by the presence of invited foreign scientists and local celebrities, while days were spent listening to presentations given to the different Sections. This was the first meeting of the 'Parliament of Philosophy' that Cornelia had attended and she was delighted and entranced. She was particularly impressed by Murchison's observations on the geology of the Hartz and Thuringerwald, and a paper by General Sir Edward Sabine (1788-1883) on terrestrial magnetism. Passions began to run high at this meeting between Murchison and Sedgwick. These two distinguished geologists had been great friends for many years, had gone on field trips with each other and together had formulated a theory on the formation of the ancient world. However, their friendship had ended when they had a serious falling out over the classification of the Palaeozoic rocks. At this meeting Sedgwick and his supporters declared war on Murchison and his supporters and loud arguments broke out in the Sections.

On the last day Sedgwick stood up and forcibly denounced his old comrade's geological views, and verbally attacked anyone who disagreed with him. Professor Sir Andrew Ramsey (1814-91), a Scottish geologist, at that time lecturer of the Government Royal School of Mines, stood and made a vehement defence of Murchison. Following this Edward Forbes (1815-54), a respected naturalist and marine biologist who had carried out research all over Europe, tried to calm things down by making a temperate speech, saying that the dispute was merely a question of nomenclature. Cornelia found all this passion very exciting, although this was certainly not Andrew's view!

That evening Cornelia was taken in to dinner by Whewell, and felt it would be wise to keep off the subject of science so, being a confident young lady, she asked him if he had read the latest new novel. Other members of this very distinguished company may well have regarded this as a frivolous question, but she was delighted to find not only had he read it, but regularly borrowed novels from a circulating library and was able to talk about all sorts of works of fiction. He told her that he was so fond of the works of Jane Austen that he read her novels once a year. He further impressed Cornelia by praising another novel, *The Favourite of Nature*, which she had also read, but had never met anyone else who had done so. Someone opposite Whewell asked him, probably mischievously, for his view on a recently published book, *The Plurality of Worlds*, which put forward the view that the earth was the only planet that was inhabited. This had been published anonymously but it was generally rumoured that Whewell was the author. He very carefully avoided acknowledging any authorship in his answer and discussed it as if it were the work of another person. Cornelia was convinced he had written it and so could not resist saying to him 'But, Dr. Whewell, though you make out that all the other planets are uninhabited, what do you say to the man in the moon?' To which he replied, joining in the joke, 'Oh yes, I will leave you the man in the moon; we can all see his face, so there's no denying him.' His answer amused the whole table. Having this beautiful, intelligent and vivacious young girl at their dinner must have made this, and the other dinner parties she and Andrew attended, very enjoyable occasions for all concerned.

On another evening Sir Roderick Murchison took Cornelia in to dinner. This was the day they had heard about the Battle of Alma, the first major engagement of the Crimean War, which took place on 20 September 1854. During the dinner Joseph Yates proposed they all drink a toast to the 'success of the British arms.' To her surprise Sir Roderick, sitting next to her, reversed his glass as the servant was about to pour out the wine. Cornelia said to him 'Not drink the health of our army, and you a soldier, Sir Roderick!' 'No' he said 'I cannot drink to the success of an unnecessary war; my long friendship with the Emperor Nicholas has made me aware that all this might have been prevented, and I believe before many years are over that statesmen will acknowledge that this is a political mistake.' This attitude shocked a number of those present. He had got to know the Czar when he had spent a few years in Russia when preparing his work, *On the Geological Structure of the Northern and Central Regions of Russia in Europe* (1841), but before taking up science he spent eight years in the British army and had seen action in the field. In 1808 he landed with the Duke of Wellington in Galicia north-west Spain, was involved in battles at Rolica and Vimeiro, and took part in the retreat to Corunna and the final battle there.

Andrew had an enjoyable time renewing his acquaintanceship with many scientists who he had not seen for a long time, although he often corresponded with them. He had the opportunity to meet a new generation of scientists, many of whom were now professionals employed by universities and in industry. Science had changed a great deal since Andrew had started his investigations nearly fifty years earlier. At that time there were few professional scientists, and those were almost exclusively to be found in the universities, but even there only a few of the colleges included this subject in the curricula, as the main emphasis was still on the classics and theology. While in Liverpool, Andrew and Cornelia went to many other social events, dinners, soirées, concerts and various festivities. Towns would compete to host British Association meetings. They were among the thirty-five guests who attended a dinner party in the Mayor's Parlour, and on another occasion they went to a soirée at the Town Hall, but found it very crowded, as many people had turned up to look at an exhibition of modern paintings, valued at fifty thousand pounds. Andrew simply commented that they were 'lit in the most tasteful and well-judged manner.' At these events they met Liverpool artists, architects and merchants, and what made a deep impression on Andrew was how these 'non-scientists' held both science and literature in high regard and were easily able to talk about them in a knowledgeable way.

Liverpool was a booming and immensely rich city at this time. Something else that made a big impression on him was a conversation he had with a rich Liverpool merchant. 'We have too much money' said this gentleman. He then continued 'To give you our definition of the word good will explain what I mean. By a good man simple hearted people mean a moral, virtuous man; at the universities I understand it means a first rate scholar, with us a good man is a man of capital, a safe debtor!' One wonders what Andrew thought of this remark! They also went to the newly built St. George's Hall on 20 September to hear the oratorio of the Creation played on the magnificent, 8,000 pipe organ. St. George's Hall was regarded as the most magnificent public building in the country at that time, and indeed the finest neo-classical building in Europe, and its opening was timed to coincide with the British Association meeting. Extracts from a letter to Miss Douglas written when Andrew and Cornelia were staying with friends at Clifton, Bristol, dated 28 September 1854, shows what he was doing at this period both in his scientific research, in which Cornelia was making her own contribution, and in making improvements to the estate:

Theresa is to return to us on Saturday, after a long series of visits. Our oldest babe is growing a fine fellow, with all his mother's love of mischief; he runs about like a lamplighter. He is the delight of his grandmother, to the discomfiture of Theresa, who is a jealous animal. I have of late been engaged in following up closely my favourite science, and have been highly successful, in the 'dropping' experiment near the laboratory, which was set in action when you were with us. I have crystals of arragonite growing at the negative end of the piece of clay-slate in some quantity; and, also what I am almost certain are crystals of quartz growing in considerable numbers on the positive end. I have also formed an entirely new mineral in brilliant octohedral crystals, now forming upon a coil of platinum wire. These crystals are composed of oxygen, silver, and copper, and such are not known in Nature, nor have they hitherto been formed by art.

Cornelia and I have been a second time to Battleborough, to prepare for the erection in the ensuing spring of some new buildings necessary for the farm. We are much pleased with the situation, which is indeed most beautiful, and which commands one of the finest views in our beautiful county. At Broomfield we are cutting down a large quantity of laurel and under cover round our house, to give a better view of the large trees, and admit the air. We have lately built a new cow-house, and taken in hand twenty-five more acres, so that Cornelia is becoming a she farmer. I have nothing to do with her farming. A new school house is now building in Broomfield, near the church; and the singing gallery is taken down in the church, and considerable improvements about to take place.

The reference to Cornelia being a 'she farmer' is because she took on the personal management of sixty acres of land she rented, and was generally successful at this enterprise although, like all farming, sometimes things were not as good as they might be, usually due to weather conditions. She had a 'factotum' who assisted her, and while he could read and write he did not seem to have had much initiative. Because Fyne Court is so high in the hills, spring was often a difficult time for the fruit trees as it was noticeably cooler there. One day Cornelia asked him what he thought of the possibilities for the fruit trees. He replied 'Please God, we shall have a terrible fine crop, but please Him or no we shall have a goodish lot.' Andrew paid for the construction of the new school house (plate 21), but had been supporting local education for many years. Initially there had only been a small, privately run 'Dame School' at Broomfield, but from 1835 Andrew was paying the salary of a teacher, although it not clear where lessons were held. The new school served the people of the village and neighbourhood until its closure in 1933. It is now used as the village hall.

In October Andrew spent a few days with his relative Henry Porter at Winslade House near Exeter. While there he received requests from some of the local Literary and Mechanics Institutes to give them a talk, something he was very happy to do. Described as the 'life of the party' while at Winslade, he amused the younger members of the household with humorous stories, of which he had a great stock. The winter was spent quietly, but not comfortably at Fyne Court as it was one of the harshest winters for many years, even in a period when winters were notably cold. He and Cornelia spent the evenings reading to each other from Gibbon's *Decline and Fall of the Roman Empire*. A letter written by Andrew, dated 16 February 1855, shows just how bad it was and how he and the family must have suffered, especially as Cornelia was seven months pregnant that February:

The weather has been the most awful I ever witnessed. Every large tree was laden with tons of ice, and when the thaw took place there was an incessant rain of icicles, which brought down with them the boughs and limbs of some of our finest trees; literally, they came 'cracking, crashing, thundering down', doing incalculable mischief to the woods and plantations. I never saw so universal a destruction of timber. The season has been very remarkable. The supply of water has been unusually scanty. The leaves had remained longer on the trees than I ever knew them. The oaks, only one month before Christmas, had all their leaves on, and were not even touched by the autumnal tint.

Today with a large fire in the music room, the thermometer is two degrees and a half [Celsius] below freezing. In endeavouring to open the lid of a tea-pot, we found it frozen hard to the pot, with a rim of ice all round it! This in front of a large wood fire. The wind is roaring awfully, and the windows are rattling in their frames. My electrical glasses are exposed to imminent danger from their fluid contents being turned to ice. I am obliged to have fires in all directions. The snow on Broomfield Hill is drifted in some places to six feet deep or more. Last night the thermometer out of doors was thirteen degrees [Celsius] below freezing, and this before midnight.

That Christmas the Crosse children were invited to a party at Miss Durant's house in London, and they had reached the point where the children had exhausted the usual games of forfeits and prizes, and had all got their fingers burnt by Snap Dragon, a game where raisins, currants and dried fruit was heaped in a shallow dish and brandy poured on top. This was set on fire and the children had to snatch the fruit, blow out the flames and eat the fruit without getting burnt. Seeing the children were getting bored, Dr Emanuel Deutsh (1829-73), a Semitic scholar and an Orientalist at the British Museum, offered to give them an entertainment. Using a towel wrapped round his head for a turban and a tin tray on his knees below the table he told them a story of a great storm, using the tray to make the sound of thunder. All were entranced by this.

Once again Andrew had bad news concerning his family, as on the 25 February 1855 his tenth grandchild, Robert Davy Hamilton Foster, the son of Isabella and Thomas, had died aged three months. However, his family soon increased again, as on 23 April Cornelia gave birth at Fyne Court to their third son who was named Ormonde. Despite this, only a few days later, she and Andrew were staying with friends in London, at 36 Russell Square. Ormonde and the other two boys remained in Somerset in the care of Cornelia's sister Theresa. Andrew was still carrying out his experiments on various aspects of electricity, presumably at Charles Street, and had considered, but decided not to go to the BAAS meeting that was to be held in Glasgow that year. Cornelia's recent ordeal did not seem to have slowed her down as they both attended a geology lecture given by Sir Charles Lyell at the Royal Institution in Albermarle Street on the 27 April, only five days after giving birth. The tickets for the talk had been supplied to Andrew and Cornelia by their old friend Michael Faraday, only three months before he died. They took tea the following day with 'poor Spence, who has lately lost his wife.' The reports from the Crimean War were concerning Andrew at that time, as they were many other people, and he was particularly moved by the letters from ordinary soldiers being published. This was the first time that the public had received so much information about a distant war almost as it happened, which had a huge influence on public opinion.

They took the opportunity to visit the Botanical Fête, which was very popular, and both were impressed by the magnificent flowers on show. On 10 May they breakfasted with Andrew's old friend John Kenyon, and there met for the first time Henry Crabb Robinson (1775-1867), a well-known diarist who travelled extensively on the continent and knew all the major figures in literature of Britain and Germany including a son of Wordsworth and a brother of Southey. The following day they dined with John Kenyon and John Eagles, which was to be the last time these three old friends would all be together. On 11 May Andrew wrote a letter to Theresa with the not too surprising news that 'Your sister is much fatigued, I therefore write to give directions about our carriage meeting us at Bridgwater station. We return on Tuesday ...'. Further on, after noting that the weather was 'horridly cold', he says 'We hope to have a letter from you to-morrow, bringing accounts of the three dear children.' They returned to Broomfield on 15 May. Ormonde was baptised in Broomfield church on 20 May. Shortly afterwards they had some friends, the Coxs, to stay, one of whom remarked that they had never seen Andrew in such good health or higher spirits. On the 22 May he had to go to a distant farm on business, and so Cornelia decided to accompany him. That day they walked seven or eight miles (11-13 km) easily with neither feeling any fatigue on their return.

The following day Andrew decided to set up the experiment that had been suggested to him at the British Association meeting the previous year. He arranged twelve Daniell batteries in series, took a large jar filled with dilute sulphuric acid, and in the bottom placed a small square of white marble and a solid piece of chemically pure gold moulded into a coin shape which he had bought from Messrs. Johnson and Matthey, gold assayers of Hatton Garden, London. About the size and shape of a florin coin, it weighed 201 grains (11.872 g). Using this setup he managed to get the carbon dioxide gas to knock off, apparently by mechanical action, twenty three grains (1.358 g) from the gold. In a previous experiment with a lower current he had succeeded in detaching six grains (0.354 g). He was very pleased as this proved that he had answered the objections of Miller, Hopkins and the others that it was the disintegration of copper that had caused the gold to break away. The chemically pure gold had no copper in it. The result was obtained in less than twenty-four hours, but Andrew decided to let the experiment run for as long as the battery charge was strong enough to cause the evolution of gas.

On Friday 25 May he gave his annual rook shooting dinner for a number of local tradesmen and tenants, having gone out in the morning to join them in their sport, and was reported as looking particularly cheerful. That evening he and Cornelia took a walk in the grounds, and he complained of a heaviness in the legs, but it passed off and they took no further notice of it. They later retired to bed. The next morning, while dressing, Andrew suddenly complained of dizziness, and initially Cornelia was not too concerned as she assumed it was one of the nervous attacks to which he had been subject for most of his life. However, he then threw himself on the bed and immediately felt a deadness on the left side of his body – he had had a stroke. Turning to his wife, who was now standing anxiously at the side of the bed, he said 'Cornelia, I have a paralytic seizure, send for Mr. King.' At first she could not believe what he had said. She tried to attribute the sensation he was suffering to other less serious causes, but Andrew knew what had happened, and had enough experience to know it was likely to be fatal. In a calm voice, but with deep emotion, he said 'My dear wife, bear it as I must bear it. Do not deceive yourself, this is my death stroke.' It took three hours for Dr King to reach Fyne Court as Abraham King, physician and surgeon, lived in Blake Street, Bridgwater, but was probably absent from home when the message summoning him to Fyne Court came, which would explain the delay in his arrival. While waiting for the doctor, Andrew said to Cornelia 'If by moving my finger I could restore myself to perfect health, and to the certainty of several years of life, I would not do it if I knew it to be contrary to the will of God.'

While his body was affected and Andrew lay in his bed, rarely sleeping, Cornelia would keep watch, usually alone, at his side all through the night. He was perfectly lucid, and through the dark hours of the night or in the bright light of the summer days, he would talk about all sorts of subjects, ranging from religion and philosophy to poetry. However, when she spoke of his last experiment regarding the breaking down of gold, which was still set up, he said 'Don't talk to me about it now', although he willingly discussed all other aspects of science almost until the end. At times Cornelia said his mind was intensified by his illness and his conversation was such that she had difficulty following it. At other times an extreme physical weakness came upon him and he seemed to be ebbing fast, and at these times he would become anxious for a visit from Dr King, who regularly visited him. Andrew was always much calmer after the doctor had attended him. Towards the end of June he started to suffer intense pain, but bore it with great fortitude, and without ever complaining. He said on several occasions 'I have no reason to complain, I have lived my time. Morning and evening seem all the same to me now, but I pray constantly.' One day, feeling better, he recited to Cornelia and his eldest son John by his first wife, who had been at Fyne Court for some days, his translation of Horace's *Ode to Augustus Caesar*, a work of 120 lines, showing that his stroke had not affected his phenomenal memory. About a week before the end he quoted one of his own poems, 'To the Chamber Clock', as an allusion to his own situation:

> List to the chamber clock,
> As it measures the time with regular knock!
> As the pendulum sways from side to side,
> It beats to the fall of mortal pride.
>
> Beat! beat! the Spring draws near,
> And promises fair for a future year;
> The Summer awakes – it glows – it flies,
> Then quick gives place to autumnal dyes.
>
> But withering Winter triumphs in turn,
> And scowls o'er Nature's funeral urn.
> Beat! beat! In the glare of day,
> When the dream of life is bright and gay.
>
> Beat! beat! in the calm of night,
> When darkness shrouds the waker's sight:
> When memory views with unclouded eye
> The faces of friends that are long gone by.
>
> Beat! beat! in love or strife -
> Every beat is a slice of life,
> And when the listener's dead and gone,
> Another shall hear the clock beat on!

His great friend John Eagles came down to Fyne Court and stayed for some days, something that greatly pleased Andrew. He received the sacrament from the parish priest on 1 July. Towards the end the other surviving children of his first marriage came, Robert, Rector of Ockham, travelled up from Surrey and Isabella, who came from London, attended him as he was getting rapidly worse, and his symptoms more painful and distressing. Two days before his death he sent for his three sons, Andrew, Landor and Ormonde, and blessing them said 'I do not pray that they may be great, or that they may be rich, but I pray that they may be good.' On the morning of the 6 July Andrew died in the same room in which he had been born seventy-one years earlier. The following day *The Somerset County Gazette* reported his death:

Death of Andrew Crosse Esq.

We are deeply pained to have to announce the death of this estimable gentleman, which melancholy event – the result of a paralytic seizure – took place at his residence, Fyne Court House, this (Friday) morning.

On 12 July Andrew was buried in the family vault at Broomfield church, the service being taken by his ordained son Robert. The experiment that Andrew had set up investigating the mechanical breakdown of gold by electricity was still running. After four days the action had become noticeably weakened but was not refreshed as Cornelia was then nursing Andrew who had taken to his bed. However, after Andrew's death, she made careful notes of what had happened:

Looking edgeways at the florin-shaped piece of gold, I observed that it had the appearance of being separated into collateral flakes; and I found, on taking apart the experiment, that such was the case to a considerable extent. Indeed, one large piece had become separated or scaled off from the solid mass, which measured an inch and a quarter on the outer circle, and was half an inch in breadth, and of about the thickness of writing paper.

A stain of the purple oxide of gold was perceptible, as in the former experiments, fully proving that this appearance had nothing to do with the presence of copper. After most carefully washing the broken pieces of gold in nitric acid, and after careful drying, I found that these portions weighed exactly twenty-three grains, which was precisely the amount which the coin-shaped piece of gold was proved to have lost.

So Andrew was vindicated, the breaking up of the gold was not due to the presence of copper, something he knew he had proved just before he took to his bed. The results were noted by Cornelia and written up as a paper 'The Apparent Mechanical Action Accompanying Electric Transfer.' This was read by Dr Lyon Playfair, President of the Chemical Section of the British Association meeting in Glasgow in 1855. Following this Sir Roderick Murchison wrote to Cornelia:

September 16, 1855.

My Dear Mrs. Crosse,

It gave me great pleasure to be in any way useful in bringing before the Chemical Section your interesting and clear explanation of the processes which your late lamented husband had completed, to establish his ingenious and original discovery. I took the paper myself to the Chemical Section, and impressed forcibly on the president the propriety of doing every honour to the memory of Mr. Crosse.

Dr Playfair also wrote to her:

Your paper was read to-day to a crowded audience, which evinced much interest in it. I supported the views which you had given, and expressed the opinion that the experiment was conclusive, paying you a deserved compliment for continuing the enquiries left uncompleted by your husband. Professor Miller followed, and expressed himself perfectly satisfied with the experiment; and Mr. Gassiot passed a high eulogy on your husband and his labours, and admitted fully your experiment ... .

She also received a letter from William Hopkins who had also doubted the veracity of Andrew's initial findings at the British Association meeting, and had read a report of the Glasgow meeting:

I gave up my visit to the British Association this year very reluctantly. You will perhaps recollect I heard Mr. Crosse explain his experiment with characteristic clearness last year. I considered then that something was wanting to the complete demonstration of his views, and I am truly glad to learn that that something has been supplied.

Andrew had been vice-president of the Somerset Archaeological and Natural History Society since its inauguration in 1849, and at the first meeting following his death they expressed their regret at his passing and referred to him as 'one who took so lively an interest in the well-being of the Society, and whose scientific zeal and attainments reflected so much lustre in this his native county.' Cornelia was later to set up a memorial obelisk (plate 25) in the corner of the churchyard bearing the inscription:

SACRED

TO THE MEMORY OF

ANDREW CROSSE

THE ELECTRICIAN

BORN JUNE 17TH 1784

DIED JULY 6TH 1855

HE WAS HUMBLE TOWARDS

GOD AND KIND TO

HIS FELLOW CREATURES.

THIS TRIBUTE OF

AFFECTION IS RAISED BY

CORNELIA HIS WIFE.

CHAPTER ELEVEN
A Deathbed Reconciliation: 1855–80

A letter written to John Moore at Minehead by John Crosse, the eldest son of Andrew Crosse, the day after his father died, shows that there had been a serious family rift:

Fyne Court
July 7th 1855.

My dear Sir,

    My Father died yesterday morning at 5 minutes before 11 o'clock, after an unusually distressing illness of 41 days – during which time the mind remained calm & unshaken amidst the sufferings of the body. He knew us to the last.

There were, as you know, most painful dissensions in the entire family, but an entire & most affectionate reconciliation united us all during this anxious time. All intervals of ease were employed in discussions on philosophy & poetry, or on those solemn subjects that befit such a moment. Three or four days before his death we all received the Sacrament together.

Will you inform the Richards of Alcombe of this sad event.

Very sincerely yrs.
John Crosse

Pray give my affectionate Regards to yr. Aunt.

Considering Andrew's forgiving nature and his wish to avoid conflict and causing hurt to other people, traits that he had demonstrated all his life, it is surprising that there was this breakdown in relations within his own family. Something else that shows just how serious this was is the fact that nineteen days into his illness, on 30 June, Andrew revoked his previous will and wrote a new one leaving almost his entire estate to his second wife Cornelia. This will was proved under oath by Cornelia in London on 4 August 1855. Until that point it was generally assumed that Andrew's son John (born 1810) by his first wife would inherit the estate. So it must have come as a huge shock to him when this new will was read:

> This is the last will and testament of Mr. Andrew Crosse of Fyne Court in the Parish of Broomfield in the County of Somerset Esquire. I give unto my two sons John Crosse and Robert Crosse in token of my sincere love and affection for them the following legacies namely To my said son John Crosse the organ in the Music Room and all the books in my Library and to my son Robert Crosse my telescope and the sum of nineteen guineas to be paid to him by my Executive hereafter named at the expiration of six calendar months next after my decease. I devise all and singular my real estate and bequeath all the residue of my personal estate whatsoever and wheresoever unto my dear wife Cornelia Augusta Hewitt Crosse absolutely and I appoint her sole executor of this my will and I hereby revoke all former wills by me made. In witness whereof I have hereunder set my hand this thirtieth day of June one thousand eight hundred and fifty-five – Andrew Crosse signed by the said Andrew Crosse the testator as and for this last will and testament in the presence of each other have hereto subscribed our names as witnesses. Witnesses: John Eagles A.M. Clarkson Orders, Redland, Bristol; Henry Bisson Harman, surgeon, Bridgwater.

The bequest to John of only the organ from the music room and his library of books suggests that the rift was between John, the oldest son by Andrew's first wife, and Andrew, and possibly between John and the rest of the family. It would seem, by the letter John wrote the day after his father's death, that the two had been reconciled, and there is no trace of any bitterness in what he says, so it is unlikely that he knew of this alteration until the will was read. Was it ironic that Andrew, left John the organ and books 'in token of my sincere love and affection …'? One can imagine John's dismay and anger on learning that the estate that he had expected to inherit had been left to his step-mother, a woman who was thirteen years his junior and forty-three years younger than his father. There were also now three children as a result of his father's remarriage. Andrew's second marriage to Cornelia could well have caused resentment among the children of the first marriage, but there was another likely reason why John and Andrew had fallen out.

To understand the origins of this it is necessary to go back a number of years. It involved a very famous figure in both science, mathematics and society. Augusta Ada King, Countess of Lovelace (1815-52), the only legitimate daughter of the poet Lord George Gordon Byron (1788-1824). She was a close friend and collaborator of Charles Babbage (1791-1871) who began to construct the precursor of a computer in 1822. This was his small-scale model Difference Engine, a device to produce error free numerical tables of various kinds. However, for various reasons, mostly connected with lack of funding, he was not able to build a full size and much more advanced machine until the 1830s. It was in 1833 that Babbage met Lady Lovelace, or Ada, as she preferred to be known, at a party in London, where he was demonstrating his machine. She was able to understand the Difference Engine and impressed Babbage as she had read differential calculus, and obviously had a natural aptitude for mathematics. Captain Luigi Menabra wrote an article on Babbage's Difference Engine which appeared in the *Bibliotheque Universelle de Geneve* in October 1842. Shortly afterwards Ada translated it into English at the suggestion of Professor Charles Wheatstone for *Taylor's Scientific Memoirs*, a journal featuring the latest foreign scientific and technical papers. When Babbage heard she had done this he asked why she had not written an original paper on a subject that she was so 'intimately acquainted' with. Ada said that the thought had not occurred to her. He than suggested that she should add some notes to Menabrea's work. This she agreed to do.

When Babbage saw she had added her own original and advanced calculations and thoughts, he wrote 'That the whole of the developments and operations of analysis are now capable of being executed by machinery.' In effect Ada had devised the prototype programs for an advanced calculating machine – a century before anyone built a programmable computer. She understood the concept of a stored program, as well as looping, indexing, sub-routine libraries and conditional jumps. She was a mathematical genius. The Lovelaces had a country house, Ashley Combe Lodge near Porlock Weir on the Somerset coast. Despite the term 'Lodge' it was a fairly substantial building, to which a clock tower was added in 1840. In 1845 it was described as 'An old irregular building to which additions have lately been made in very bad taste.' As relatively near neighbours, Ada (plate 22) had been acquainted with Andrew Crosse for some years. According to *The Taunton Courier* of 14 November 1838:

> The Earl of Lovelace and his lady called at Fyne Court House with a large party, but Andrew Crosse was away from home. However, the distinguished visitors were much gratified by their inspection of the elaborate electrical, chemical and philosophical adaptation of the premises to the scientific pursuits of the indefatigable owner.

In 1842 she wrote to Andrew about his 'mite experiments' of 1836. Her interest may have been aroused by reading or hearing about the positive results of Dr William Weekes who repeated, under very stringent conditions, Andrew's experiment in which *Acari* had appeared. Reports of his results appeared in the *Proceedings of the Electrical Society* and *The Times* that year. It was in 1844 that she decided to become a house guest of Andrew at Fyne Court in order to learn more about the practicalities of experimenting with electricity. She wrote a letter to him a little before her visit as 'you may require a little preparation possibly for the purpose' explaining her interest: 'Some of my own views make it necessary for me to use electricity as my prime-minister, in order to test certain points experimentally as to the nature and putting together (con-sti-tu-tion) of the molecules of matter … By eventually bringing high analysis to bear on my experimental studies I hope one day to do much.' Ada had suffered from a variety of illnesses, some serious, all her life, and in another preparatory letter to Andrew before her visit mentions what to do if she became ill while staying with him. Andrew was quite used to illness in his own family and probably wondered what he was letting himself in for:

I think I may as well give you a hint that I am subject at times to dreadful physical sufferings. If such should come over me at Broomfield, I may have to keep to my room for a time. In that case all I require is to be let alone ... With all my wiry power and strength, I am prone at times to bodily sufferings, connected chiefly with the digestive organs, of no common degree or kind.

It was on the 22 November 1844 that Ada arrived at Fyne Court. She was not accompanied by her husband, William, and the following day she wrote to him describing her journey. This also gives a fascinating insight into the chaotic domestic arrangements of Fyne Court, very different to the normal regimented upper class household of the time:

Finding no symptom of either breakfast – or human beings, I have sat down to write to you, in my shawl & bon[net] in their very cold sitting room. I was down at nine, having been told there [would] be breakfast. We all sat up reading & talking philosophy till one o'clock last night. I suppose that is the secret of the dawdle this morning. My head is very muzzy this morning, from that cause I think, & shall take the liberty this evening of calling my hosts to the recollection of Time. The droll thing was we were discussing the metaphysics of Time & Space, &c. in so doing we forgot real Time & Space ... Our journey was agreeable. In the course of it I was able to give Crosse a complete outline & vista of all my scientific plans & ideas. He seemed to think there is much merit in them & remarked 'I see no mere enthusiasm in all this. It is all so quietly reasoned, so soundly based.'

What is significant is that this letter goes on to describe her meeting John Crosse, Andrew's oldest son, for the first time. He had been away in Germany and even at their first meeting the attraction that seems to have been sparked between the two can be seen, a relationship that was to eventually lead to the rift between John and his father. Although very taken with John and impressed by Andrew, she found Robert, the second son and his sister, Isabella, rather disagreeable:

I find my visit is of more importance to me than I had anticipated. The eldest son John is giving me information as to scientific doings in

Germany which is of utmost importance I should be in possession of, & he will undertake, if I choose, to be my organ to any extent he can in procuring me every means of keeping au courant as to German mathematics & natural philosophy. He is most extensively read, & also a very clever young man. I can get from & by means of him, what I could from no one else. He is 6 months at Berlin next year, & he will occupy himself in catering for me. John Crosse says that in Germany books of dry science sell even better than light works. That for instance such a one as Wilkinson's would pay richly, to get more information upon; for my own future purposes.

The next day, 23 November, she wrote to William again, and this throws further light on the Crosse household, as well as her growing feelings for John, who she had only met the day before:

This is certainly a most extraordinary domicile to visit at. It appears to me to be the most unorganised domestic system I ever saw ... All this is just so much of a novel field for observation & analysis of the human atom, and as the interests of my avocations will doubtless oblige me at times to be more or less a guest in this dwelling, I am obliged to study how to fall into the circumstances for the time being, in the most easy & agreeable manner. There is at least one very unusual & agreeable circumstance. I am treated without let or hindrance, & left to do exactly as I like ... This is just what I want. I am nobody here ... The oldest son is a frank & cordial person; & we take to each other I think. He has a mine of reading & references in him to me quite invaluable. Me he evidently regards more as he would a young man than a fine lady. I do not mean to say that he is wanting in any point of manners to a women. Far from it, but the lady & the woman are quite merged in his simple consciousness of the intellect & pursuits. He addresses them, not Lady Lovelace...

There is another reference to Andrew's 'method' of working:

There is in Crosse the most utter lack of system even in his science. At least so it strikes me. I may be mistaken. Perhaps I don't see enough, as yet, to discover his system … I have quite a difficulty to get him to show me what I want. Nothing is ever ready. All chaos & chance.

Mary Ann Crosse, Andrew's first wife was, at this time, an invalid, and had suffered poor health for some years. This may explain in part the chaotic domestic household arrangements. Her letter written to William the next day, 24 November, provides further insight into this singular household, and John also gets a telling mention:

Dearest mate,

All well, but not much time. I could stay here a fortnight with my advantage. I have made the whole family laugh heartily with my witty fun about the chaotic nature of the establishment & proceedings. Old Crosse delights in my quizzing him. The playful bird, you know!! … Young Crosse is an excellent mathematician as well as metaphysician &c.; & he works my brain famously for he opposes everything I advance, intentionally; but with perfect good humour. This is very useful & good for me. He will be an addition to my catalogue of useful & intellectual friends, in many respects … There is no order. Everyone straggles down whenever he pleases … The post &c. ALL by chance, & at all sorts of hours. I never saw the like.

After Ada left Fyne Court she wrote a letter to Andrew:

My dear Mr. Crosse,

I found my gold pencil this morning in the pocket of my gown I wore on Tuesday evening. I believe I had put it there to prevent losing it, as I went up to bed that night. My journey was very wretched, so late, so cold, so dreary. I could not help lending my cloak to a lady who was my companion, and who seemed to me more delicate and in need of it than myself. This did not, however, add to my physical comfort. Many times after it became dusk did I think of your hospitable 'chaos', and wish myself back, and imagine to myself if you are all sitting down to dinner, and if you missed me at all or not. In short, I had in my own brain a very comical chaos composed of what I had left behind, and a thousand heterogeneous ideas, all of them but half alive and stagnant through physical cold … My gold pin does not come forth – but it is not a thing of much consequence. If a stray gold pin, however, does develop itself, don't fancy it is an electrical production, but send it to me.

On returning to London Ada wrote to William to say that her enthusiasm for experimental laboratory research as practised by Andrew had waned, but went on to describe a five hour visit to her by Professor Charles Wheatstone. She also said that he had suggested that she should try to become Prince Albert's Scientific Advisor, something that John Crosse, apparently, had also urged her to pursue. She also mentioned that Wheatstone had urged her to study German philosophy and science. This gave her the opportunity to suggest it would be useful to spend more time with John Crosse, and even get him into her house:

> As far as the German studies are concerned, they cannot be carried on while on a visit; and it is at home only that I should make any real progress as such. If young Crosse stays with us, some hours can be daily given for the time-being, to that purpose; but when one is visiting a family one must be diluted a little amongst all the members of it … .

Once again this letter gives a snippet of everyday life at Fyne Court:

> There are certainly inconceivable oddities there. For instance: The water closet can only be got thro' the Drawing Room; & of course it is perfectly evident the errand one is going on, since the exit leads nowhere else. I don't mind that sort of thing in the least, when it is inevitable, & I take everything cooly & as a matter of course. That is the only way. Sometimes they lock up the water closet, & then one has to make a hue & cry after the key.

Ada now went to great lengths to get 'young John Crosse' into her house. Her many references to John as 'young' in the letters to her husband may have been designed to allay any fears he may have had. In fact John was six years older than she was! John had gone to Exeter College, Oxford, reading Classics. He graduated in 1833 with a Second in Classics, went to Lincoln's Inn to study law, but this did not work out and so left within the year. At the time that he and Ada met, he seems to have spent most of his time travelling and was somewhat at a loose end. However, he had married Susanna Eliza Bowman, the daughter of Charles Bowman of Ipswich, in July 1840 at Kelso in Scotland. Under Scottish law at that time all that was required was for a couple to exchange vows when they would be considered married. The reason for English people marrying in Scotland was usually because they had eloped, but when they married John was aged twenty-nine and Susanna was twenty-two. While in England in 1840 the age of consent was only thirteen, men and women could not marry without parental consent until they were twenty-one according to the Marriage Act of 1773. This Act did not apply to Scotland, where parental consent was not required for people under twenty-one. John and Susanna did not need parental consent to marry, so why marry in Scotland? Was it a romantic impulse or was the marriage opposed by one or both of the couple's families? Was it therefore a secret marriage for some reason? Later events suggest this was indeed the case.

After their first meeting in 1844, John spent much time in Ada's company, and gave her a lot of encouragement in her scientific work. With John's urging and the backing of Wheatstone, she began an essay on the molecular structure of matter. In 1846, in consultation with John, she wrote a review on an *Abstract of Researches on Magnetism* and on certain allied subjects including a supposed new 'Imponderable' by Baron von Reichenbach. What is interesting is that there are corrections and alterations to her manuscript in another hand, although in many cases it does not improve her prose, and some of these changes make the sense more muddled. This looks very much like John's handwriting and it is significant that she is allowing someone else to meddle with her writing – something she forbade Babbage and others to do. In the margin of one page there is a note, in pencil, written by Ada: 'Here follows the extract of occurrence in Pfeffel's Garden &c. To be given when T.C. returns me the rest.' By now Ada had given John Crosse a nickname! Although it is not known what 'T' stood for. This paper was not submitted for publication, probably due to a similar review being published by James Braid that year. John and Ada spent more and more time together, and he was accepted in the Lovelace household as a friend. John was a 'gentleman', that is he seemed not to have had an occupation, and his income presumably came from an allowance that he got from his father, another reason why Andrew was always short of money.

The Earl of Lovelace was a fanatical builder, particularly in the 'Gothick' style popular at that time, and used every penny he had on expanding and consolidating the holdings that he had inherited. He also brought a large neighbouring estate next to Ockham Park, the family seat in Surrey, and from 1846 occupied this new property, East Horsley, which he renamed Horsley Towers, as his principal house. He transformed it from a pseudo-tudor house to a mock medieval castle. Not only was Lord Lovelace short of money, he was always lecturing Ada on household economy. She had an income of £300 a year but, on the death of her mother, Lady Anne Byron (1792-1860), she would inherit an income of £7,000 a year. In the meantime she found it impossible to manage on £300, an allowance that Lord Lovelace refused to raise, regarding this as a 'most liberal' sum, despite her desperate entreaties, but he would give her the occasional cheque for court dress and other items that he regarded as essential. So, in an act of desperation, Ada borrowed £500 in May 1848 without the knowledge of her husband from Mr Currie, a neighbour who was a banker. It seems that it was also in this year that John's relationship with Ada changed from a friend to something much more intimate. Ada wrote many letters to John in that year, but unfortunately they do not survive. That year she also lent him a large sum of money with which to buy furniture for a house he had at Reigate, Surrey, eleven miles (17.7 km) from East Horsley. The money presumably came from her loan. However, that year John was also resident in Park Street, Grosvenor Square, London, presumably with his wife, since on 26 March she had a daughter, Mary Crosse, who was born in Kensington.

Ada was now in debt, and never did repay Mr Currie's loan. In 1850 she got involved in gambling in an attempt to raise money to pay her now increased debts and provide sufficient spending money. As an expert mathematician it could be expected that she had a 'system' but this does not seem to have been the case. Her interest in racing began quite openly, and it was only the size of her losses that were a secret. She bet on the Derby in May 1850, and while the horse she said she would back won, she wrote the day after the Derby 'I have such a horrible head today (owing of course to despair at the great pecuniary losses I have sustained by betting) that I can't write the long letter I intended.' Either she had not backed the Derby winner after all or, more likely, had lost heavily by betting on other races at Epsom. In the late summer Ada and her husband took a tour of Northern England, and she anticipated attending a number of race meetings. With this in mind she accepted a gift of money from her mother, but did not tell her how she intended to use it. There was a three day meeting at Doncaster, and Ada was so eager to attend that she went on ahead of her husband, who had no particular interest in racing, and spent two days admiring local architecture. He only turned up on the last day of the meeting. Ada seems to have been lucky as she later wrote that she did not need to spend the £30 her mother had given her – she had won it back with possibly more on top. By early 1851 Ada was deeply involved with racing and had formed a racing syndicate from a small group of associates, which included John Crosse, but not Lord Lovelace.

They were working out a betting strategy, and Ada suggesting they make a book. There is some evidence that she was trying to dazzle her colleagues, who were as inexperienced in betting as she was, with her mathematical prowess. Ada was determined to back Voltigeur against the Flying Dutchman at the York Spring Meeting, having been at several races where it won. Unfortunately, Voltigeur lost. When she met her partners some days later to settle her debts, her losses amounted to £3,200. In addition she had somehow persuaded Lord Lovelace to give her £1,800 to lend to one of the poorer members of the 'group'. Her health, always poor, now deteriorated and she was confined to the Lovelaces' London house. She, with the help of John Crosse, pawned some of the Lovelaces' heirloom jewels, a diamond *parure*, a set of matching jewels designed to be worn together. Her mother found out about this and took prompt steps, through her solicitors, to recover the jewels for £800 plus £100 interest. It seems Lord Lovelace was not aware of this. John was a regular visitor to the house, as was Babbage, and they were often there together. John was placing bets for her, and at some point persuaded Ada to obtain a letter from Lord Lovelace saying he agreed to her gambling, and she was successful in getting him to supply such a letter, although he was obviously quite unaware of how deeply in debt she had got.

John was a frequent visitor to her sickbed, and he called on her on 25 July 1852 although he himself was recovering from a serious illness. That same day Lord Lovelace was walking with his solicitor, Woronzow Greig, when a sudden thunderstorm broke out and they took refuge in a shed. As they sheltered Greig casually mentioned John's wife and two children. He had learnt of them the previous Christmas from an acquaintance at his law office who was a neighbour of Johns at Reigate. Lord Lovelace had no idea he was married and asked Greig, as his family solicitor, to look into the matter. Greig was later able to report that Crosse's name had appeared on the Voters Register at Reigate for at least two years, and that his wife was a 'young and charming person.' He asked if he should look any further into the matter? Lord Lovelace mulled this information over for a few days and then confronted Ada with it. She denied any knowledge of John being married, so this news would have shocked her. She agreed to ask John about it when he visited her that evening (3 August). The answers he gave, or at least those she conveyed to her husband, were obviously not satisfactory as Lord Lovelace said he would talk to John on his own. Ada was now very anxious in case John's visits were stopped. Lord Lovelace wrote to Ada from East Horsley:

> I told Mr. C. that in saying I did not wish to withdraw my countenance from him, I did not thereby imply that I desired to receive him as formerly – that discussion and explanations of the sort that had passed between us rendered it less agreeable for the respective parties to meet often – and that knowledge with which I was fixed with regard to his proceedings at Reigate rendered it undesirable that he should frequent my house – but of course your wishes were sacred in my eyes. He told me that his position was most painful & that your wishes were very strong – & rather asked for advice & suggestion from me. I replied that I could give him none – that my position & feelings were at least as painful & he must judge for himself – but that your wishes must be a paramount consideration with me.

The account of his 'proceedings' at Reigate that John gave to Lord Lovelace were later summarised by Greig. John claimed that for the first year he had shared his house at Reigate with a married cousin on his father's side. Upon the cousin's departure, an uncle on his mother's side had installed his (the uncle's) mistress and children, who, by a coincidence happened also to be called Crosse, and they were living in an unused part of the house. Eventually he claimed that she was his mistress and the children were his own living under his name, and that they had now moved to Godstone five miles (8 km) from Reigate. What he did refuse to admit was the fact that he was married! However, his involvement with Ada probably made it easy for him to convince himself, after he had become infatuated with her, that he was not legally married as the ceremony had been carried out in Scotland. This must have made things very difficult for Susanna when he moved them out of the Reigate house to live in Godstone, or had she walked out taking the children with her?

In the 19th century the possession of a mistress and illegitimate children would not have been sufficient to bar John from friendship with the Lovelaces as long as he did not try to introduce them into society. Despite Greig's informant who suggested something to the contrary, John maintained he had never tried to do this. However, the possession of a legal wife who was not taken into society was quite different, as the only conclusion that could be drawn was that there was either something shameful about the wife or there was something disreputable about the husband's intentions. What is surprising is that the Lovelaces were not aware John had a wife. They were sufficiently often in contact with Andrew Crosse for descriptions and discussions of his second wife to appear in their correspondence in the early 1850s. Letters from Andrew were long and chatty, and it is surprising that he would not have mentioned in one to Ada that his eldest son had married Susanna in 1840, and he and Susanna had a son, John Jennings Crosse, in March 1848, and a girl, Mary Crosse, in 1851. One wonders if Andrew and his first wife (who died in 1846) were even aware John was married, and if Andrew and Cornelia his second wife, even knew that John and his wife had children, Andrew's fifth and sixth grandchildren. Though they must have found out at some point.

On 19 August Lord Lovelace recorded that he and Ada had a row about 'Mr. Cr.' John had apparently complained to Ada about the interrogation to which he had been subjected. She took her husband to task and a row ensued that was to further jeopardise John's chances of visiting Ada. She was so desperate that she persuaded her doctor, Charles Locock, to write to her husband in such a way that it appeared to be his idea and nothing to do with her. A copy of this letter survived:

> I know that for several years Lady Lovelace has had a great friendship for two or three gentlemen to whose society she had much devoted herself. I allude especially to Mr. Crosse and Mr. Babbage – I know also from recent conversations with your Lordship that from not personally liking one of these gentlemen, you might be led, either by word or manner, to prevent him from being so much with Lady Lovelace as she herself would anxiously desire. I beg particularly to urge your Lordship not to needlessly disturb Lady L. by depriving her of so much of Mr. Crosse's society as she wishes or has the strength to bear – for I know the dread of such being the case has often much harassed her & I think in her present deplorable state it would be both cruel and mischievous to debar her from what has been such a source of comfort & happiness.

Ada's fear of losing John was for practical as well as emotional reasons. She was still trying to make secret payments to and through John including, as it later turned out, taking out an insurance policy on her own life. He was her intermediary with the outside world as she could no longer even post letters. Her mother, now in attendance as Ada's illness became worse, was reducing her possible 'agents' and had already forbidden Babbage to visit and was now threatening to ban her trusted maid, Mary Wilson. Ada was now in a panic. During their brief meeting on 3 August 1852 she gave John the diamond *parure* that he had pawned the year before, and which had been redeemed by her mother, to be pawned by him once again. A week later she tried to make Babbage her executor and gave him a number of papers, letters and keepsakes, with a letter that she hoped would enable him to sort out and settle her complex financial affairs without her husband or mother interfering. Babbage reluctantly agreed to this, as by now Ada was in a great deal of pain and was obviously dying. On 19 August Mr Fleming, one of her gambling partners, managed to get in to see her, and took away a cheque for another instalment on the life insurance policy John had arranged on her behalf.

Fearing her coming death she confessed to her mother on 20 August that she had had an affair with John Crosse, but said she did not regret it. Although shocked but not totally surprised, Lady Byron kept this to herself. However, on 1 September, Ada told her husband about her infidelity with John. He received this news bitterly, and left the room with the parting words, according to Lady Byron, 'God be merciful to you!' He later said he 'was forced to listen to the most degrading excuses', while Lady Byron called John 'A Swindler & a Brute ...'. Among Ada's papers is a list of titles of her poems, two of which have 'T' added in parenthesis. On the review of von Reichenbach's paper that Ada wrote in 1846 she referred to T.C. in an obvious reference to John Crosse. 'T' was her nickname for John. One of these poems goes:

> One thought of thee and I am calm
>> Midst bitter wrongs that stun and crush,
> One word of thine is heavenly balm
>> That bids warm soft'ning tears to gush.
> Though friends (or those I thought my friends)
>> Drop off like withering autumn leaves,
> And rising scorn my spirit rends,
>> Yet thou canst still the heart that heaves!
>
> For thine's the touch my soul doth own;
>> And thou hath tuned my heart-strings oft,
> And bid them mildly, gently, moan,
>> And made them vibrate sweet and soft.
>
> For thy dear sake my life I prize,
>> And feel there is a God of love;
> And then each demon discord dies,
>> For thou the chords of hope dost move!

A further demonstration of the tenderness with which she held 'T' was a bequest among the papers she gave to Babbage, but which he later returned to her mother. Wrapped in a piece of paper marked to 'B' [Babbage] on the outside, was another marked 'To T', which contained a bequest:

My gold pencil-case (Morden's Patent) having my name & Coronet on the top as a seal; with the bequest that he will use it habitually, in remembrance of the many delightful & improving hours we have jointly passed in various literary pursuits. Also I request him to select from my Books, any 12 WORKS (not vols.) which he may prefer ... Also for the sake of the same pleasant memories, my very shabby dark-coloured leather writing Box which is always on one of my tables, & which I have had for very many years & have habitually used, I wish T. to have this with all its contents ins[ide] – some seals, minerals, etc. etc. exactly as they happen to be found. There is nothing in it of any value, excepting for old association's sake; & in fact it always contains much rubbish, – odd bits of paper, pins &c. &c. but I wish it delivered to T. as it is with its contents, & no attempt made to clear it of anything or to put it tidy. Its value would cease, if it & its contents were in any way altered after I had last used it.

This is obviously a sentimental bequest to John, something that would mean a lot to him. However, Babbage was forced to hand this and other papers entrusted to him back after Ada's death, and so John never received the items, but Ada did give John some mementoes, possibly even before she had her final illness. This was a gold ring that had belonged to her father, a locket containing a lock of Byron's hair, and a miniature portrait of his entitled 'Maid of Athens'. In his will John left the gold ring to his son John, the miniature to his daughter Mary, and the locket to his daughter Susan. Towards the end of September, having suffered convulsions and considerable pain for some time, with an impaired memory, possibly due to the drugs with which she was being treated, and having, apparently, become addicted to the opium, she confessed to her mother she had pawned the Lovelace family jewels for a second time. Lady Byron immediately ordered her lawyers to redeem them again, and this time they were placed in the safekeeping of a Dr Lushington. Lord Lovelace was not to learn his family jewels had been twice pawned until after Ada's death. On the 27 November 1852 Ada's sufferings finally ended. She died of uterine cancer and as a result of the blood-letting by her physicians aged thirty-six, the same age as her father when he had died. It seems that John may have made an attempt to see her almost at the end, as Lady Byron wrote that she had stood between John and Ada 'in the very last hour. John seems to have really loved her.

Ada had left not only debts of seven to eight thousand pounds, but a financial tangle that Greig, the family solicitor, was never really able to sort out. Among her many papers were letters from John Crosse during the years 1848, 1850, 1851 and 1852. Babbage was intimidated into handing over all the papers, bills and receipts, plus the bequest to John Crosse that Ada had given him. These included receipts for payments on the insurance policy and instalments on various secret debts. Babbage seems to have been aware of her affair with John for some time, and acted as a channel of communication between the two after Lord Lovelace found out about his family. Babbage himself seemed to also have been very smitten with her, both for her character and mathematical ability. Ada's racing partners now claimed that they were owed various sums of money, but Greig was able to dispose of most of these in various ways, leaving only two, Mr Fleming and John Crosse to deal with. Ada had made Fleming a beneficiary of the insurance policy, but Greig pointed out a number of reasons why it would not be valid, so he withdrew his claim. However, despite saying this, the insurance company were in fact willing to pay out on the policy. This now remained something of an embarrassment, for if Lord Lovelace claimed it, he would appear to be associated with the betting syndicate whose claims he and his solicitor had beaten off.

John now laid claim to the £600 insurance payout, pointing out that he had, in his possession, certain letters from Ada, plus one other document. The most serious of these, from the solicitor's point of view, was not one written to Crosse, but the one provided to Ada by Lord Lovelace to say he had agreed to her betting. John agreed that he would ceremonially burn these for a payment of £600 in the presence of a lawyer. He provided a list of Ada's letters, numbering eighteen, although Greig knew, having read Ada's correspondence, she had sent him at least one hundred and eight. However, as Greig wrote:

> Being satisfied from these facts, not to mention others, that I am dealing with a man destitute of honour and principle, I have determined to allow him to receive the money under the policy, provided the 18 letters are destroyed in Karslake's presence – one of these letters being the most injudicious one referred to from him to her – and another being her letter to C. of the 22nd of last August.

Grieig asked John to sign a statement that the eighteen letters in his possession were the only ones he had, that no copies or extracts from them had been made, and that these were the only ones that existed. However, John refused to sign such a document, and had his own demand, a letter from Lord Lovelace and Lady Byron exonerating him from all blame respecting the racing transactions in which he had been involved with Ada. The significance of Lord Lovelace's letter authorising Ada's betting becomes clear. If John handed it over, it would open him up to legal proceedings as he would be implicated in running up racing debts with Ada. Greig refused his demand as it would look, if either document was disclosed, that John or Lord Lovelace had something discreditable to hide. There was a stalemate. In the end John allowed the letters to be destroyed, he was paid the £600 from the insurance policy and he never seems to have attempted to use any of her letters he may still have had in his possession.

In 1854 John's wife Susanna gave birth to a daughter, Susan Hamilton Crosse, at Godstone, where she had been living since 1852, so presumably John had now moved to Godstone from Reigate, or was at least regularly visiting his, apparently, estranged wife! A turning point came for John in 1859 when he inherited £10,000 from an uncle, Colonel John Hamilton, and seems to have used this to buy the Fyne Court Estate from Cornelia. A condition of the inheritance was that he change his name to Hamilton, which he did, also taking the Hamilton coat of arms. John Hamilton, as he was now, became a reformed character, and a pillar of the community. In the 1861 edition of Kelly's *Directory of Somerset* it shows that the residence of John Hamilton was Fyne Court, and notes that 'The living [of Broomfield] is a perpetual curacy, worth £100 yearly, with a residence and 17 acres of glebe, in the deanery of Bridgwater, archdeanery of Taunton, diocese of Bath & Wells, province of Canterbury, and in the gift of John Hamilton Esq., who is lay-rector, and receives the great tithes, worth £400 per annum.' By 1866 John is a Justice of the Peace and, as far as society is concerned, a respectable married man with three children, John Jennings, Mary and Susan.

In July 1875 his son, John Jennings, got married at Marylebone Church. Three weeks later, on 6 August, his mother and father, John and Susanna also got married, (for the second time), at St. Thomas's Church, Portman Square, London. It seems that having married in Scotland in 1840, the couple now felt, thirty-five years later, that they should legitimise their marriage as far as English law was concerned. John was now sixty-five and Susanna was ten years younger. In the 'Condition' column of the marriage certificate, where it usually says Bachelor, Spinster or Widowed, theirs says 'Married July 1840 at Kelso according to the Laws of Scotland.' So it may be that John, and possibly Susanna, had not really regarded themselves as being properly married. This particularly applied to John in 1852 when he told Lord Lovelace that Susanna was his mistress and the children illegitimate! John died on 30 March 1880 and was buried in Broomfield Church on 6 April. Susanna continued to live at Fyne Court House until it was destroyed by fire in 1894.

John's life in the late 1840s and early 1850s was an unsavoury episode that does no credit to him. If his father had found out about his involvement with Ada he would have been very shocked, having very firm and high principles all his life, particularly if their affair was initiated while both were under his roof in 1844. The shock and hurt would have been even greater if Andrew had also been unaware that John was married and had children! Could this have come to light when Greig or Lord Lovelace were trying to find out more about John and his family in 1852? Lord Lovelace had appointed John's younger brother, Robert, Rector of Ockham, where his original house was located, early in 1852, and he retained this post during the revelations of John's affair with Ada, and remained Rector for twenty years. The obvious and most easily accessible person to ask about John's domestic arrangements would have been Robert, so Lord Lovelace may well have discussed the matter with him. Did Robert know his brother had a wife and family? If he did, Lord Lovelace obviously did not blame him for failing to mention it earlier, but if, as it appears, Andrew and Cornelia were unaware of John's family, then it is probable that Robert would also have been unaware of the situation, so he too would have been shocked by the news. There is little doubt that such a revelation would have caused a major rift between father and son.

However, the deathbed reconciliation, despite the change in the will, seemed to have worked. Writing in April 1885 Cornelia, talking about John, said 'I was much attached to him, he was a man of cultivated understanding and of considerable mental capacity – though he had never done anything in literature which was his forte.' Unfortunately, like father like son. Although Cornelia liked her stepson John, she did not like his son John Jennings, and after her stepson's death in 1880 had little further to do with the family. She still had fond memories of Fyne Court and was not happy about how John Jennings treated it, noting 'I regret to say the family who are now at Fyne Court have no feeling for Andrew Crosse's scientific achievements – nor interest in scientific collections', suggesting that much of his scientific equipment, and perhaps his geological collection were still there. In another of her letters she said: 'The present Mr. Hamilton (whose father was my step-son, John Crosse, afterwards Hamilton) has fallen into pecuniary trouble.'

CHAPTER TWELVE

Fyne Court – A Fiery End

On Andrew's death Cornelia was left a widow with three children, Andrew Frederick, aged three years, Landor Richard, aged thirteen months and Ormonde only three months old. She was now the owner of the Fyne Court estate following the change to her husband's will during his illness which, in effect, disinherited his oldest son by his first wife. Sir Roderick Murchison, who had been a close friend of Andrew for many years and had got to know Cornelia since her marriage, was very impressed by her ability to tell a good story and her memory for recalling interesting incidents. So he urged her to write an account of Andrew's life. This she did and published *Memorials, Scientific and Literary, of Andrew Crosse the Electrician* in 1857. Cornelia seems to have left Fyne Court soon after Andrew's death, and she wrote *Memorials* while at Comeytrowe House near Taunton.

Some of the happiest days of her life had been spent at Fyne Court, and everywhere she turned in the building or on the estate brought memories of her late husband and the short but happy time they had spent together. So it seems to have been just too painful to continue to stay there. While *Memorials* was very successful at the time, after its publication Cornelia concentrated on bringing up her children and providing them with a good education. This took up much of her time so she does not seem to have produced much other writing for many years. However, it is intriguing that in the 1851 census she is described as 'authoress', so she may have been writing the occasional article for magazines even at this time.

In the autumn of 1856 John Kenyon, Andrew's life-long school friend, had lent his house at Wimbledon to the Barrett Brownings, as he was away ill in the Isle of Wight. Cornelia met Elizabeth there and heard about her plans to go to the Isle of Wight to join Kenyon. She did so, but her visit was very brief as Kenyon had become seriously ill and died a few weeks later. In 1859 Cornelia was still resident in Somerset. Over the next few years she spent some time travelling on the continent, usually with a friend, Miss Lucas. She spent some months in Heidelberg in Germany, and travelled to other parts of the country. She also visited Italy meeting up with friends in Rome, and travelled in Switzerland, France and Hungary where she stayed in Budapest. This may have been at the time her eldest son visited that country in the 1870s, but if she was there earlier, it may have encouraged her son Andrew Frederick to undertake his extensive travels in the country. With her many social skills and connections, she seemed to have easy entry into the society of all those countries which she visited. She often met up with English friends when they were travelling on the continent.

Cornelia maintained a friendship with many leading scientists and literary figures she knew when Andrew was alive, and continued, through them, to meet other scientists, many of whom made major contributions in their fields such as Johann Galle of the Berlin Observatory who discovered the planet Neptune in 1846. She and her sister Theresa were sometimes the guests of Dr and Mrs Percy in London for two or three weeks at a time. She was welcomed by William Hopkins in Cambridge and, as an attractive and intelligent woman, and the widow of Andrew Crosse, a well-known and respected name in scientific circles, was welcomed not only in society but at scientific meetings. When in London she regularly went to Michael Faraday's Friday evening lectures at the Royal Society, to Sir Charles Lyell's geological talks at the British Institution, and to meetings of both the Royal Society and the British Association for the Advancement of Science. At some point she bought a house at 32 Delamere Terrace, Paddington, London, which, at the front, overlooked the Grand Union Canal, and was only a 10-15 minute walk from Kensington Gardens. Cornelia went to the British Association meeting at Bath in 1864 with a friend, Miss Hall, and when they got there found, to their dismay, that all the places were taken. She managed to get a pencilled message passed to Sir Roderick Murchison, and both were immediately admitted to the stage where they were seated with those scientists who were to read papers to the assembled company.

So they got an excellent view of the proceedings. Cornelia said she was often pleased in these later years when she heard about the latest new use of electricity in everyday life and recalled how, years before, Andrew had predicted that it would happen.

In the 1861 census Fyne Court seems to be occupied by tenants, Mary Gardiner Felicia Warre, her son Edmond and daughter Margaret. There were also eight servants employed. The 1861 edition of Kelly's *Directory of Somerset* shows it was the residence of John Hamilton (formerly Crosse) and Henry Warre. This suggests John owned it but at that date he and his family had not moved in. Cornelia seems to have been quite happy to have sold the Fyne Court estate to John, and he was able to buy it as he came into a £10,000 inheritance in 1859 from his mother's unmarried brother, Colonel John Hamilton of the Coldstream Guards. However, that was conditional on changing his name to Hamilton, which he did by royal licence, and assumed both the name and the coat of arms of Hamilton. In April 1861 John and his family were resident at Park Street, Westminster, the same address his uncle, Colonel John Hamilton had occupied since at least 1838. However, a letter from John's daughter, Susan (born 1854) shows that his family were 'in residence' at Fyne Court in the earlier 1860s when she was a small girl:

> In a long passage called the corridor at Fyne Court there stood a beautiful old mahogany cabinet which was the admiration, and awe of my childhood. The cabinet's one key, which was handed down from father to son, was given to my father John Crosse (afterwards Hamilton) by his father Andrew on his death bed. I remember well how when we were children the cabinet used to be opened in a ceremonial way on Sundays and holidays and its contents exhibited to our wondering gaze. It was on these occasions that I have often seen the grant of the crest to Sir Robert in 1584 which the family still bears. This paper was a copy of the original in the college of arms ... .
>
> Numerous other papers in Elizabethan script were shown to us and old letters as well as embroidered coats and waistcoats worn by Richard Crosse at the French court. I remember an apron and christening cloak and a

curious old map of the manor showing the old trees which are still standing, in the avenue then, as large trees.

This cabinet was also described by Cornelia Crosse in 1893, although she says it was made of oak and bore a coat of arms, initials and the date 1704. Inside it contained recesses and drawers, some of which were secret, which would have greatly intrigued the children of the house. Besides a quantity of letters dating back centuries, including a large bundle of letters sent home by Andrew's father Richard while travelling in 1770, it held family mementos such as a child's toy and a worn shoe which were bound together with white ribbon bearing a seal, a keepsake of a deceased child. Other 'treasures' included an 18th century hand-written recipe book which included medical advice and cures and an early newspaper dated 17 September 1660 with others of the 18th century. Richard's court clothes are described, and their cost shows one of the reasons why he was often short of money! There was a 'white satin coat beautifully embroidered in colours, and to be worn with it a long, square-flapped pink satin waistcoat, stiff with gold lace and embroidery. Another suit, a pale blue satin coat and waistcoat of the same colour, was if possible, still richer quality.' The 1871 Census shows that John and his family were in residence and that they employed considerably more house servants than in his father's time, as they had a butler, footman, lady's maid, housemaid, cook and kitchen maid. By the 1881 Census, when John had died and the house was occupied by his widow Susan, the household servants had decreased to three, and by 1891 had reduced to just two. An intriguing entry appeared in a notice of an auction to be held at The Vicarage, Bishops Hull near Taunton on 12 September 1894:

> ... set of mahogany dining-tables, with fluted legs and rounded ends, also forms two centre or one centre and two side tables (formerly the property of the late Mr. Andrew Crosse, of Fyne Court, Broomfield) ... .

The reason for this sale was because the Rev. W. P. Williams was leaving Taunton. However, this was not one of the items rescued from the a fire at the house on 1 September, as the notice of the auction and list of items to be sold was published on 25 August, so must have been sold by either Cornelia or John Hamilton some time previously. Cornelia wrote the occasional article for such publications as *The Queen, Once a Week, Blackwood's Magazine, Chambers Journal* and *The London Quarterly Review*. However, it was not until the 1880s that Cornelia once again seriously took up the pen, encouraged by her old friend George Bentley, who persuaded her to write some reminiscences of the many scientific and literary figures she had known. These appeared in the *Temple Bar Magazine* and were so successful that they were compiled into two volumes, *Red Letter Days of My Life*, in 1892, which was a great success. Following this work, she contributed many further articles to *Temple Bar* and other publications, and was preparing to compile these into a second work of reminiscences when she died.

She was a brilliant conversationalist and a delightful addition to a dinner party, although nothing bored her more than music which, she said, 'spoils conversation'. In her later years she continued to entertain a variety of interesting people on Sunday afternoons, and visitors to Delamere Terrace were certain to pass a pleasant hour or two. For many years she had lived with her unmarried sister Theresa who kept house, allowing Cornelia to write peacefully in her small upstairs study each morning. The afternoons were spent in receiving guests and paying visits, while evenings were often spent in playing whist. During February 1895 she and the rest of the household had been ill, stricken with influenza. Towards the end of the month she was very much better, and only an hour before her sudden death from syncope (a rapid drop in blood pressure) on 2 March, was discussing plans for the future and planning a trip to the country when the days got warmer. She was sixty-eight years old. An obituary appeared in *The Queen Magazine* on 16 March 1895 that concluded:

> Socially she is a great loss, for it mattered not to whom she was introduced her hostess was quite certain that that person would be interested, and that Mrs. Crosse would be amused. She had the happy power of gaining social success wherever she went, possibly by her own brilliancy, genial interest, and kindly sympathy. Her death will be mourned by many a friend, as well as regretted by her large number of literary admirers, for Mrs. Andrew Crosse was a well-known figure in the intellectual life of London, where she was as remarkable as she was charming.

Andrew's first son by his first wife, John, and his wife Susanna eventually settled at Fyne Court, occupying it by 1865. He died on 30 March 1880 and was buried in Broomfield Church on 6 April that year. Andrew's second son Robert had four children, and his youngest daughter Alice, born 1845, caused a major scandal in 1865 when she eloped with their former groom, George Smith. Eventually the couple were traced and Smith appeared in court. The judge found that the elopement had been instigated by Alice, no theft had occurred and eventually all charges were dropped. Later that year Robert agreed the couple could marry and this caused a great stir with accounts of their story and wedding appearing in national newspapers all over Britain and even in America. Robert died on 4 December 1871 in Mentone, France during a walking holiday. Andrew's only living daughter, Isabella, was living in Orsett Terrace, Paddington from the 1860s and had four children. Her husband Thomas, who became an eminent lawyer and later a QC, died in 1882. Isabella died on 4 May 1887.

Andrew and Cornelia had three children. Andrew Frederick was educated at Westminster School, and at some point he joined the Naval Volunteer Reserve, but later said that the only skill he learnt from them was the ability to sleep in a hammock! He developed an interest in chemistry and by 1871 was described as a 'student of chemistry' and resident at Cornelia's House, 32 Delamere Terrace, Paddington. He later became a Fellow of the Chemical Society. Like his mother, he was keen on travel and by 1875 he had visited Norway and the Austrian and Swiss Alps. That year he embarked on a tour of Hungary and Transalvania, much of it on horseback. In 1878 he published an account of his travels, *Round About the Carpathians*, and Bram Stoker, author of *Dracula* (1897), lists Andrew's book among those he consulted before beginning his novel. In 1877 he married a Polish girl Emilia Pawlowska, and settled at Tállya in Hungary growing vines for wine production. They had four children. They later moved to South Africa where Andrew was employed as a consulting metallurgist. In 1909 he was back in London and was granted a patent for improvements in 'Extracting Gold and Silver from Crushed Ore and Ore Slimes, and means therefor.' Andrew died in Cape Town, South Africa, in 1925.

Their second son, Landor, was described as a scholar in 1871 when he was resident with his mother in Delamere Terrace. Little is known of his later life. At one point he was the Berlin correspondent for *The Daily News*, and he died in Fissau, Holstein, Germany in 1885. The youngest son, Ormonde, was also living with his mother in Delamere Terrace in 1871, and matriculated at Wadham College, Oxford in 1876, where he graduated with a BA in 1880. In 1881 he was described as a Classical Tutor, and the following year graduated from Wadham College with an MA. By 1891 he was again described as a Tutor and was resident at 32 Delamere Terrace, but ten years later he was 'living on his own means' and resident at Upper Westbourne Terrace, Paddington.

The Fire

Just six months before Cornelia died, Fyne Court House, the place where she had spent five happy years and Andrew had conducted much of his scientific research (plate 3), was almost completely destroyed. On Saturday 1 September 1894 Emma Morgan, a live-in servant, was about to accompany Susanna Hamilton, John's widow, into Taunton at 11 am. Emma was due to be married that day. Just before she left, Emma asked Jane Brinson, a kitchen maid, to bring a lighted candle up to the bedroom they shared, located on an upper floor close to the library which was on the first floor above the laundry. Emma wanted to look her best and so used the candle to heat curling tongs with which to curl her hair. Unfortunately she forgot to blow out the candle. About 1 pm Jane re-entered to room and, to her horror, saw that the dressing table and part of the floor were alight. The room was full of smoke as was the adjoining bedroom. She rushed downstairs and found Ernest Wildon, the gardener, who was the only person around at that moment. Wildon ran up to the bedroom, but one glance showed him that the fire was already too great for them to tackle alone. He told Emma to close all the doors and windows and then ran to get help.

He summoned help from a farmer and some of his men working in the nearby field. Several of them got buckets of water and attempted to extinguish the fire, but by this time the flames had got a firm hold and it was clearly beyond their abilities to deal with it, and they were forced back. In the meantime Wildon had saddled a horse and ridden to Kingston St.

Mary, one and a half miles (2.4 km) away to use the telegraph to summon the fire brigade. Unfortunately, when he got there he found the telegraph wire was being repaired, so he had to ride into Taunton, a further four miles (6.4 km). On arrival in the town he raised the alarm and the men of the volunteer fire brigade began to gather at the fire station in Corporation Street.

In the meantime, back at Fyne Court, more local people, including the vicar, the Rev. Percy Bulstode, had arrived to help. Fortunately it was harvest time so there were many people in the nearby fields. They began removing furniture, paintings, valuable china and other items from the building. Not an easy job as the front entrance and the doors to the principal rooms were all locked. So they had to smash the windows and force open the window shutters to get into the rooms on the ground floor. The items were then handed through the windows and placed on the lawn out of harm's way. Thanks to their help most of the family portraits were saved, along with paintings by Rubens, van Dyck and Sir Peter Lely, and most of the furniture from the drawing and dining rooms. Enough books were removed from the library, by being thrown out of the windows after wrenching the locks off the book cases, to fill a couple of wagons. One of the rescuers, Samuel Haste, the local blacksmith, cut the veins and tendons in the wrist of his right hand very badly on some broken glass. His injury was quite serious and he had to be taken to Taunton Hospital where he was kept in to have his injury treated.

There was some firefighting equipment at Fyne Court, but it is not certain what it consisted of, and unfortunately it was locked in the stable close to where the fire was raging. It does not seem to have been used, and either the helpers were unaware it was there, or the outbuilding could not be reached because of the intense heat from the flames. Most large isolated houses had their own firefighting equipment, and staff were often trained to use it which saved many buildings from loss. If the Hamiltons had provided hand-pumps and cisterns filled with water located at various places within the building, as was common in many large Victorian properties, then the house might still be standing today! Taunton had a volunteer fire brigade, so its members had other occupations and, like today's lifeboat crews, members would leave their jobs to respond to an emergency. They gathered together, brought the horses, four in this case, to the fire station and harnessed them to the steam-powered fire engine. They set off for Fyne Court at 1.45 pm. However, the Brigade Captain, Mr H.T. Coles, was away at the Leigh Hill Reservoir in the Blackdown Hills above the village of Blagdon in connection with his job as Manager of the Taunton Waterworks. He learnt of the fire from a party of newspapermen on their annual outing who happened to see him, and told him about it, but it is uncertain how they had heard about it.

He immediately returned to Taunton and, as the brigade had already left, made his way to Broomfield. Mrs Hamilton had arrived back at Fyne Court at 1.30 pm as Wildon, after summoning the fire brigade had gone to find her. She was with her land agents, Messrs. Easton and Son, and Herbert Easton immediately drove back with her to Fyne Court. By the time she arrived a portion of the roof had fallen in, and shortly before the brigade arrived the roof and floors of the whole central section of the house collapsed with a loud crash, causing the flames to leap to new heights and sparks to whirl away over the whole area. An eye-witness account described the iron bedsteads in the bedrooms crashing through to the ground floor. Steam fire engines were usually pulled by two horses, but the fact that Taunton Fire Brigade used four shows they were well used to the steep hills of Somerset, and were aware they were heading for the highest village in the Quantocks. However, on reaching the very steep and long hill leading from Kingston St. Mary to Broomfield, the horses were struggling, so the men had to get off the fire engine and help by pushing it. The firemen arrived at Fyne Court at 2.30 pm and were confronted with a massive fire. The central section of the building had partly collapsed and was well alight, so the firemen immediately got to work. They coupled hoses together and took water from a large fish pond near the walled garden supplied from a spring, and so constantly refilled. They began to play water on the burning building.

So fierce were the flames that fruit hanging on trees at the rear of the building was later found to have been scorched and partly cooked. The brigade, urged by Easton, devoted their efforts to preventing the flames spreading to the music room, which Andrew Crosse had used as his main laboratory, and the library on the opposite side of the building, although so fierce was the fire, the firemen were not confident they would be able to save them, but they were to be successful in saving both parts. The music room, with its cream and gold plaster work (plate 6), oak floor and a large and handsome organ on a gallery at one end of the room was fortunate to survive as it was connected to the burning portion of the building by wooden folding doors. At one point part of the wall of the central section collapsed and two or three of the firemen narrowly escaped injury, and later one fireman, Mr Sully, had a very near miss. He was engaged in pouring water onto the burning building when a large piece of iron fell from the side of the porch over the front door, and he was struck on the arm and chest. If this massive piece of iron, an architectural element, had hit him on the head he would undoubtedly have been killed. However, he got back on his feet and continued fighting the fire, although he would have some serious bruising the next day.

Mrs Hamilton remained on the scene until 1 am on Sunday morning, when she went to the vicarage to get some rest. Police Sergeant Blacker of the Somerset Constabulary had arrived at Fyne Court from North Petherton some four miles (6.4 km) away soon after the fire broke out. He later requested the assistance of PC William Bartram from Taunton and another constable. During the night the firemen continued to pour water onto the remains of the building to damp down the smouldering ruins. The police remained alert to protect valuables still not packed away or removed. The brigade succeeded in confining the fire to the central portion of the building, and were at work for twenty-four hours, not packing up and leaving for Taunton until about 2 pm on Sunday afternoon, by which time they judged that, although the ruins were still smouldering, there was no danger of the fire breaking out again. They had saved the music room and the kitchen with library above, but the bedrooms and living rooms which were located in the central part of the building were in ruins. All the bedroom furniture, linen and plate had been destroyed. The coach house, stables and other outbuildings around the rear courtyard had also survived (plate 27). The wine, which was stored in the cellars, had also escaped the flames. The rescued books and some other items were temporarily stored in an outbuilding.

Easton had sent a messenger to Taunton on Saturday afternoon to request two furniture vans and men from Robert White, Furniture Mover, so that furniture and other rescued items could be placed in them. When they arrived, so efficiently did the men pack them, that by midnight all the rescued furniture and paintings had been packed away. The vans stood on the lawn until they left for Taunton on Sunday to place the contents into storage. Large numbers of sightseers came out from Taunton on the Sunday to view the still smoking ruins, despite a heavy downpour of rain earlier that day, and they continued to emit smoke until that evening. The police were kept busy controlling the crowds, and did not finally leave the site until the Monday. Mrs Hamilton was back again on Sunday morning and engaged several men to search the ruins to try and find a tin box containing a large number of deeds and family papers of great value, but by the afternoon they had not had any success. A large iron safe was discovered and dragged out onto the lawn, but this was found to be empty. They were also searching for £25 in gold which she had in the house, but this too could not be found, and the only coins recovered were a Jubilee halfpenny and a farthing. Mrs Hamilton was present at the ruined house all day Sunday as the search went on, and was in a state of considerable shock at the loss of her home. The Rev. Bulstrode invited her to stay on at the vicarage.

She later moved into Fyne Court Cottage (also called the Old Rectory) which the estate had owned since 1786, to which the china and rescued books were removed. This building (plate 28), which was being used as a shooting lodge at the time of the fire, is situated just above the site of the ruined building. The house and contents were insured with the London Assurance Company, whose local agent was Richard Easton. The records of the London Assurance Fire Committee for the 7 February 1895, note that 'We suffered also to the extent of £4000 through a fire in a Mansion, Fyne Court near Taunton.' This was the second highest loss suffered by the insurance company in the previous twelve months, only being exceeded by the loss of a leather warehouse and its contents in Bermondsey, which cost them £10,464. The majority of losses during this period were for sums ranging from £2.10.0 to £30.0.0, with only occasional losses falling outside this range, most at the lower end. Susanna Hamilton remained in Fyne Court Cottage and did not rebuild Fyne Court House, despite the fact that for the sum paid out by the insurance company she could have created a house with all the modern comforts lacking in the old one.

Why she did not do so has puzzled people, but Mrs Hamilton was seventy-three at the time of the fire, a widow, and may simply have been happy to live in the much smaller, but still substantial, Fyne Court Cottage with just one or two servants (although not the one who burnt the building down!), and could not be bothered with all the problems and decisions required to rebuild Fyne Court House. She continued to live in Fyne Court Cottage, dropping 'cottage' from its name, until her death in 1916. So ended the story of Fyne Court House as a dwelling house and the laboratory of one of Britain's pioneering and unique early scientists. On the death of Susanna Hamilton the estate passed to her grandson John Andrew Charles Hamilton (1876-1958), since the eldest son of John and Susanna had died in 1887. In 1954 the estate passed out of the Crosse family after three hundred years when he sold it to John Adams who, on his death in 1967, left it to the National Trust, the present owners, although legal complications meant they did not take possession of it until 1972.

Select Bibliography

Anon. [Shelley, Mary Wollstonecraft]. *Frankenstein, or the Modern Prometheus.* Lackington, Hughes, Harding, Mayor & Jones, 1818.

Anon. 'The Accidental Production of Animal Life – Mr. Crosse.' *Magazine of Popular Science*, 3, 145-8 (1837).

Atkinson, H.G. and Martineu, H. *Letters on the Laws of Man's Nature and Development.* John Chapman, 1851.

Bladon, J. 'A Note on *Acarus horridus.*' *The Entomologist*, 1, 307-8 (1842).

Crosse, Andrew. 'Experiments in Voltaic Electricity'. *Philosophical Magazine*, 46, 421-46 (1815).

Crosse, Andrew. 'On the production of insects by voltaic electricity.' *Annals of Electricity, Magnetism and Chemistry*, 1, 242-4 (1837).

Crosse, Andrew. 'Description of Some Experiments made with the Voltaic Battery ... for the purpose of producing crystals; in the process of which experiments certain insects constantly appeared.' *The Transactions, and Proceedings of the London Electrical Society, from 1837 to 1840*, 10-16.

Crosse, Cornelia. *Memorials, Scientific and Literary of Andrew Crosse, the Electrician.* Longman, Brown, Green, Longmans & Roberts, 1857.

Cox, Edward. 'Andrew Crosse, the electrician.' *The Critic of Literature, Art, Science and Drama*, 1, 57-60 (1844).

Crosse, Cornelia. 'Science and Society in the Fifties.' *Temple Bar*, 93, 35-51.

Crosse, Cornelia. *Red Letter Days of My Life.* Richard Bentley, 1892. (two vols.)

Davidson, Brian. 'Andrew Crosse and his Acarus'. Quekett Journal of Microscopy, 41, 585-97 (2012).

Haining, Peter. *The Man Who Was Frankenstein.* Frederick Muller Ltd., 1979.

Hytch, E. J. 'Mr. Crosses's Revivification of Insects Contained in Flint.' *The Lancet*, 1, 710-11 (1837).

Noad, Henry. *Lectures on Electricity Comprising Galvanism, Magnetism, Electro-Magnetism, Magneto- and Thermo- Electricity.* G. Knight, 1849. (rev. ed.)

Porter, John. *Crosse Connections: A 19th century scientist and his family.* Private Publication, 2006.

Mead, Audrey. *Andrew Crosse: Scientific Squire of Broomfield.* Somerset Wildlife Trust, 1979.

Mead, Audrey. *The Story of Fyne Court and Broomfield.* Somerset Wildlife Trust, 1997.

Opitz, Donald L. 'Crosse, Andrew' in *The Dictionary of Nineteenth-Century British Scientists.* Thoemmes Continuum, Bristol, 2004.

Roth, N. 'Bugs and blasphemy: Andrew Crosse and the *Acarus electricus.*' *Medical Instrumentation*, 13, 357 (1979).

Secord, James A. 'Extraordinary Experiment: Electricity and the Creation of Life in Victorian England.' In *The Uses of Experiment: Studies in the Natural Sciences.* Cambridge University Press, 1989.

Sidney, Edwin. *Electricity: its phenomena, laws and results,* (1843)

Singer, George. *Elements of Electricity and Electro-Chemistry.* Longman, Hurst, Rees, Orme & Brown, & Triphook, 1814.

Smee, Alfred. *Elements of Electro-Biology, or, The Voltaic Mechanism of Man, of Electro-Pathology, Especially of the Nervous System, and of Electro-Therapeutics.* Longman, Brown, Green & Longmans, 1849

Stallybrass, Oliver. 'How Faraday produced living animalculae: Andrew Crosse and the story of a myth.' *Proceedings of the Royal Institution of Great Britain*, 41, 597-619 (1967).

Telescope, Tom. [Pseud. John Newbery]. *The Newtonian Philosophy, and Natural Philosophy, and Natural Philosophy in General, Explained and Illustrated in Familiar Objects.* Thomas Tegg & Son, 1838.

Turpin, P. J. F. 'Note on a kind of *Acarus* presented to the Academy.' *Annals of Electricity, Magnetism , and Chemistry*, 2, 355-60 (1838).

Turpin, P. J. F. 'Note on a kind of *Acarus* presented to the Academy.' *Annals and Magazine of Natural History*, 2, 55-62 (1838).

Weekes, William Henry. 'Details of an Experiment in Which Certain Insects, Known as *Acarus crossii* Appeared.' *Proceedings of the London Electrical Society,* 1, 240-56 (1842).

Index